THREE HUNDRED YEARS
IN PAPER

THREE HUNDRED YEARS IN PAPER

G. T. MANDL

Set in Monophoto Bembo
Printed on Antique Laid 100 gr
made by Thomas & Green Ltd.
Bound in Eska Board, 40 oz
made by Cartonfabriek Beukema & Co, Holland
Glindura Bookcloth made by Thomas & Green Ltd.
Illustrations printed on Silverblade
made by Silverdalen Paper Mill, Sweden.

The Publications in Paper Trade Press are reprinted with kind permission of
Benn Publications Ltd and Paper Technology and Industry (PITA)

The Watermark on the title page is
Smith, Pine & Allnutt, Lower Tovil Mill, Maidstone 1813
(from Edward Heawood: Watermarks, Horn No. 2767, PL 354,
Paper Publications Society, Hilversum 1950)

Printed in Great Britain by
Butler & Tanner Ltd, Frome and London

CONTENTS

LIST OF CONTRIBUTORS

Dr Julius Grant

Herbert Green

Edward Grierson

Prof. Peter C. G. Isaac

Michael Lambert CBE

G. T. Mandl

L. John Mayes FLA

John Barcham Sedgwick

INTRODUCTION

This is a book spanning a number of countries and paper mills which have all contributed in one way or another to each other's survival. History itself is nothing but a record of survival and just as great empires rise and fall, so mighty Companies go down and others rise to take their place. Ours has been a fight for survival with no ambition for greatness. Greatness means much misery for the majority in order to fulfil the ambition of the few. This ambition has never been my motivation.

Survival in our case has been against extreme odds and the fight has by no means ended. It has brought unhappiness to no-one and whilst some have gained, no-one has lost. It was performed in probably the last remaining decades of free enterprise as we knew it and its development and history are an anachronism, a constant struggle of swimming against the tide or going up a down-going escalator. The sole reward has been the pleasure of achievement against such odds.

Within the British paper industry we are the only public company that has become private and the last remaining paper mill in the UK owned by one individual.

I hope this book will provide a record for future paper historians in which they may hopefully take as great a delight as we now do when reading the fascinating accounts of papermakers in the distant past. I should like to end the introduction with a quotation from the epilogue from Dennis Lyddon's History of the Trinity Paper Mills, *Paper in Bolton* published in 1972:

"The stories have covered the age of the master papermaker and of the individual who dominated and controlled a Company and so was, in every practical sense, a master. For better or for worse, that age is now ended. The taxation and Estate Duty laws of recent times (even without the help of future Gift Tax and Wealth Tax) have tolled the bell for the family papermaker; the egalitarians have ensured that the capital cost of progress is now beyond the purse of any one man. They have driven the individual into the hands of the monoliths that they likewise profess to despise.

"From this time on, progress or otherwise may be determined by Committee; by the votes of the hopeful and the hapless, even by Government itself. Government interference in, yet callous indifference of, the British paper industry has been the most frightening development of modern times. Since Industry as a whole is already the slave of Government as tax collector, debt collector, whipping boy, milch cow, Means Test victim and sole provider of the Nation's wealth, it is not surprising that Government should seek to extend its control to ensure no escape. And should the scurvy fellow collapse and die under the burden then it will not be the fault of Government but of the slave who proved too inept to carry the load while dragging his ball and chain."

ACKNOWLEDGEMENTS

Rather than attempt a continuous story of four British and two Continental paper mills* and the circumstances which led to their acquisition, I have decided that a more accurate historical record will result from the publication of various articles which are all, in one way or another, connected with the history and development of the Group.

The resulting lack of coherence will perhaps be made up by letting the individual authors speak for themselves and permitting the reader to form his own opinion.

The historical notes on Thomas and Green from 1860-1930 were written by Herbert Green (1855-1940, of Barcham Green, Hayle Mill, Maidstone, Kent), son of the founder—John Barcham Green (1823-1883), and can be considered to be almost an eye-witness account. They were subsequently supplemented by John Barcham Sedgwick (1885-1944), son-in-law of Roland Green—Herbert Green's brother (1856-1927). Subsequent notes were prepared by Miss N. R. Wicking, Assistant Company Secretary, who retired after 50 years' service with the company in 1967.

The historical notes in my centenary speech at Stationer's Hall, as well as the article on the paper mills in the district of High Wycombe, were written by Mr L. John Mayes, FLA, Librarian and Curator of the Library and Museum at High Wycombe from 1935 to 1971.

My articles and speeches which were published in the trade press are reprinted in full as far as they are relevant to the history and development of the business and relate to the state of trade at the time. They, and Mr Michael Lambert's Gold Medal Paper on Industrial Relations of 1971, are reproduced by kind permission of Benn Publications Ltd, and PITA.

The introduction to the Fourstones section was written by the late Mr Edward Grierson, well known author and local historian in Northumberland, on the occasion of the mill's bicentenary in 1963, as an introduction to the company's history, which it was intended to publish at that time. It is followed by Professor Peter C. G. Isaac's

*Fourstones Paper Mill, Hexham, Northumberland, 1763; Thomas & Green, Soho Mill, Wooburn Green, Bucks, 1705; Towgood & Beckwith, Arborfield Mill, Helpston, Peterborough, 1856; Henry Allnutt & Son, Lower Tovil Mill, Maidstone, Kent, 1686; Papierfabrik Netstal, Netstal, Switzerland, 1679; Ernst Naundorff Merklin, near Carlsbad, Czechoslovakia, 1870.

paper on abstracts from Fourstones Paper Mill deeds "Documents speak".

I am greatly indebted to Miss G. M. Dann and Mrs Hilary Sutcliffe for patiently typing and editing most of the manuscript.

To set the scene the following two Papers of a historical nature follow:

Michael Lambert CBE, *Industrial Relations in the Papermaking and Boardmaking Industry* (Gold Medal Presentation Paper given at Stationers' Hall on 12 November 1971 prior to Mr Lambert's retirement as director of the Employers' Federation of Paper and Boardmakers after 30 years service) and G. T. Mandl, *The Case for Common Sense* (Gold Medal Paper for 1981).

INDUSTRIAL RELATIONS IN
THE PAPERMAKING
AND BOARDMAKING INDUSTRY

by Michael Lambert CBE

Thirty years have gone swiftly by since, completely green and a little bewildered by war, I knocked hesitatingly at your gates.

I will not pretend that you welcomed me with open arms—indeed why should you? Instead, you accepted me, understandably with some misgivings, extending to me that kindly courtesy tinged with caution for which you are famous. But, wherever I went among you—and what a romantic list it is—whether it was in my home waters of Lower Thames and Medway, or in the higher reaches of the Wye River; among the king-cups of the Golden Valley, in historic Wells and Avalon, in the Devon coombes, the Welsh hills or the Cambridge fens; in the industrial North—in the counties of the red rose and the white; by Tyne and Tees; through Rother Glen, on the Road to the Isles; by the banks of the Dee and the Don; in the Kingdom of Fife, in the shadow of Castle Rock or in a quiet fold of the Pentland hills—wherever I went among you, I found the same kind welcome, the same understanding of the stranger within your gates. Now, as if that were not enough, when the time has come to loose me from a long apprenticeship, you all invite me here today, you accord me the greatest honour the Industry can bestow and ask me to talk to you about what I have found and what I have seen in this strange, puzzling, fascinating, "looking glass" world of Industrial Relations into which I stumbled, almost by accident, thirty years ago.

As I moved into this world and stood awhile to take stock of my new surroundings, it was borne in upon me that it was, in very truth, a "looking glass" world. The broad features of the landscape were the same but my own viewpoint had changed and closer inspection showed things to be the other way round from the way they had appeared to me before. Suddenly, my business was other people, who rarely act logically—usually emotionally. Here was I in a world in which it seemed that people neither said what they meant, nor meant what they said; a world in which common sense was at a discount and non-sense at a premium; where everyone was unreasonable except oneself; where people rushed from one crisis to another trying to present the appearance of being calm, but in fact,

1

adding to the confusion. The rules of the game, if any, were difficult to follow.

The negotiating table seemed, at times, to bear a surprising resemblance to the Mad Hatter's tea-party—the conversation having a curious logic all its own.

The parties to the negotiations, like Tweedledum and Tweedledee, were linked to each other by unbreakable bonds. For this reason, they operated most of the time within their own immediate circle, oblivious of the wider interests of others.

It was inevitable that the parties would resolve to do battle from time to time. In fact, it had become a tradition for them to do so and they dared not draw back from any challenge.

It was a relief to turn from this confusing scene and look back five hundred years into the Industry's past. Suddenly the mists cleared and it was possible to discern the important landmarks and the river of progress in human relations winding its way through them.

It was not possible to see exactly when papermaking emerged from the home or cottage, to establish itself in mills operated mechanically by water power. This was when industrial relations began for us, but we know the recorded date of the first mill was 1490. The progress was gradual as the corn millers found it profitable to fill the time of their mills by making paper, though it did not follow that they thereby ceased to grind corn. There was evidence that they carried on both activities in the same mill using the same labour. The early papers made were therefore coarse, for the level of skill was not high. The establishment of the business in fine papers was a long and arduous task against intense foreign competition and the failures and mill closures among the early papermakers were frequent. (The scene is not so very different today). However, by 1711, about 200 small mills had become established; the number of persons employed was around 1,500, and their total output was some 2,500 tons yearly.

The end of religious toleration on the continent with the revocation of the Edict of Nantes in 1685, brought a change in the labour market, when refugee papermakers sought sanctuary in this country. This influx of papermaking skills, together with the unsettled state of affairs abroad, gave a tremendous boost to the Industry, so that by the end of the eighteenth century there were over 500 mills operating in the British Isles. The number of employees had risen to somewhere around 5,000, and the total annual production was about 17,000 tons. Productivity had doubled.

Up to the end of the eighteenth century, paper had been made by the hand process based on a 12-hour day. The mill, as we know, consisted primarily of the rag-house, where women and children were employed sorting and cutting the rags; the preparation house where the stamping or grinding operation was carried out by men and

2

boys, and the vathouse, the heart of the mill, where the skilled journeyman "the vatman" reigned supreme. His skill lay mainly in the manipulation of the mould and his own particular "shake" by which he ensured a strong uniform sheet of paper of the required thickness. His was a closely guarded craft for which he served a seven-year apprenticeship, at the end of which he obtained his "Card of Freedom".

The indentures of 1715 contained some interesting restrictions. "He must not commit fornication nor contract matrimony within the said term. He must not haunt ale houses, taverns or playhouses. At cards, dice or other unlawful games, he shall not play, so that his master has damage." In return, the master undertook to instruct him in the mysteries of papermaking and at the end of the apprenticeship, to provide him with a new suit of clothes.

The vatman's job was a heavy one from the physical point of view—particularly when handling the heavy moulds for the "antiquarian" or "double elephant" sizes, which required the services of two vat crews working in tandem. It was also a thirst-raising job and the wage structure soon became encrusted with special abnormal payments such as "beer money", not to mention the "Five in two Rule", and the practices of "Skinning" and "Shuffling". Occasionally, a vatman, for no particular reason, would lose his "shake" and would have to be rested for a considerable time. Sometimes he would never recover it. To rest and to enable others to practice their skill, he would "change out" with the coucher, the second man. This was the first practical training programme in the Industry.

The other occupations in the vathouse were the layer, the parter and the dryerman, known as the "dryworker", who operated in a separate drying loft.

All these operatives were described as "following the vat". They were paid not on an hourly basis, but by "measured day work", i.e. their production was literally measured against a post set up on the bench, which measured the height of the stack of sheets and felts ready for the press. It was a matter for negotiation, depending on the size of the sheets, on how many posts constituted a "day's work". This method of payment gave rise to the first incentive scheme, so that after the passage of a hundred years or two, the vat crews were happily completing an eight day week in four-and-a-half days! (And "measured daywork" is now being sold by the consultants as a modern management technique!)

The grievance procedure in the hand-made mill was simple. If a matter arose between Master and men, either side could demand a "bull ring". The men formed a ring with the employer in the middle seated on an upturned box. The "ring" was not broken until the discussion was finished and the matter in dispute resolved. If called by the Master, he supplied the beer for the occasion; if by the men

3

they had to provide their own beer. If the men held a meeting of their own they were said to be "in divan".

The method of terminating a contract of employment is interesting. Either party could determine the contract by giving 14 days' notice or alternatively by placing one golden guinea on the counting house table.

Stirrings of labour unrest became apparent towards the end of the eighteenth century. In 1784, and for the next few years, occasional strikes had occurred in paper mills, mainly over wages. The first evidence of a labour dispute involving an organised strike, appeared in the Manchester Mercury as early as 8 July 1788, as follows:

> Whereas a combination has arisen amongst the Journeymen Papermakers for an increase of wages and they have circulated a paper full of complaints against their masters for refusing to comply with their unreasonable demands. We, whose names are subscribed, making it our duty to prevent any imposition which the public may suffer through a misguided pity, beg leave to assure them, that if they will give themselves the Trouble to enquire of us, or any other Papermakers in the Town or neighbourhood of Manchester, it will be found that the Journeymen Papermakers receive much greater wages, have more consistent Employment and derive superior advantages than most other Artificers or workmen, earning from 10s 6d per week and upwards, according to their Merit.

There follow the signatures of employers famous in the trade— Seddon, Crompton, Appleton.

In the South, James Whatman of Maidstone, sold his business to Hollingworth in 1793 and retired from papermaking, expressing (it is said) disgust at the labour agitations. The record of this might have been the opening paragraph of a Jane Austen novel—

> The late Mr. Whatman ... had not, for many years of the earlier part of his life, much of opposition to meet with from the workmen; and by a judicious application of moderate encouragement they were stimulated to aid his endeavours by contributing their due portions of care and attentive workmanship. At that period each individual stood singly; no associations were then in existence; and the employer could extract from the labourer a just return for the wages paid him. But the latter years of this gentleman were crowded with regret at finding his plans opposed on every stage of their progress by his workpeople, and, foreseeing nothing but an increase of the evil, and no means of establishing a just and necessary control, he retired from the manufacture with disgust and disappointment.

Three years later Parliament was petitioned by the papermaking employers, and an Act was passed making journeymen's clubs and combinations illegal, but this did not stop their activities, because it proved too difficult to trace the offending ringleaders and bring them to justice. So this early attempt to control industrial relations in our industry by law was ineffective.

In defiance of the Act, the journeyman papermakers formed their first trade union in 1800. Called "The Original Society of Papermakers", it was limited to skilled journeymen and within a few years it wielded great power in the industry.

It fell to William Balston in Kent, the most important papermaking centre (there were 37 mills in Kent alone), to organise the employers to meet the increasing demands of the journeymen papermakers. (Wages in Kent, even at that time, were 20% higher than elsewhere.) The employers formed "The Society of Master Paper Makers of the Counties of Kent and Surrey", associated for the express purpose of "resisting the illegal combinations among the Journeymen Paper Makers".

They met in the Star Inn at Maidstone.

Twenty-three firms joined this first attempt at Federation and the level of subscription was £20 per vat.

But the pressure on the mills from the journeymen became so intense that the need for a "lock-out" became imperative and William Balston, as leader of the Southern Employers, was requested to visit all mill owners in the south and west of England. This he accomplished in the space of twenty-eight days and it was, by any standard, an astonishing performance. "He started on December 11th and in the next four weeks, on the bad roads of that period and in the depth of winter, travelled 787 miles and visited more than sixty mills—as far west as Plymouth and north-west to Tintern, travelling about thirty miles and visiting two or three mills, weekdays, Sundays and even Christmas Day alike, with only one day's rest in twenty-eight." (This is a programme which would daunt even a District Secretary of our Federation today.) The journey was followed by a "lock-out" which history records was only "moderately successful"!

But if the journey of this employer is to be regarded as a feat of endurance, what do we think about the performance of the unemployed journeyman papermaker? He had no alternative but to become a "trade union tramp". He had to tramp the whole country walking from one mill to the next in search of work. This was known as "the Round" and it was 1,190 miles in length. There were 51 "turning points", which were listed on a card which he obtained from his union. At each "turning point" was a mill at which a union secretary might be found in the evening, who signed the card, arranged for the journeyman's meal and lodging for the night and provided him with sixpence for the next day's tramp. He was allowed sixty-four days to complete the round with ten Sundays to rest. After completing the round without finding work, he could get a new card from the union to start his journey all over again! And this system of tramping lasted until the middle of the nineteenth century when the union replaced it with unemployment benefits.

In 1803, occurred the event which changed the whole face of the industry—the erection at Frogmore of the first continuous paper machine. Its impact was such that three years later some twenty of these machines were producing about one tenth of the total output of the country.

The same William Balston inspected one of these machines, but after a careful assessment, turned down the idea, despite the fact that he had been assured that the machine would produce, in a twelve-hour day, the output of eight vats, "so that one machineman at £2 9s a week would do the work of thirty-two men and there would also be considerable saving on fuel and felting. Though the machine would cost £1,500 and there would be £380 per annum payable to Fourdrinier for the licence to use it, it would save at least £1,000 yearly."

Yet William passed the invention by, but to what extent he was influenced by his wife Catherine, we do not know, for she wrote to him "If you adopt it, I hope it will not be at the expense of your popularity, for I would rather see you generally beloved than rich".

From that significant date, the industry was destined to change from labour intensive to capital intensive and the impact of this on the labour relations of the industry and on the skilled man's first trade union, the Original Society of Papermakers, was dramatic.

The skilled men saw the new paper machine as an evil thing, which would destroy them and their craft. Most of them could not come to terms with it. There was discord within the union as the continuous paper machines gained acceptance. At the same time, trading problems in the industry, together with the mechanisation of the process, led to widespread failures and closures among the hand-made mills. Reductions in wages were enforced and unemployment amongst their skilled journeymen reached serious proportions. There was hardship and bitterness as the mills struggled to exist, the men to live and the union to survive. The number of mills fell to 377 but the number of persons employed overall in the industry rose to over 20,000 and the production level to around 80,000 tons. In 1853 the union split and an offshoot of those who were prepared to embrace the new paper machines was formed called "The United Brotherhood".

Through all these times the other great citadel of papermaking in the South, namely Portals in Hampshire, was relatively free of serious labour troubles. The River Test ran more softly than did the Thames and Medway, and the brown trout basked undisturbed in the stream that ran through the forecourt of Laverstoke mill. But the chronicler of their history (the present Sir Francis Portal) tells us that there was "a *suggestion* of labour trouble" in 1826. News of this was sent in a report from the Mill Manager, Mr Dusatoy, to Mr John Portal who was in London. It is worth listening to his report for it has a familiar ring!

3rd April 1826

On Saturday I told Morrell to put a quire more of felts into each post. A short time afterwards the men sent a message, desiring me to come to them in the 2nd workhouse. I desired their messenger to tell them that I was in the Counting house and that they might come to me if they pleased. Accordingly, they all came. Joshua Webb (as Vatman of the 1st Vat) said "We don't think it right to have the quire of felts put in". I replied that nothing could possibly be more right.

There followed full details of the dispute.]

"Is this true Joshua? Or is it not?" He answered that it was true. "Then", said I, "where is the difficulty now?" ... Cullerne then, in rather a loud manner, said "I won't make another sheet." I said "You never did make a sheet here fit to be called a sheet and many a pound has Mr Portal lost by his good nature and my folly in giving you so long a trial ... You are and always have been a bother to us; and that which you are now doing, a child would do full as well for a quarter of your wages. So that I advise you to hold your tongue. This mill is not going to be governed by *your* laws!"

I then addressed the other men and said: "Do not be misled by such a silly fellow as this. Is there throughout England a journeyman that can, as you can, show a rack full of bacon, and a good wholesome beer in his cellar? Is there a mill where *each vat* receives five guineas a year for feasts? Where £24 5s is paid, as was paid last week to you, for beer money for 12 weeks, which is at the rate of £100 per year? In what part of England will you find comfortable houses and gardens at 40s a year; which are, you know, in this neighbourhood worth three times the sum? Behave like men—fulfil your agreement. What is a man worth that does not? Keep up the character of the mill, for your families' sakes, and for all your sakes. Take a friend's advice."

They are now going on steadily.

It would be interesting to hear the end of this matter, if I had time to tell you. It must suffice to read you the next sentence of the chronicler—"On receipt of this report, John Portal was outraged! And his reply to Mr Dusatoy came down sizzling, in the Salisbury Coach."

One hundred and forty years were to pass before Sir Francis Portal himself was to meet, and overcome, the same sort of challenge.

By 1869 another small union for skilled men in the machine mills, called The Society of Paper Makers, had been formed, this time in the North of England.

But it was in Scotland that things came to a head. The demand was for shorter hours, which was hardly surprising. The girls employed in the rag houses worked 66 hours a week—10 to 12 hours a day. (Hours were somewhat shorter in winter because candles could

7

not be used with safety in the rag house.) They were paid on piece-work, earning about five shillings a week. The boys in the grinding mill, did three spells of 24 hours each, i.e. 72 hours per week, with time for a few hours sleep. They too earned about five shillings a week. The men also worked at least 72 hours per week, often 80, and their wages were from 25s to 33s per week for a skilled man. Holidays were almost non-existent; they varied from one day a year, i.e. Christmas or New Year's Day, at most mills, to eight days at the very best mills, i.e. three at Christmas, two at Easter and three at Whitsun. There was no such thing as a summer annual holiday.

The approach to the mill owners met with a dusty answer and one mill under pressure declared a "lock-out", demanding that its workers should undertake not to join a trade union. The inevitable happened. The men responded by forming a new union in Edinburgh on 1 February 1890. It was called "The National Union of Paper Mill Workers" and it catered for the unskilled and semi-skilled workers in both hand-made and machine mills. It was the forerunner of our present major union and it started with a membership of 3,106. Now the writing was on the wall!

The United Brotherhood and the Society of Papermakers amalgamated, thus creating one union for skilled men in the new machine mills, leaving the Original Society of Papermakers to cover the skilled journeymen in the hand-made mills.

It took 23 years for the new union organisations to gather their strength. In 1913 they attacked in Lancashire and the Northern mills responded by forming a Federation with C.R. Seddon as chairman and John L. Merchant as part-time secretary. There were many strikes and just as things had reached a really serious state, the first World War was declared.

As soon as the war finished they were at one another again. The Southern Mills established a board under H. Green and Wm. Nash, to deal with their labour affairs and a year later, William Wallace and John Tod, succeeded in forming a Scottish Section. The Federation's headquarters were located in Manchester and it operated through an Executive Council consisting of all the members of all the District Boards.

The battle between the unions and the newly formed Federation was joined in earnest and it resulted in a strike two months later. The Ministry of Labour intervened and eventually on 10 July 1919 the first national agreement in the history of the industry was signed. This was exactly thirty years after the first reasonable request had been made by the men for shorter hours. The new agreement put the industry on the three 8-hour shift system with an average week of 44 hours for shift workers and 48 hours for day workers. The wages per normal week for a day worker and shift worker in the same class of occupation were identical. The "shift differential" was therefore created not by way of extra money but in the form of four extra hours of leisure per week in favour of the shift worker.

This first national agreement also set minimum rates of wages. The rate for a skilled machineman was 1s 8d per hour, an unskilled labourer received 1s 2d per hour. The agreement was hailed by the unions as the "Paperworkers' Charter". It meant that the unions had arrived and had been recognised as a force in the industry. The pattern of collective bargaining had been set for many years to come.

The twenty years from 1919 to 1939 were years of hard and sometimes bitter bargaining between the Federation and the unions, including, as they did, the years of the great depression, when prices collapsed and reductions in wages had to be negotiated. The Employers were held together by a strong and wise president, Arthur Baker. Six more national agreements were negotiated and signed by him and John L. Merchant during those years, but at the end of that time the wage rates were 2d per hour lower than at the beginning. The No. 3 Agreement linked wages to the cost of living index by a sliding scale, which was to prove a source of conflict and was to lead to the unions withdrawing from the national agreement for five years—although the Employers continued to operate it throughout. The conceding of an annual paid holiday of one week was made in the No. 8 Agreement.

1938 had seen the appointment of the first full-time General Secretary of the Federation, E. M. Amphlett, who made a great contribution to the industrial relations of our industry, particularly by the negotiation of Recognition and Procedure Agreements with all the unions with which we were then dealing. They had increased to twelve in number—three on the process side and nine representing the various trades of the maintenance craftsmen. These agreements provided a three-stage machinery for dealing with disputes round the negotiating table rather than by strike or lock-out. They gave the industry the chance to achieve labour peace and they have proved to be the Federation's greatest asset. The other aim was achieved in 1951 when a national agreement was signed with the craft unions covering all the maintenance tradesmen. Thus, thirty-eight years after the foundation of the Federation, the main objective had been achieved, whereby all the manual workpeople in the papermaking and boardmaking industry were covered by national agreements. (And now Lord Donovan has questioned whether this is a good thing and suggests that we might reverse the process!)

I have talked at length about the past because it is necessary to see things in perspective; for in industrial relations, in particular, the past is always a part of the present and the present is already a part of the future. For me "the immediate present" covers the last fifteen years during which you have called on me to act as your pilot (if I may so describe myself?).

What was my contribution to be—what the objective and what "leading marks" must be set up to show the way?

All the main battles had been fought—the very existence of trade unions, their recognition, the granting of negotiating rights. Basic agreements had been made; the machinery for dealing with disputes had been fashioned—at least on paper. Those who had gone before had been fighters and builders and they had achieved much. There seemed little left to do! Gradually the task became clear. The industry desperately needed a period of labour peace, free from the debilitating wounds, sustained during the creating period.

The task ahead was to try to use that which had been built by our predecessors; to turn the Procedure Agreements into reality at the mills; to throw a bridge of understanding across the divide of mistrust, which separated the parties and which the battles of the earlier years had brought into being. If we did not succeed in doing this, the mistrust would become a river of hatred and the chance would be lost. The time had come for reconciliation. In this task we were greatly helped by three far-sighted trade union leaders. E. B. White of the Paperworkers, John Boyd of the Engineers and Mark Young of the Electricians. During the past twenty years we have held over 1,000 conferences under our procedure agreements for dealing with individual mill disputes. Well over 50% of the Federation's time has been spent on this aspect of our work and all but two or three of those disputes have, in the end, been solved peacefully. The subjects of those conferences have, of course, been mainly concerned with wages and working conditions; with dismissals and suspensions. But there have been some strange ones—they sound like a book by Conan Doyle.

The thorns on the stolen rose bush.
The light on the mill chimney at West Hartlepool.
The pipe band at Bullionfield.
The love life of Betty Sugg.
The Plymouth Brother of Keynsham.
The unpredictable behaviour of Rae Smith.
The mystery of the missing mill manager.

Of course, a good deal of constructive work has been done—the move to four-shift operation, shorter working hours and longer holidays. The standard of living of the workers has been increased rapidly and social security benefits lifted—perhaps too far and too fast.

But possibly history will show in due course, that in the labour field, the past twenty years in our industry have been an "interlude"—a period of consolidation (in more than one sense!) during which our relations with the unions have been improved and some preliminary steps taken towards the distant goal of true partnership,

10

which others who follow us must seek to attain. "Participation" is the main dream of the future, but with it must come the true acceptance of responsibility by unions and men. In this concept, middle management must also be encouraged to play a part and, if it is clearly shown to be their wish, the unions which cater for them cannot long be denied a place. But let us have no illusions, there will always be two sides to the table of industrial relations, no matter what shape you make the table.

To achieve this long-term task, it will be necessary first to train the future managers, their departmental heads, supervisors, union officials and mill representatives in the arts and skills of human relations. They must, above all, acquire the art of speaking and know the power of words—for the spoken word is still the most powerful instrument for good or ill. We have only just begun this task of training and the new Industrial Relations Act is a spur. The Act does one great thing—even if it creates at the same time a host of other complications for us—it lays a foundation stone for a new structure— a code of civilised behaviour. But the creation of a code does not, of itself, achieve anything. We shall have to translate the code into practice ourselves and those who accept responsibility for our labour relations in the years ahead must do this within the mills themselves, within the board room itself, where an industrial relations policy must be fashioned and kept under review. These builders for the future must commence their work at once. We have given them, I believe, a good foundation on which to build, which should sustain them against the stresses and strains that building always brings. But they must guard that foundation well, for it can so easily be undermined and let them not forget that the bridge of trust of which I have spoken, is not made of steel or concrete. It is made only of men with a desire to serve.

But, build they must, for there are urgent tasks to accomplish. Going into Europe will call for the gradual "harmonisation" of labour costs and the levelling up on conditions. This will mean further increases for Britain, particularly in relation to holidays, holiday pay, state pensions and social security benefits. The boundaries of the labour market will extend—for the movement of labour in Europe must be free under the Treaty of Rome. Some people fear that a wave of unskilled labour will surge upon our shores. Rather, we should take care to see that our competitors do not start a "skill drain" in the reverse direction. "Equal pay" already poses the question of the future role of women in our industry and, taken to its extreme conclusion, will accelerate the reorganisation and in time might mean the virtual disappearance of our Salles. Or does it constitute a challenge to us to develop far more intensely than hitherto, the undoubted skills that women possess?

There is a need to consider afresh the frontiers of our industry and to realise that the various sectors of a wider paper industry—mills, converters and merchants—are at present negotiating separately with one major union, which can find advantage in a divided house.

Now, for these tasks you have taken a new pilot* on board; his skilful hands are even now feeling the kick of the wheel. This is right; for the channel is changing; the landscape is opening out; the tide slips faster under our keel and there is "white water" ahead. But I know that he, with his wide experience and with the loyal help of those who sail with him, will serve you very well.

For myself, I shall be aboard for a little while yet—just until the launch is alongside to take me off. But this, I promise, will embarrass no one. For after all, I have learned some of the lessons of my Looking Glass world!

> Alice looked up, and there was the Cat again sitting on the branch of a tree.
> "Did you say pig, or fig?" said the Cat.
> "I said pig" replied Alice "and I wish you wouldn't keep appearing and vanishing so suddenly: you make one feel quite giddy."
> "All right" said the Cat; and this time he vanished quite slowly, beginning with the end of the tail, and ending with the Grin, which remained some time after the rest of him had gone.

* John Adams, Director General, British Paper & Board Industry Federation 1972-1983.

A speech by Michael Lambert CBE, director of the Employers' Federation of Papermakers and Boardmakers, on the occasion of the award to him of The World's Paper Trade Review Gold Medal for 1971, at Stationers' Hall, London, on 12 November 1971.

The text is reproduced by kind permission of Benn Publications Ltd.

THE CASE FOR COMMON SENSE

by George T. Mandl

(Reprinted from *Paper*, 6 April 1981.)

Common sense is not very common. This old proverb applies particularly to the paper industry, and we may well ask ourselves how it is possible that a sophisticated capital intensive industry could get itself into such a mess throughout the whole of Western Europe

In order to understand the present, one has to look into the past. The examples I shall give are drawn from Britain, but the same situation would equally apply to any major paper producing country in what is now Western Europe.

The earliest available records show that approximately 500 tons of paper a year were consumed in the British Isles in the year 1600, to cover the needs of the population of some five million. This represents a per capita consumption of some 0·1 kg per year. During the following four centuries, the population of Britain increased from five to 55 million and the latest figures for 1980 show a paper consumption of seven million tonnes—an incredible increase from 500 tons to seven million tonnes a year and a consumption growth from 0·1 kg to 130 kg over the past four centuries.

When one pauses to contemplate this unbelievable growth in both volume and per capita consumption, one might be led to believe that the industry producing such a growing commodity would have had four centuries of uninterrupted expansion and prosperity, and that failures might have been confined to the incompetent few who, in spite of continuing demand, were unable to keep in business through mismanagement of their paper mills.

Unfortunately, the very opposite has been the case throughout the entire period, from the early days of primitive hand-made production through the years when Huguenot immigrants brought the necessary secret skills of papermaking to Britain, right up to the invention of the papermaking machine, which led paper manufacture into the industrial revolution.

The first paper mill established in Britain was founded in Hertfordshire about 1490, but failed a few years later. Its owner is on record as giving the reason that "he could not fourd his paper as good cheape as that come from beyond the seaze, and so he was forced to lay downe making of paper. And no blame to the man: for men would give never the more for his paper because it was made heare".

Let us leave, for a moment, the reign of the first Elizabeth and have a look at the situation in the late 17th Century.

The first known joint stock company engaged in the manufacture of writing paper was formed in 1686 under the name of "The Governor and Company of White Paper Makers in England". It had a large share capital of £100,000 divided into shares of £50 nominal, and claimed to produce some 100 000 reams in 12 mills with 20 vats, although this figure appears exaggerated.

The state of the paper industry is reflected in the price at which the shares were traded. They rose from a low of £41 in May 1692 to a record of £150 in March 1694, but by 1698 the company disappeared and its shares were worthless.

The following example from the 18th Century shows the picture to be no brighter. William Hutton, who set up as bookseller and retail stationer in Birmingham in 1750, records in his diary in 1756: "Robert Bage, an intimate friend and paper maker, ... proposed that I should sell paper for him, by commission or purchase, on my own account. As I could spare two hundred pounds, I chose to purchase, appropriated a room for its reception, advertised, and hung a sign: The Paper Warehouse—the first in Birmingham. From this small hint I followed the trade for 40 years and acquired many thousand pounds".

Prospering in his new trade, Hutton was moved to write in his diary two years later: "if there was a profit to the seller, I concluded there must be one for the maker. I coveted both. Upon this erroneous principle I wished for a paper mill".

He then set out acquiring knowledge of paper making, had a model of a mill constructed, took a lease of two acres of land and started to build. For reasons which he does not make clear his plans miscarried. By 1761 he had abandoned the idea; the next year he sold the mill.

While all this was happening in the days of hand-made paper during a period when annual consumption increased from some 500 tons in 1600 to 15 000 tons in 1800, involving 450 mills in the British Isles with some 750 vats and the population had doubled, much worse was to come with the advent of the paper machine in the 19th Century.

The Fourdrinier brothers, who purchased the Robert patent and spent their entire fortune as very prosperous paper merchants in the City of London in developing what is known today as the Fourdrinier machine, went bankrupt in the process.

In spite of exploding increases in consumption and population during the industrial revolution that followed, production was always several steps ahead of consumption. Between 1800 and 1860, consumption increased to 100 000 tons a year, while prices fell from £170 a ton in 1800 to £95 per ton in 1836 and £60 a ton in 1860.

Between 1851 and 1867 the number of newspapers alone increased from 563, including 17 dailies, to 1294, including 84 dailies. "The Times" increased its circulation from 2000 copies in 1790 to 10 000 in 1830 and 65 000 in 1861, when it also reduced its price from four pence to three pence per copy.

By 1872 the situation became so desperate that the three most important paper making countries in Europe—Germany, Britain and Austria/Hungary—founded national associations of paper makers in order to try and find ways of improving the situation.

Gladstone told the newly formed Paper Makers' Association of Great Britain and Ireland "... to apply science to their manufacture, and drop their constant appeals to the Government for help", to which the president, John Evans, of Dickinsons, replied "that no amount of manufacturing skills and new inventions, of which there were plenty, can make up for the 50% increase in the import duty of rags, while allowing foreign paper to enter duty free without let or hindrance". Mr Evans pointed to the "profitless condition of late years, unnatural foreign competition and grave lack of unity among the paper makers, whose reckless competition was forcing some owners to cut prices down to the point where their mills were losing money".

At a general meeting of the association in 1879 he stated that "the present unsatisfactory condition of the paper industry had been caused mainly by over-production; when profits began to sag, manufacturers tried to reduce their losses by making more paper. The regulation of prices was the most pressing need of the industry at that time".

Combinations against paper makers had sprung up on every side. Suppliers of materials to the industry had already combined to raise their prices, while newspaper owners were combining to keep down the price of paper. The similarity of the situation with the present time is frightening.

Pioneers of the British paper industry such as John Evans and Thomas Routledge, who between them put an end to the shortage of rags by developing the first alternative and plentiful fibre—esparto grass—later followed by Edward Partington's introduction of chemical woodpulp to British paper makers, did not bring the necessary relief from recession.

Within 10 years the output of British mills doubled from 150 000 tons in 1870 to 300 000 tons by 1880. There was little the association could do to help its members "... who wrung their hands and looked dolefully into the future". The situation was made worse by many new mills that were being opened, in spite of falling profits. The plentiful availability of raw materials and the explosive growth in consumption served as encouragement for an enterprising man to gather a little capital and open a new paper mill or revive an old one. Between 1860 and 1900 two new mills were being established in Britain every year, and it is not surprising that many of them did not survive for very long.

In 1876 no less than 37 bankruptcies among paper makers and stationers were recorded, and they numbered 40 in the following year.

The chances of finding export markets were dismal. While foreign paper continued to pour in duty free, most European countries were levelling import duties up to 50%, in Russia even 100%. Protected continental domestic markets were therefore easily able to dump their surplus output at up to 25% lower prices on the British market.

The Paper Makers' Association was powerless to persuade a Government, set on free trade, to re-instate an import duty.

By 1900 some 540 paper machines were installed in Britain producing 750 000 tons, while the number of mills declined to below 300.

In 1912 the UK first reached the landmark of one million tons of output, a tenfold increase from 100 000 tons in 1862 over a period of 50 years. While wages and living standards continued to rise, paper prices fell from £60 to £20 per ton.

During the last 100 years per capita paper consumption of the major industrial nations in Europe has risen from 4 kg in 1879 30-fold to an average of 120 kg in 1979, while their population almost doubled. This represents no less than a 50-fold increase in European output during the period.

The decade before the First World War was one of calm and stability before the storm. Imperial Germany became the world's largest producer of paper with an output of almost two million tons in 1150 mills and a per capita consumption of 25 kg.

After 1918 instability resumed at once with ever increasing cycles of boom and depression. The post-war shortages soon collapsed in the early 1920s and prices came crashing down to well below pre-war levels. The introduction of protective and prohibitive trade barriers, coupled with the departure from the Gold Standard, created large-scale unemployment and lack of liquid capital, which triggered the economic crash in 1929.

The Second World War left most of the European paper industry either totally destroyed, or severely damaged. Consumption of paper in Germany dropped to only 15 kg per head of population in 1948, but rose to 50 kg after the monetary reform and Marshall Aid in 1952. In the following seven years it doubled again to 100 kg by 1965 and reached the ninth place in the world in 1972 with 125 kg.

German domestic production rose from 1·7 million tonnes in 1950 to seven million tonnes in 1979 with a most remarkable increase in productivity from 10 to 85 tonnes and value of DM 8,500 to DM 85 000 per person employed, per annum.

While production in the UK declined by almost one million tonnes and 50 mill closures in the late 1960s and 1970s, Germany invested an average of 8·5% of its sales each year so that 50% of its machines are less than 30 years and 20% less than 10 years old.

Due to inflation, comparison of ratios except in Germany are difficult, but German productivity can be gauged by the fact that between 1958 and 1978 wages rose by 300%, while selling prices of paper in terms of Deutschmarks barely moved and the percentage of wages and salaries on sales remained constant at around 20%.

Sweden and Finland too had enormous increases in output taking an ever increasing share of the traditional domestic European markets.

This expansion brought no profits to anyone. Company indebtedness rose to over 80% of capital employed in the manufacture of paper and the industry became unable to turn over its funds even during one year. Ever increasing costs of labour, materials and taxation, as well as environmental expenditure, now estimated to cost the industry 3% of sales, prevented the generation of necessary capital for the maintenance and future replacement of plant without direct Government intervention.

This sad and brief excursion through four centuries has now brought us to the present time. It should make it easier to appreciate, if not to comprehend, the present situation.

Having established the fact that paper makers have steadfastly refused to learn anything from historical events, we should not be too surprised that they have learned nothing from lessons of the more recent past, particularly the 1974 boom and the 1975 depression.

I first became involved in speaking at Technical Section meetings and elsewhere some 12 years ago with the object of publicising and highlighting this situation, of which the industry appeared to be blissfully unaware. I should like to quote some of the things I said in order to show how futile it was, and how the lone voice was lost in the wilderness, in view of the events which have overtaken us since then.

First, let me quote from a paper I gave at a public meeting organised at my instigation by the Northern District of the BP & BMA at the Manchester Club on 8 May 1970.

"The 1969 Spring Conference of the Technical Section was entitled 'Technical Changes Resulting from Economic Pressure on Paper Mills'. The two-day conference discussed a wide variety of subjects, how the industry could best meet economic pressure, which has gradually been building up over the past 10 years.

I should like to examine here some of the circumstances which have led to this economic pressure which threw our industry into one of its deepest depressions during 1967 and which led to the closure of over 30 paper mills in Britain.

This depression was not confined to Britain but due to the international nature of the paper trade had world-wide repercussions, embracing all the major pulp and paper producing countries of the world.

The root causes of the trouble lie in the structure of our industry. From the smallest one-machine paper mill to the largest of the pulp-producing giants, the problem of capital intensity is common to all, whereby the capital employed by each unit is as a rule turned over only once a year. In such circumstances it is relatively easy for production oriented management to pursue very aggressive sales policies, based on lower cost of additional production being squeezed out of each unit. This policy has led to what is known as marginal costing, whereby only the direct costs of the additional capacity are calculated in order to secure substantial additional business.

The production oriented management which, in the Nordic countries, was almost entirely technical, was unaware of the disastrous consequences of such policies, carried out without any attempt at fundamental marketing.

Prices calculated on marginal costing soon became ruling market prices and management then proceeded to defend their policies as being 'The survival of the fittest' and the elimination of excess capacities by bankruptcy and closure of the smaller and weaker economic units.

Although price levels expressed in terms of the cost of living index had reached an all-time low throughout the world, capital investment continued, regardless of return on capital employed, as long as companies were able to borrow substantial funds based on their previous profit records and the security of their fixed assets.

The inevitable consequences soon followed; both shareholders and bankers realised that the profits earned on the new investments did not cover depreciation and interest.

Let us examine a little more closely some of the criteria which have led paper and pulp producing industries as varied as those of Scandinavia, the UK and the Common Market into the same situation of over-production.

The British paper industry produces paper on some 500 machines, of which 50% are more than 50 years old. These machines were written down on the books and it was possible for a limited period of time to produce increases in capacity at very low investment costs.

Due to marginal costing, no new units could compete. This became increasingly evident from the loss figures being returned by mills with substantial new capital investment. The return on capital employed fell to levels at which no investor was willing to risk his

18

money and the price of pulp and paper mill shares throughout the world continued to fall far below net asset values, until a level of yield was reached which brought them in line with other industries.

The exploding consumer boom of pulp and paper since the war should have put our industry among the leaders and certainly not at the bottom of the list. It is an incredible fact that shareholders were finding themselves in a situation whereby the value of their shares in real terms dropped far below previous levels after a very extensive investment and modernisation of their mills.

As a result of all this, new thoughts began to emerge. The late Mr William Tait, the well-known Scottish paper maker, put this into a nutshell when addressing the Technical Section in London: 'Many of you think you are in business to make paper. You are wrong, you should be in business to make money.'

Quite apart from our interest in forestry, we have failed to see the wood for the trees.

The three main factors which have brought about the present unhappy situation and should be very seriously investigated are, in order of importance, the following:

Continuing overproduction has led to marginal costings and resulted in a low return on capital employed throughout the industry. It is an established fact that the lowering of selling prices has stimulated no increased demand for paper and it can therefore be safely assumed that consumption cannot be stimulated by price. Once we accept this fact, we should be able to discard any attempt to increase an individual market share based on the mistaken belief that this can be achieved by price cutting.

The second point we should look at is the rationalisation through product swaps, of which a very good example has recently been given by the Swiss paper industry. Too many grades per mill causes a great deal of loss of production and streamlining of these through swap arrangements would clearly benefit all concerned. The Swiss mills, which have, for many years, enjoyed tariff protection and high carriage charges to their home market, have been forced into this step by the duty-free importations from EFTA countries, including both Scandinavia and Austria. This is a very good example of rationalisation of an industry under pressure.

The third is an entirely domestic question and concerns the substantial additional costs incurred by mills stocking their output.

A very substantial tonnage of paper consumed in Britain has to bear the cost of double handling: first into mill stock, then out of mill stock into merchant stock and finally to the consumer. We know from inter-firm comparisons how high the costs of putting paper in and out of stock are to a merchant. It has so far not been assessed that similar costs are being incurred by the mills putting the paper into their own stock.

19

There is virtually no price differentiation between a making order and a delivery from mill stock, although the on-cost absorbed by the mill could well be in the region of up to 15%. If the product is to be distributed to the consumer without a very substantial increase in price, allowing for the double stocking operation, an elimination of one of the stock operations is clearly necessary.

The resulting saving could then be equitably shared between the mill and the merchant, resulting in an improvement of extremely poor profitability of both parties. This will inevitably mean that merchants will carry fewer lines with a larger and faster turnover to allow only making orders to be delivered to their warehouses.

Where the mill, for reasons of type of product, is still obliged to stock, the upcharge for the stock should go to the mill that carries such stock and delivery should, wherever possible, be arranged mutually between the merchant and the mill direct to the consumer so that double handling is eliminated.

These are some of the outlines which could lead to an improvement of our position. They presume a very much closer co-operation between companies within the industry and indeed between different paper producing countries throughout the world and very much better horizontal communications than we have at present. Also, within individual companies and groups, vertical communication must be improved, as large numbers of responsible executive personnel are unaware of some of the major problems facing the industry. Without this improvement, the great technological advances and skills of our industry will continue to be wasted."

In an article published in "The World's Paper Trade Review" on 28 January 1971 I drew attention to the fact that between 1954 and 1967 the price index for paper and board was some 20 per cent below other manufactured industrial goods, while its raw material index was actually 4% higher than for all other industries, resulting in an incredible pressure on margins for paper and board manufacturers.

On 22 November 1972 I gave a paper to the Technical Section which could also just as well have been given today. I should like to quote from it as follows:

"Looking around the paper industry in Europe today is reminiscent of a battlefield scene where neither side has won and both sides have suffered very heavy casualties. The area is littered with the dead and wounded.

In human terms it is a relatively harmless situation, for instead of blood only money flows into the ground, but like human resources the dead cannot be revived and the rehabilitation of the wounded is a very long and costly process. We may well ask ourselves the question why it happened and whether it was really necessary in an industry that is far from declining, involving a production for which demand is rising at a higher rate than most other industrial commodities in the western world.

It is well known that the basic reason for this situation is that more paper was produced than the market was able to consume. Although consumption has risen steadily, the increases have not taken place in regular annual steps and they have been tied to the growth of the Western European economy in general.

Following the recession of 1967, we had a rather sharp increase in consumption during 1968–69 followed by a levelling-off and an actual minor decline in 1970–71. This is now being caught up by another sharp increase during this year. All appears therefore to be set fair for 1973, but we can already forecast the next recession, based on the cyclical experience of previous years, to take place some time in 1975.

If, as individuals and indeed individual companies and mills, there is very little, or nothing, we can do about this highly unfortunate situation, we can at least try and analyse the reasons behind it and the motivation of those who bring about the consequences.

In theory, the responsibility is wholly collective and rests squarely on the shoulders of the pulp and paper industries of the world. Basically, the individual motivation is aimed at achieving a profit for the company, but the ways to this rather desirable end are extremely strange.

The first of these is the assumption that new units installed at very high capital cost, but low labour cost, would out-compete older written-off units operating their mills on a low capital but high labour cost. The initial calculation shows a loss on account of high depreciation, interest and capital charges in spite of low labour costs, but anticipates a reversal of the situation when, through the passage of time, the depreciation will have been reduced and the low labour cost will win over the older unit, thus producing a profit.

The second motivation is one of strength and power of the big corporations and those who lead them. We have a situation very similar to that in politics, where the interests of the shareholders (in politics, the electorate) are thrown overboard in favour of winning a great victory over their opponents and after they have forced them into closing their mills, profit will be their ultimate end result.

The third motivation is one of pure technology without marketing, utilisation of natural resources and subsequent conquest of markets through price.

The immediate result of all three motivations described above is very clearly a net loss. They have one thing in common—no marketing, ignorance of the basic fact that demand cannot be stimulated by price. In each case, however, there is a justification.

In the first instance, the ultimate strength of the modern unit with its lower labour costs over the older mills; in the second, the greater market share after eliminating the competition through forcing it to close; in the third, the ultimate victory of the technologically perfectly sited units basing their output on enormous resources of raw materials and cheap power. As in politics these promises are hardly ever fulfilled. In the last few decades, no war has ever left a nation better off than it was before it started and no electorate would have voted voluntarily in favour of going to war unless in sheer defence of their lives and freedom.

The same applies to our industry. The war which has now been raging for some 10 years has involved all those mills who were not prepared voluntarily to close down their production and hand over their orders to their competitors. The electorate, that is, the shareholders, were never consulted and certainly would never have agreed to the rather irresponsible course that our industry has taken, although it is all supposed to be for their good in the long term.

We can next ask ourselves what defence a mill, region or country has against this situation—what lessons can be drawn from past experience?

The possibilities of a company's defence depend entirely on its size, production and location. A newsprint mill, for example, can survive in Southern Germany, close to the scarce forest resources in continental Europe and far away from the ports that bring in cheap Scandinavian and North American imports. A similar company situated, for instance, in The Netherlands or in the UK would be facing the greatest difficulties.

A de-inking waste mill has failed in Sweden, but has succeeded in the UK. The processing of waste is generally the best defence in a market with a high density of population and far removed from the forest resources of integrated mills. A small speciality mill can survive in a large market, but it would soon be out of business if it exported its entire output of speciality papers.

Retreat into specialisation can only take place, therefore, for a limited number of mills in a limited number of large markets, otherwise overproduction of specialities will result with the same disastrous consequences that have already overtaken the rest of the industry.

Defence can also be taken on a national basis through the active intervention of trade associations, such as in France, or governmental intervention through tariffs, such as in Spain or the Republic of Ireland. These usually have very severe repercussions, as most advanced nations have substantial bilateral trade and any restrictions on imports, or trade tariffs for any commodity, bring with them immediate reciprocal disadvantages from their trading partners. Therefore, this is a rather difficult course to follow for any of the highly developed countries, such as the enlarged EEC, and the

22

matter rests as it always has done, collectively on the industry as a whole.

Many companies still operating today do so in an economically much weaker position than they did 10 years ago, having been depleted of their resources and reserves and unable to borrow any more money to maintain their mills at an efficient level. Many machines are still being operated at a direct loss, although the majority of these have now been closed down.

Unfortunately, most of the closures took place after involving the mill in very substantial losses that could have been foreseen as all cost factors and selling levels were known. Yet, incredibly, the obvious step of closing *before* the losses had piled up was, in many cases, not taken, perhaps in anticipation of some miracle that did not materialise. When they finally closed down, the losses involved often exceeded the value of the machine. Therefore, the cost of hanging on is extremely high and a closure before the loss is clearly preferable to a closure after the loss.

What is going to be the future pattern? The old school of thought that this or that country or region is *our* market is clearly no longer viable. Among the free trading nations, pulp, paper and board is one market and each unit must take a detached and highly critical look at itself and ask itself the questions—*how* viable is it? How profitable is it now? How much money is being generated to *maintain* that profitability? How should any funds, either generated or borrowed, be invested in the mill?

Clearly not in increasing the output unless this is backed by a tangible demand for the product, for any increase under present circumstances, based on reducing production costs without existing demand, worsens the situation and reduces overall profitability to the industry.

Whichever way is chosen, whether rationalisation or diversification, or ultimately closure, the reason must have been clearly analysed beforehand rather than left to luck or providence, or a combination of both.

We must also recognise that we cannot make paper without employing people. These employees are not in the least concerned with the resources, or power politics, or technological advantages of certain companies that have brought about a collapse of the price structure to levels that no longer bear any relation to costs.

While the price of most commodities is based on costs, but subject to the law of supply and demand, the price of labour is not. There is now almost one million unemployed in the UK. Yet the cost of labour continues to rise. We can expect, therefore, all our costs to go on rising however much governments may try from time to time to put a brake on inflation.

It is not my objective here to go into the economics of inflation, but to point out the necessity of charging those who use our products a realistic cost for paper and board, as indeed we are being charged for whatever we purchase or consume.

If, as a result of all this, we can one day achieve a balance between supply and demand, then we can look forward to a happier future. For it will only be then that we will be able to sell our products at a price reflecting a true relation to our costs and start slowly and laboriously to replenish our reserves and to repay the debts for which we are at present barely earning the interest."

A balance between demand and supply has clearly not been achieved and the situation is now worse than ever.

The only people who appeared to have got their marketing right were the forecasters of wishful thinking who, for high fees sold to the paper industry what it apparently wanted to hear, on the same basis as the gypsy at the fair ground would sell the handsome dark stranger every girl wants to meet, and in this way justified the wrong investment decisions of management.

It is therefore not surprising that after more than two decades of overproduction and subsequent lack of profitability, the paper industry, particularly in Britain, was quite unable to face the latest onslaught in the form of high energy costs, high interest rates and completely artificial pulp and paper price ratios, manipulated through the international cartel of the suppliers of wood pulp.

In a growing number of countries bankrupt companies continue to manufacture paper under the management of Government receivers, thus distorting the natural adjustment consequential upon closures resulting from over-production and accumulated losses.

We ought not to deplore the lack of assistance to bankrupt industries in Britain, but rather condemn the maintenance of artificial employment through government intervention elsewhere. This does not mean, however, that I condone the present Government's completely irrational policy of energy pricing and interest levels, which in themselves ought not to be a sufficient reason for the wholesale closures we have been witnessing if the companies concerned had been able to accumulate sufficient reserves over the past two decades.

We still have all over Europe a small number of profitable paper companies in spite of this situation. They are those who, through outstanding management, have succeeded not only to survive but continue generating sufficient profits to be able to add to the reserves which have enabled them to keep alive.

Whether they have achieved this through high productivity, right investment decisions in their particular circumstances, or vertical integration, or good marketing is immaterial. It shows that where average management is struggling, outstanding management can show a profit.

It is gratifying to be a prophet who has been proved right, but it is very much less so when the doom that I have forecast has actually materialised. At present I have no intention of selling you a handsome dark stranger, but like all optimists, I never give up hope. A spark of hope that perhaps one day a few of those responsible will see the light that is there for everyone to see.

G. T. MANDL HOLDINGS LTD

The roots of the history of this company go back into Central Europe where my grandfather bought the small Mechanical Pulp and Board Mill near Carlsbad from Mr Ernst Naundorff in 1920.*

He had inherited and developed a prospering liqueur distillery and fruit juice business in Troppau from his father and intended to diversify into another industry, as he had two sons. My father, Dr Gottfried Mandl (1886–1941) was put in charge of the Mill without very great enthusiasm after his return from the war with the Austrian army. Having studied philosophy in Vienna and commenced work with a firm of publishers in Leipzig, he was set on an academic rather than commercial career and initially hoped that the Mill would take care of itself whilst he could pursue his interests in the academic field. The dishonesty of his mill manager which came to light in the year of his father's death, brought him abruptly back to reality and he started to take a serious interest in the mill. After his marriage and the investment of my mother's entire dowry in modernising the mill, it became his major interest in life to such an extent that he never took a holiday. He was one of the founder members of the Czech Association of Board Makers "Kartonia" in 1928 and succeeded in keeping the mill employed during the great recession of 1929 to 1933. Vertical integration into carton and box-making commenced in the late 1920s and by the outbreak of war the entire production of the mill was being converted.† It was his intention that I should follow him in the mill and he brought me in as an apprentice in the summer of 1937, which has given me the opportunity of completing almost 50 years in the paper industry as an occasion for the publication of this book.

The mill processed both pulpwood and waste paper, generated its own energy through steam and a water turbine and thus with its 200 employees, provided me with a very good training ground in all major aspects of our industry.

One of my father's greatest limitations was his inability to learn foreign languages. He spoke only his native German and did not even acquire an elementary knowledge of the Czech language which was used in our household. In order to avoid this particular handicap, my father sent me to Czech, German, French and English schools,

* A brief history of this mill, which was founded in 1870, was published in German in the Swiss Paper Historians *Kontakte*, see page 347 (reprinted in full).
  † British Patent of 1938, see page 351.

not realising that he was providing me with a greater asset than the value of the mill.

I was at school in England when war broke out and joined the Allied forces at the age of 18. After the end of the war and subsequent upon my father's death, I took over the management of the mill at the age of 22. This was not to be of long duration, as Czechoslovakia soon disappeared completely behind the Iron Curtain and the mill was nationalised without compensation in February, 1948. I attempted to continue working in another division of the nationalised corporation but soon found out that the conflict of outlook would make any future co-operation impossible. I left with great difficulties for England in February 1949 and took up employment with the Buckinghamshire Paper & Box Company in West Drayton as a Costing Clerk in the Sales Department. Whilst still in control of the mill in Czechoslovakia, I had registered a company under the name of London Boxboard Company Limited in 1947, which was intended as a sales agency for the marketing of our boards and boxes in export markets, but nothing other than the registration and an unpaid bill for the formation expenses had remained by the time I arrived in England. I arranged to take over the registration and the bill on the understanding that I should return it if I was unable to repay the debt. I duly started an attempt to generate some foreign agencies not competing with the boxmaking trade of my employers but before any business could result I was given the option of either transferring the future business to my employers or getting the sack.

Having found suitable partners in the persons of two wartime colleagues from the Czech forces—Arnost Polak and Ivan Schwarz—I duly set up in business at their office at 56 George Street, London W.1, as managing director, salesman, typist and office boy all in one, at a salary of £9 per week, which was a great improvement on the £6 per week I was earning in West Drayton.

In order to accelerate the viability of this one-man business, I imported some of the first knitted shirts from Hong Kong, which were sold at 2s 6d each to the warehouse merchants, Bradbury Greatorex, and I believe it was one of these that had the doubtful honour of being thrown across the floor of the House of Commons at the time.

In 1950 our office moved to 245 Knightsbridge where an amicable separation from my partners was arranged. I moved to 129 Cannon Street and finished paying off my partners by 1954. The brief departure from the paper industry into Hong Kong shirts and similar articles was carried on by a newly formed Company, Goodall Young & Co. Ltd, in which I remained a partner, and which operated successfully, trading mainly in West Africa until the virtual expulsion of UK-based companies precipitated the closure of its head office and branches in Ghana and Nigeria.

27

The 7 years from 1950 to 1957 spent in Cannon Street can truly be described as the foundation years for the present business. Through our mill in Czechoslovakia I knew Ihlee & Sankey, Board and Paper Merchants, at 38 Wilson Street, London E.C.2, one of the great names of British paper merchanting which have sadly disappeared from the scene. It was a partnership originated by the two founding partners in 1866, handed down to succeeding generations of partners who were drawn from senior employees. Thus the firm continued not unlike a family business but without any blood relationship between the owners. Amongst the last generation of four partners was Mr A.G.W Freeman, head of the Fancy Paper Department of Ihlee & Sankey, who regularly accepted my invitations to the Paper Agents' Dinner in place of Mr D.H. Potton, who was by tradition otherwise engaged for that particular function with the party of the United Board Agencies of Finland. Thus Mr Freeman attended our party each year without personally doing any trade with my company, which he tried to remedy by first recommending me for the vacant agency of La Turnhoutoise in 1954, which brought me into the fancy paper field. It was also he who was instrumental in recommending my company for the vacant agency of Thomas & Green Ltd for the North of England in 1956 which, together with my agency for John Pitts & Sons Ltd of Exeter, created the first connection with British mills.

Having come from the board industry, the initial years of my activity as a mill agent were concentrated in the area of boards, so familiar to me from previous years. In 1952 I was appointed Agent for N.V. Cartonfabriek Beukema & Co., one of the market leaders in Dutch strawboards.

The formation of G.T. Mandl & Co. in 1956 saw our entry into the paper market, first in flexible packaging papers from Sweden, and subsequently adding writings and printings, so that by the beginning of the 1960s the agency covered practically all types of paper and board. Our Swedish agency of Pauliström Mill first brought me in touch with cellulose wadding, which was subsequently produced at Fourstones Mill with the active technical assistance of my Swedish friends. During all of this time my business interests were not only confined to selling foreign papers in the UK but business was simultaneously being built up in selling paper in other European countries, notably Belgium, Germany, Denmark and Austria. In the 1960s branch offices of the agency were established in these countries in partnership with local men and group sales exceeded 100,000 tons a year.

All appeared set fair for a prosperous and well-established agency business had it not been for the structural changes taking place in Sweden.

The growing concentration of the paper industry eliminated the

Ernst Naundorff Board Mill. Merklin near Carlsbad Czechoslovakia in 1946

A view of Netstal village Switzerland, with the Upper Paper Mill, founded in 1679 in the right bottom corner. It was closed down in 1974. In the background Mt Glarnisch, 2.950 m

Aerial view of Netstal Paper Mill Switzerland in 1977

G. T. Mandl & Co A/S Otterup
Denmark, Makers of Coffee Filters

Pallet of Coffee Filters for Super
Markets

Indupa NV Zaventem, Belgium.
Makers of Coffee Filters

Thomas & Green Ltd. Arborfield Mill, Helpston, Peterborough, formerly Towgood & Beckwith,
taken in the 1960s

Filtration Exhibition, Olympia 1979 *l. to r.*: ALEC SCOUGALL, G. T. MANDL, BILL LIVINGSTONE

The Board of Directors of the Swiss Linthesa Holding AG taken in
Netstal at the Annual General Meeting on 1 June 1985. *From left to
right:* Willi Fischer, Hans Maier, G. T. Mandl, Richard Sauter,
Anders Tullberg.

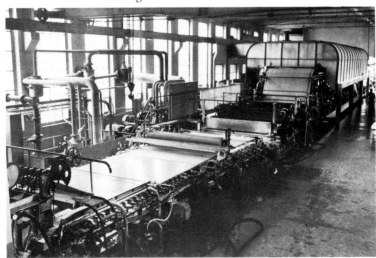

The Filter Paper Machine
225 cm wide at Netstal
Paper Mill in 1974

The Board of Directors of Thomas & Green Holdings at the Group Management Meeting at Arborfield Mill on 7 June 1985. *From left to right:* Roy Gamble, Poul Grönbech, Tage Miskov, George Robinson, G. T. Mandl, Michael Klimes, Harry Pollak, Emile Vanhamme, George Meadows.

use of the independent paper agent and substituted him with the groups' own offices in the major European markets. We were thus first pushed out from our major agencies which included Brusafors-Hällefors (part of Modo), Strömsnäs Bruk (part of Södra), Cellva (part of Klippan and Modo) and Stora Kopparberg, the United Paper Mills of Denmark and many others.

In 1962 I acquired a majority interest in Fourstones Paper Mill, followed by my appointment to the board of Thomas & Green and its subsidiary H. Allnutt & Son in 1963 which ultimately led to the control of both companies and their merger into Thomas & Green Holdings in 1972.

What was at first intended as a diversification from agency back to paper manufacture soon proved to be the main future for my company. A very large tail had begun to wag a very small dog.

EXTENDING INTO EUROPE

We opened our first office in Vienna in 1964 in partnership with Mr Josef Leitner. It was intended to produce coffee filters for the Austrian market based on paper production at Fourstones and at the same time to represent foreign mills for the Austrian market which, at that time, began to dismantle its extremely high protective tariffs under the EFTA Treaty. Whilst the agency, which still represents leading Scandinavian companies including Munksjö, Union, Follum and others, became an immediate success, the introduction of a new domestic coffee filter proved to be rather difficult and the project was subsequently transferred to Denmark.

Our Brussels office was opened following the granting of the Klippan Group agency for Belgium and subsequently represented a large number of mills for different kinds of paper and board on the Belgian market.

In 1966 an office was opened in Düsseldorf representing mainly corrugated case-making materials and packaging papers. With the growing success of the two UK operations, it was my intention to acquire a mill in Germany with the object of integrating it with the agency. An opportunity arose in 1972 with the bankruptcy of Fritz & Co. KG, who were operating a board mill in Laufen in Southern Germany with an annual capacity of 20,000 tons of white lined and coated boards, founded in 1733. There was also the great temptation to return to the industry from which my family had started only some 250 miles away in a mill situated close to the West German border.

The project got off to a bad start and had to be closed down again during the severe recession of 1975.

Our interests in Denmark commenced with the export of filter paper from Fourstones in 1964. We had built up sufficient volume by 1966 to register our own company in partnership with Mr Poul Grönbech, who is still the General Manager. We started with one converting machine in Mr Grönbech's coffee warehouse in Odense but soon moved into our own premises. In 1972 we bought a freehold site in the village of Otterup and the new factory was officially opened on my fiftieth birthday on 8 August 1973. Since then, further land has been acquired to a total of four acres, and the factory has been extended several times. Denmark has definitely proved to be one of the most successful of our operations and its future in vertical integration through direct sales to supermarkets seems to be assured.

In 1974 we entered into an agreement with Papierfabrik Netstal AG in Switzerland to transfer some of our filter production for the Danish factory from the Thomas & Green mill due to lack of capacity there at the time. At the same time the Netstal Mill was rebuilt and restructured from glazed mechanical printings, for which it was no longer viable, to filter and other speciality papers.

Very considerable difficulties had to be overcome from the very beginning. The recession of 1974 prevented the full utilisation of capacity and short time working had to be maintained until 1979, before outlets for coffee filter paper could gradually be created. The original object of selling a substantial proportion of the mill's output on the Swiss domestic market could not be realised and vertical integration in the coffee filter market, involving the export of more than 90% of the mill's output, finally brought it to full employment as from 1980.

Whilst the market shares in the Nordic countries were increased through the Danish converting company, increasing quantities of filter paper were being taken by the Belgian company, Indupa NV in Zaventem, which became an associated company through the acquisition of a substantial shareholding in 1982, now being supplied with its entire requirements of coffer filter paper from the Netstal Mill.

On 4 April 1979 the Netstal mill was able to celebrate its tercentenary and published a separate book about its history.

The mill is now the third oldest still working in Switzerland and was in the ownership of the founders' familily from 1679 until 1921. In 1765 the government of Glarus issued a prohibition of the sale of rags with a specific directive to deliver these to Ludwig Zweifel, the then owner of the mill, to secure its supply of raw materials. Hand-made production continued into the 1860s.

The history from its foundation up to 1853 was published in German in the Swiss Paper Historians (SPH) Year Book 1978, "*Die Geschichte Der 7 Papiermühlen im Kanton Glarus*" and the full history was published by Papierfabrik Netstal AG in 1979 bringing the history of the mill right up to date, under the title *G. T. Mandl: Dreihundert Jahre Papierfabrik Netstal*.

30

The long drawn out negotiations for the acquisition of the freehold land and buildings due to the substantial increase in the exchange rate of the Swiss franc since 1974, were finally concluded in 1982 and a majority shareholding in the company of the previous owners, Linthesa Holding AG, was acquired, the Netstal Mill becoming a wholly-owned subsidiary of Linthesa Holding AG. At the same time a 50% interest in the Linthkraft AG hydro-electric power station was acquired, integrating the mill with more than 80% of its electrical energy supplies.

Looking back over the past 25 years, I should like to quote from the speech of Sir Rupert Speir, at that time MP for Hexham, at the bicentenary celebrations of Fourstones Mill: "The mill has been known as a village industry. Now its future may be going to be on a wider, more global scale."

Perhaps "global" is not quite the right description but there is nevertheless some truth in the statement.

Having reached a peak of 550 employees during 1974, we were down to just under 250 in 1985, firmly set upon a course of consolidation and optimum utilisation of our resources.

HISTORY OF FOURSTONES PAPER MILL

Family Tree of the Rumney papermaking family of Fourstones Paper Mill

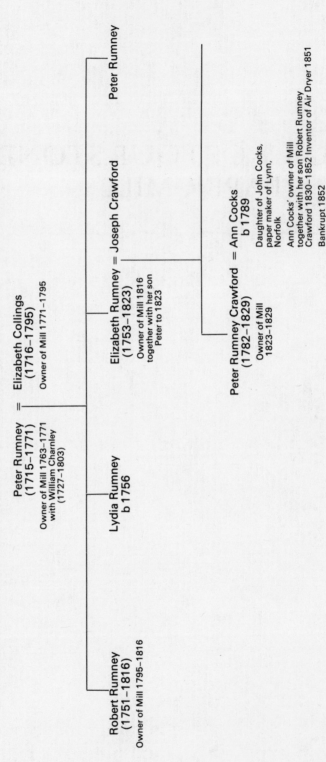

Peter Rumney
(1715–1771)
Owner of Mill 1763–1771
with William Charnley
(1727–1803)

= Elizabeth Collings
(1716–1795)
Owner of Mill 1771–1795

Robert Rumney
(1751–1816)
Owner of Mill 1795–1816

Lydia Rumney
b 1756

Elizabeth Rumney = Joseph Crawford
(1753–1823)
Owner of Mill 1816
together with her son
Peter to 1823

Peter Rumney

Peter Rumney Crawford = Ann Cocks
(1782–1829)   b 1789
Owner of Mill
1823–1829

Daughter of John Cocks,
paper maker of Lynn,
Norfolk

Ann Cocks' owner of Mill
together with her son Robert Rumney
Crawford 1830–1852 Inventor of Air Dryer 1851

Bankrupt 1852

Edward Grierson

PREFACE TO FOURSTONES HISTORY

Two centuries ago, on 21 April 1763, the mill now known as The Fourstones Paper Mill Company Ltd was founded at Warden on the South Tyne, two miles west of the market town of Hexham, which King James the First and Sixth in a moment of rare tact once called "The heart of all England."

The name Warden appears as such in the Border Survey of 1542, but before that time was spelt in a variety of other ways—Waredun, Wardon, or Wardun—but always with the same meaning of "Watch Hill", so appropriate to a hamlet set under the tumulus shaped height that dominates the junction of the North and South Tyne rivers. Fourstones village is three quarters of a mile away to the west, and here antiquaries have advanced no fewer than four possible derivations for the name, which may be connected with the quarrying which had gone on here for centuries or with the presence of four stone altars that were once said to have stood in the open fields, one of which, called "the fairy stone", was supposedly used as a secret letter box during the Earl of Derwentwater's rising in the "Fifteen".

People have lived in this laboured place far longer than written records go. Traces of a bronze age burial of a woman and child of the so-called "Beaker Folk" were found near the banks of the river in 1928, including a tool-worked covering stone weighing over a ton, and another stone cist, containing a male skeleton, was found near the confluence of the Tynes in the last century. No traces have come to light of the wattle huts, like kraals, which may have laid among the strips of cultivated land on the lower slopes, but the whole area of the North Tyne is rich in tumuli, standing stones and other prehistoric works of man, and on the six hundred foot heights of Warden Hill itself a mound and three concentric horseshoe-shaped ramparts of dry stone walling mark the site of the war camp of the people of the valley. From such a position, high among the whinns and heather and the remains of primaeval forests, the first Northumbrians may have seen one day the glint of sunlight on the breastplates and eagles of the legions advancing to the very limits of the known world.

Britain had been familiar to the Romans for three hundred years before Julius Caesar made his raids upon it in 55 and 54 BC. But not before the 'eighties of the first century after Christ did the great general Julius Agricola overrun the island to the Forth–Clyde line and begin the wonderful network of roads, some of which, such as the Stanegate between Corbridge and Carlisle, can be seen to this day.

In 122 Hadrian, "the Imperial Tramp", came in person and decided to build a wall—he is commemorated in the district by an important paintworks and an excellent inn, which would have pleased this busy and progressive man.

In fact, the Wall owes less to Hadrian than to the legate Aulus Platorius Nepos, under whom the main construction was undertaken, though it was not finally completed till some time after AD 130. Of its many and great vicissitudes historians learned and unlearned have written by the score. Devastated by civil wars and barbarian invaders, it was nearly in ruins by AD 200; was then rebuilt under the great emperor Septimius Severus, who taught the tribes a lesson that was remembered for nearly a hundred years; was burnt again about 300 by the Picts, making their first enigmatic appearance on the stage; was rebuilt and flourished till the disastrous year of 367, when a combination of invasion from the north and sea raiders from the German coast overran and devastated almost the whole province of Britain as its Roman masters knew it. There remained to it one last brief assertion of imperial power under Count Theodosius in 369, before the legions were recalled to Rome and an island which had in large part accepted the dominion of the world-state was left to fend for itself and relapsed gradually into barbarism.

At the height of its efficiency the great work ran 80 Roman miles from Wallsend on Tyne to Bowness on Solway, covering the whole northern frontier with a complex of forts, milecastles and military roads. It was planned not so much to contain the Picts as to act as a base for policing them in their territory and for counter-attack if necessary. The aim was to pacify and embrace all the South Britons, and this was substantially achieved in the last years, when the use of the Wall as a barrier had lost its meaning.

Considered purely as a defence work, it was formidable enough. In cross-section, to the north was a V shaped ditch and berm; then the wall itself, twenty feet high, eight or ten feet wide, and bristling along its course with the fortified turrets known as milecastles and no fewer than 36 major forts, each capable of housing a cohort of five hundred men. Behind it was the ditch called the Vallum, which was apparently a boundary line marking the limits of the military zone, and a lateral road crossed by a series of north–south turnpikes communicating with other forts, both to the rear, at strategic points, and out in barbarian territory on the Pictish side.

Even in ruins it has about it an extraordinary air of authority and grandeur. "Verily," wrote Camden, the great antiquary of the first

36

Elizabeth's day, "I have seene the tract of it over the high pitches and steepe descents of hilles, wonderfully rising and falling." In the desolation of those windswept heights along the cliffs of the Great Whinn Sill one can look back across the sixteen centuries to the time of its power, as Kipling saw it in *Puck of Pook's Hill*:

> ... a smoke from east to west as far as the eye can turn, and then, under it as far as the eye can stretch, houses and temples, shops and theatres, barracks and granaries, trickling along like dice behind—always behind one long, low, rising and falling, and hiding and showing line of towers. And that is the Wall! THE Wall! But the Wall itself is not more wonderful than the town behind it. ... a thin town, eighty miles long. Think of it! One roaring, rioting, cock-fighting, wolf-baiting, horse-racing town!

To this day the pastures are richer where Roman buildings stood; the oats and barley ripen sooner along the strips of land where the roads once ran. Roman stones from the wall find their uses still: in the tower of Warden church and St Wilfrid's crypt in Hexham, as well as in numerous houses and dykes throughout the countryside.

Of the thirty-six forts, two lie within a radius of three miles of Fourstones Mill. A small fort behind the main line, at Newbrough, is even nearer, but is hardly to be compared with the great wall fort of Chesters, the Roman Cilurnum, which with Housesteads is probably the most famous of all, as it is certainly the most accessible.

Covering nearly six acres of ground, Cilurnum guarded the southern end of the bridge that crossed the North Tyne at this point, just downstream from the present Chollerford Bridge and the charmingly placed George Hotel with its lawns by the river. It was garrisoned by five hundred men of the second *ala* or cohort of Asturians from northern Spain. The Wall was not manned by the legions, who lay in their garrison towns well behind the frontiers, the *Sixth Victrix* at York, the *Twentieth Valeria Victrix* at Chester, the *Second Augusta* at Caerleon on Usk. These crack units of the army stayed in reserve except in times of trouble, leaving the run of the mill patrolling of the frontier to the lighter armed auxillaries drawn from almost every province of the Roman world. Troops from the Dalmatian coast garrisoned the fort of Magna; Gauls, Vindolanda; Hadrian's Own Marines were at Tunnocelum; Aurelius's Own Moors from Africa at Aballaba, and one wonders how they took to the bitter Northumbrian winters on those heights.

The tendency was for the veterans of the units which had built the Wall to remain after demobilisation in the areas they had garrisoned, intermarrying with the tribal women and settling in the villages that grew up in the shelter of the forts, with temples, baths and every modern convenience at their disposal, including a wide choice of pubs. In one of these, at Housesteads, a body was found buried surreptitiously among the foundations with the point of a knife embedded in his ribs, proof of some tavern brawl that justifies the neat little notice set up by the Ministry of Works on the site—*Murder House*, it reads. As Sir Winston Churchill has pointed out, the ordinary inhabitants of these islands had to wait till late Victorian times before getting a hot bath as enjoyed as a matter of course by every Roman soldier on the Wall. At Chesters this marvellous system of hot and cold rooms, worthy of comparison with the Turkish baths of today, stands in an excellent state of preservation for all to see. No comforts were spared. Among the refuse in the camp the shells of oysters, mussels, cockles and limpets have been found strewn on the floor where the rushes must once have lain: proof of the age-old Spanish taste for sea-foods and paella and of the thoughtfulness of quartermasters who brought such delicacies to a place thirty miles from the nearest coast.

Perhaps Cilurnum, as one might guess from the cosiness of its site, was a specially comfort-loving camp. At Procolitia, the next fort in the line as one goes westward, still within three miles of the Mill, it is the evidence of the soldiers' religious needs that takes the eye, in the remarkable temple of Mithras that has been excavated in recent years, with its three statues of the god and proofs of desecration at the hands, presumably, of some Christian commander.

Procolitia was garrisoned in the fourth century by the first cohort of Batavians from what is now the Low Countries, replacing troops from Aquitaine. They seem to have acquired habits since made famous by tourists at the fountains of Rome, for at the bottom of the west slopes of the fort, in swampy ground at the source of a stream, a shrine to the water goddess of the place, the nymph Coventina, enclosed a well which has yielded up no fewer than thirteen thousand, four hundred and eighty-seven coins dating from the time of Mark Antony to that of the emperor Gratian, some of them tossed in no doubt as votive offerings, though the main hoard may have been buried there at some time of peril in the very last days of occupation by a garrison that never returned.

Soon after AD 400 two centuries of darkness descend on Britain, lit only by the legendary deeds of King Arthur, enshrining the folk memory of resistance to the barbarian invasion that fell upon the land from every side once the legions had been recalled to Italy.

In the *Morte Darthur* Mallory sets many of his hero's adventures along the line of the Wall, between Carlisle, where the king and Guinevere held court, to Lancelot's impregnable "Castle of the Joyous Gard", which some say was Alnwick and some Bamburgh. According to Mallory it was "at Fourstones Castle" that Balan met Balin, his brother and fellow knight of the Round Table, just freed from "dolorous prisonment".

Alas for legend! No trace of any castle has been discovered at

Fourstones—not even the walled meadow which in Scott's words "tracks the moor with green" on the ancient site of Sewingshields where Arthur himself held court. In a subterranean hall deep down beneath the castle, King Arthur, his queen, his knights and even his hounds still sit enchanted, so legend says, like Barbarossa and the Sleeping Beauty, awaiting the day when someone stumbling on their resting place will blow a bugle and cut a garter with a stone sword, all of which are conveniently placed there for the purpose. The story goes that in the eighteenth century a shepherd of Sewingshields found by accident the secret passage and reached the vaulted cavern, where by the light of a "fire without fuel" he saw the sleeping figures of enchanted lords and thirty couple of equally enchanted hounds. The shepherd, recovering from his terror, guessed the purpose of the garter and duly cut it with the sword; at which the king awoke, and fixing his deliverer with jaundiced eye, declaimed, before returning to the sleep of ages:

> O woe betide that evil day
> On which this witless wight was born
> Who drew the sword, the garter cut,
> But never blew the bugle horn!

Arthur was fortunate. The Dark Ages that followed the collapse of the Britons' heroic but doomed resistance to their savage foes were good centuries to sleep through. No records survive of the fate of the Romanised tribes that had lived behind the Wall, but little imagination is needed to guess that it must have been a grim one, as bad as anything that befell other displaced peoples in our own century. In the mountains of Wales and Strathclyde the defeated found sanctuary of a kind, but when Northumberland emerges again into the light a new Germanic race is ruling there and all the old landmarks of culture and language have been swept away, even their origins forgotten.

Christianity went down with the rest, submerged under a tide of paganism which only began to turn again after two hundred years, when the powerful and enlightened Edwin of Northumbria was baptised by the Roman missionary Paulinus, and St Aidan and his Celtic monks from Iona began their conversions from a base on Lindisfarne.

Civilisation was returning. Not peace, however. A series of sanguinary battles marked the struggle between the new Christian kingdoms into which the island was being divided and the doughty champion of the old pagan gods, King Penda of Mercia, who chopped off the heads of Edwin and his successor Oswald before losing his own to a third Northumbrian champion, Oswy. Oswald, St Oswald, is still commemorated by a cross and memorial chapel on the site of his victory of Heavenfield, near Chesters, over an army of Britons making their positively last appearance in the bloody pageant of the age. Nor were the Christian priests much more peaceably inclined, torn as they were between the rival claims of Iona and those of Rome, which finally won the day after a grand series of debates at the Synod of Whitby.

Bishop Wilfrid, later canonised as St Wilfrid, had been the main architect of this Roman victory which brought the Anglo-Saxon kingdoms into line with the mainstream of Christian Europe. His friend and patroness Queen Etheldrid, wife of Egfrid King of Northumbria, was moved by his success to give him a gift of land out of her dower, amounting to almost the whole of what came later to be called the Regality of Hexham, and on this site Wilfrid set to work to build a church in honour of St Andrew. In 678, after four years, the great building was completed and marvelled at by travellers as the finest north of the Alps. Only the crypt of it remains today, but we know that it was in the form of a basilica, with arcades, paintings, and even an aqueduct of its own.

Wilfrid was a saint. But even saints may be opinionated. And tactless too. Queen Etheldrid, beautiful and much beloved by her husband, desired only to live a life of chastity. This was not an ambition that King Egfrid shared. Calling upon their mutual friend the bishop to make his bride see things in a proper light, the monarch was distressed to find that she was actually being encouraged to leave him for a nunnery. To such a story there could only be one end. The king lost his wife (he soon remarried); the bishop lost his see and rushed off to Rome to beg help of the Pope. Of his later struggles we need not speak, but he left behind him a legacy of beauty and culture that was never quite forgotten in the north, even in the dark days that followed.

Between 821 and 874 waves of Viking invasions broke over the land, as savage and terrible as anything the Saxons had done three centuries earlier. The country between Lindisfarne and Carlisle at this time was known as the Waste, and in 875 Hexham (Hagustald) itself was ravaged and Wilfrid's great church burnt to the ground.

Somehow or other religious life went on in the town and the countryside that looked to it for leadership. Where bishops had ruled, and St Cuthbert had been proposed for the see, there were now simple priests who married and passed their benefices to their children along with the church lands. Perhaps things were improving a little when in 1071 William the Conqueror came north to punish his rebellious subjects and devastated the area all over again.

Nine years later the church was still in ruins, for we find Eilaf the priest being given permission to rebuild it. In that same year a new and still more deadly scourge of the unfortunate Northumbrians, the Scots, swept across the border, and enraged by the treatment given to one of their envoys in Hexham town, threatened to burn what was left of it, but were prevented from crossing the bridgeless river by mists and floods supposedly conjured up by the shades of St Cuthbert and St Wilfrid, who had *both* appeared to Eilaf in a dream prophesying this happy result.

Perhaps it was partly on this account that Hexham began about this time to gain wide renown as a place of saints and pilgrimage. The real fame of the area, however, had long depended on the peculiar position of Hexhamshire as a "Regality", a separate state in fact belonging to the Archbishops of York, where the king's writ did not run and the real ruler was the Bailiff, whose jurisdiction could impress even so ruthless and powerful a sovereign as Henry VIII. Far distant from York, the Bailiffs could easily become oppressors, interested only in lining their pockets, and as a result the whole district became known for its lawlessness, which was only modified when the first Augustinian canons arrived in Hexham, the forerunners of the great monastic house soon to rise on the site of Wilfrid's ruined church.

In 1296, however, the Scots swept down again and fired it, throwing all the previous relics into the flames and looting the gold and gems of its shrines. Not even St Andrew, the patron saint of Scotland, was spared indignity, for the head of his image was cut off and his ghost invited to return and plough his own country. Pious onlookers thought they heard the thunderous wrath of heaven at this atrocity, though a far worse one was being committed in the school, which was burnt with all its scholars inside it. The following year William Wallace was in the town after his victory at Stirling Bridge, and in 1312 Robert the Bruce sacked it, and its neighbour Corbridge for good measure, driving out the unfortunate canons, who only managed to struggle back after an exile of thirty years.

Small wonder that these were reckoned times of extreme hardship, when even a £40 loan from the Archbishop of York could not rescue the priory from destitution. And this state of things prevailed over the countryside surrounding Hexham and was perhaps most acute in Warden which had lain for years in the "Debatable Lands" between the Scottish and English kingdoms, claimed by both and often administratively split in two, so that a man claiming justice at one end of the parish had to go to the seat of local Scottish government at Wark on Tyne, whereas his neighbour at the other was in the English barony of Langley and would have his case tried at Langley Leet. King Edward I visited Warden in the course of his last expedition against the Scots, lodging at Thornton Tower, then the chief house in the parish, but even the coming of this great soldier and lawgiver did nothing to remedy things or compensate his subjects for the extreme rigours of their lives.

During the reign of the third Edward conditions began to improve—until the Black Death arrived to carry off a third of the population. One had a wide choice of horrors in those days. The Scots had given up the worst of their raiding, but it was not to be expected that so suffering a neighbourhood would manage to avoid being implicated in the ambitious schemes of the Percies, the uncrowned kings of the Border country, still less in the Wars of the Roses, one of the last battles of which was fought along the Devil's Water, a tributary of the Tyne.

About this time the celebrated *Black Book of Hexham* gives us some notion of rateable values as then understood. Warden is shown as part of the Priory lands, extending over twenty-eight acres and including six cottages, a ferry and a manor with a rental of £6 13s 4d, this money being appropriated to the cellarer for mead and wine. A canon and lay brother were in permanent residence in the village. By Henry VIII's time the once prosperous priory lands were no longer worth the two hundred pounds that the government had set as the economic level for such places, and it was accordingly decided to dissolve it along with scores of other foundations up and down the land.

The people of the north, however, were much attached to their monasteries; and on arrival in Hexham the king's commissioners were horrified to find the town in arms against them. This was in fact the beginning of the rebellion known as The Pilgrimage of Grace, which ended with executions throughout the north, Hexham Priory peaceably dissolved, and its prior packed off to a living in Yorkshire, *not* hanged at his own door as local tradition likes to insist. All the monastic buildings were pulled down, lead worth £266 being stripped off them, after which the land was leased to a worthy named Sir Richard Carnaby, who bred only daughters and was pursued in other ways by the indignation of heaven for his impiety. The church itself escaped, because the inhabitants untruthfully maintained that it was their parish church, and so it has remained ever since.

For the people of Hexhamshire and Warden peace of a kind now began to descend, marred only by a skirmish between Cavaliers and Roundheads in the Civil Wars and by a rising of the Catholic gentry under the Earl of Derwentwater in 1715, in the course of which the Old Pretender was proclaimed in Hexham market place as King James III. The area was always strong in Papists, against whom the penal statutes of the time weighed hard. Even a horse of more than £5 value was forbidden them. In 1745 Mr Leadbitter of Warden owned a particularly fine one, much in danger of falling into the hands of the government bailiffs. Accordingly it was hidden by Mr Leadbitter in a wood near Homer's Lane, but was tactless enough to neigh just when a picket of soldiers was riding by. It was therefore brought back to Warden and hoisted up by pulley into the loft above the carthorse stable, and there a wall of trusses of hay and straw was built around it. So closely watched, however, were the Leadbitters and their servants that they were unable to take water to the loft, and the poor beast, becoming restless, began to stamp furiously on the wooden floor while the search was at its height. A friend of the family, "Bowery" Charlton from the North Tyne, whom the Lead-bitters had befriended thirty-six years earlier at a time when he had been in dire trouble with the government for killing a man in a duel at Bellingham races, resolved to pay his debt. While the bailiffs were led one way, "Bowery" "lowered the horse through the trapdoor from the loft, jumped on its back and rode off over the haughs to How Mill Ford and across the floods and icefloes of the Tyne to safety in another Leadbitter house at Nafferton". All this less than twenty years before the foundation of the Fourstones Paper Mill in 1763.

It is amusing and instructive to look back on those times and see what conditions were like for others than "Bowery" and Mr Lead-bitter's horse. Beef, mutton and lamb cost 2d to 3$\frac{1}{2}d$ a pound; pork, 2$\frac{1}{2}d$; a goose, one shilling at harvest and 2/6d at Christmas. Salmon could be bought at Hexham market cross for 1$\frac{1}{2}d$—there was no Tyne pollution in those days. A labourer earned 8d a day; a carpenter 1s 4d; tailors "that do work by day", 6d, plus their victuals; the "Sunday Curate", £5 a year; the parish midwife, or gamster as she seems to have been called, 8s a month; and it is agreeable to note that of the three centenarians living in the parish about this time, one was still in general practice at this profession, to everyone's satisfaction.

In those delectable days a shirt cost 3s 4d, a penny more than a pair of shoes. Clogs cost 1s 6d; a bed gown, 5s; a sheet, the same; a surplice, £2 16s 1d; "a cloak for ye sexton", £1 4s 6d; a coffin, 9s. By contrast, port, still a luxury, was 4s 6d a bottle; ale, 2d a pint.

The drunkenness of the urban areas of the north was greatly to distress John Wesley when he came to Newcastle in 1742. "So much drunkenness," he laments, "such cursing and swearing even from the mouths of little children do I never remember to have seen or heard before in so small a compass of time. Surely this place is ripe for Him who came to call sinners to repentance." His preaching made a tremendous impression, and his brother Charles was able to establish a proper Methodist society in Newcastle and later to build a chapel costing close on £700.

In Hexham, five years later, John was greeted by "a great multitude of people who soon ran together, the greater part mad as colts". It was in the market place that he stood up to preach. "The Lord opened my mouth and they drew nearer and nearer, stole off their hats and listened; none offered to interrupt but one unfortunate squire, and he could get no one to second him."

After the preaching was over Sir Edward Blackett (perhaps "the unfortunate squire" and certainly the lord of the manor) ordered him to leave the town. Wesley announced that he would not speak again in the open market place. The only theatre he could find was a cockpit, where attempts were made to raise a mob against him. "I called in words first heard in that place," said John, " 'Repent and be converted that your sins may be blotted out.' God struck the hard rock and the waters gushed out. Never have I seen people more desirous of knowing the truth at first hearing."

Sir Edward, however, did not like to be defeated, and when a fortnight later Wesley returned to preach, servants appeared with their cocks and set them fighting, forcing the good man back into the market place again, where he had an audience four times as large as in the pit. On his last visit to the north, in 1790, he came through Hexham on his way from Carlisle to Newcastle, passing close to Warden "down the side of a fruitful mountain shaded with trees, and sloping down to a clear river which ran between this one and another fruitful mountain, well wooded and improved." Here he saw the newly built chapel—a fit meeting place for what he called "a loving people".

Wesley's visit to the district was in itself a portent: a breaking-in of the modern world upon an area that had for years been shut off from the mainstream of the nation's life. At the time of the excitements of the "Forty-five", when Prince Charles was at Carlisle on his southward march, the Hanoverian General Wade had found it impossible to concentrate against him with artillery along the appalling roads that led westward from Newcastle, and had in fact taken fifteen hours to reach Ovingham. He got to Hexham on the second day, but had to turn back because the tracks were quite impassable from that point, and the Prince was allowed to reach Derby unopposed.

As a result of Wade's reports on this unhappy incident it was decided to build a new road along the line of the Roman wall, using the original stones as a foundation, and this was completed in 1752, being known as "The Military" in the neighbourhood to this day. As the local rhyme had it:

> Had you seen the roads before they were made
> You'd have held up your hands and blessed General Wade.

It was still felt, however, that use should be made of the river Tyne to improve general communications, and in 1794 there was a project to build a canal from sea to sea. A Mr B.R. Dodd was inspired by the prospect to dream of market and passenger boats between Hexham and Newcastle, with even a buffet service provided of coffee, tea and wines.

No action followed, however. Woodroof's "single horse chaise" still kept jogging quietly along twice a week at 4s a head from the

White Hart in Newcastle Fishmarket to Hexham town, and there was still "expeditious travelling" to be had between Newcastle and Carlisle by Mr Sunderland's "diligence" at 14*s*; that rapid vehicle with its "three insides" leaving the Crown and Thistle in the Groatmarket at "half past eight o'clock" in the morning and arriving at the Bush Inn, Carlisle after precisely twelve hours.

In 1800 a paper was read to the Newcastle Literary and Philosophical Society advocating a railway, which was sufficiently necessary, since according to a Mr William Armstrong, corn could be brought to the Tyne more cheaply from the Cape of Good Hope than from Carlisle. After the success of the Stockton and Darlington Railway the local worthies began to agitate more pressingly for action, envisaging a railroad with horse-drawn vehicles, since steam locomotives were deemed revolting by the gentry. By the Act of 1829 which embodied these aspirations it was laid down that no locomotive or movable steam engine should be used on the new railway within view of various manor houses, including that of Nicholas Leadbitter, Esquire of Warden. By the time the first seventeen miles of track were opened on 9th March, 1835 these objections seem to have evaporated, as a quotation from *The Monthly Chronicle of North Country Lore and Legend* shows:

> Two trains, drawn by the Rapid and the Comet started from Blaydon for Hexham with banners and bands, triumphal arches, loud cheers and louder cannon. Swiftly flew the iron horse; and spectatotrs with good memories quoted the words of Erasmus Darwin:
>
> > Soon shall they arm, unconquered steam, afar
> > Drag the slow barge or drive the rapid car.

We may smile, but a generation that has pulled up the North Tyne line may perhaps allow the last laugh to these hardy ancestors, "closely crowded, omnibus fashion, inside and out", who rode behind the Rapid and the Comet out of Blaydon on that epic day. Actually the line was being laid from its western terminus at Carlisle as well, and in 1836 the two lengths arrived in Warden, which was served by *two* stations, one at West Boat and the other at Quality Corner, until eventually a rail bridge was built to link them across the Tyne.

We have mentioned Mr Leadbitter's objections to the Age of Steam. There had been Leadbitters in Warden for hundreds of years. A Mary Leadbitter in 1719 married a member of another well-known Roman Catholic family in the parish, Jasper Gibson, whose brother George had been "out" with the ill-fated Earl of Derwentwater in the "Fifteen". To this pair, twenty-two children were born. Four of their sons were priests, of whom two became bishops and in turn Vicars Apostolic of the Northern District, the younger being the founder of Ushaw College.

Another Catholic family, the Erringtons, had lived at Walwick since the twelfth century, building the great house of Chesters on the site of Roman Cilurnum in 1771. This estate passed in turn to Nathaniel Clayton, whose son John was responsible for the excavations at Cilurnum and the fort of Borcovicium at Housesteads, being the friend of Dr John Collingwood Bruce, the great name in the study of Roman antiquities along the Wall.

Not all the old families of the north were Catholic, though most of them were, along with half the "simple". In the Reverend John Shaftoe, who originally came from outside the parish, Warden was to produce another Vicar of Bray, almost contemporary with the hero of the song. In 1643 he was appointed under the Commonwealth to be a "preaching minister", bound to renounce bishops and all their works, including the Book of Common Prayer. After twenty years of this, however, he found no difficulty in 1663 in welcoming back a king, and having sworn his dutiful allegiance to the nearest bishop, settled down comfortably in his reading desk to exhort his parishioners to be good Anglicans. It was this nimble but benevolent man who founded the Haydon Bridge "Shaftoe Trust" schools, still with us to-day.

Less eminent, no doubt, but far more famous locally—indeed by far the most famous Warden man since Aulus Platorius Nepos built his wall—was Joseph Hedley, better known as Joe the Quilter, who had the misfortune to be murdered in the parish in 1826, in Homer's Lane.

> His quilts with country fame were crowned,
> So neatly stitched, and all the ground
> Adorned with flowers, and figured round,
> Oh! clever Joe the Quilter.

Joe's quilts indeed are still to be found in some of the big Northumbrian houses, and in his own day, he, who had started life as a poor tailor and died quite destitute, had attained a celebrity from his craft in England and even across the Atlantic which he probably never understood and which certainly brought him nothing, except the rumours of hidden riches that caused his death—

> Who raised the tale t'were vain to scan,
> But far and wide the story ran
> That there was scarce a *wealthier* man
> Than poor old Joe the Quilter.

Thus the poem by A. Wright, and in a booklet called *The Hermit of Warden or The Tragedy of Homer's Lane* the stage for the drama is set in terms very much in accord with the spirit of the age. On Sunday the 1st of January, says the pamphlet, the old quilter was seen as usual sitting at his window industriously reading the Bible.

"You make good use of your time, old man," said his visitor. "I wish I could," replied old Joe. "I look back over a long road that I have trifled on—I look forward to a place of rest—I am close upon it, but the darkness travels faster than I; I have need of help to complete my journey. May the mercy of God strengthen my spirit and speed my footsteps."

On the evening of Tuesday the 3rd January Joe returned early to his cottage from a call at a neighbouring farm. About six o'clock a labourer by the name of Herdman, returning home to Wall from work at the Fourstones Paper Mill, visited the quilter, whom he found boiling potatoes for supper in front of a good fire. About seven, a female pedlar, Mrs Biggs, called at the cottage to ask her way, having lost herself in the darkness, and Joe himself came to the door and directed her, gallantly observing that if he had been a younger man he would have been glad to act as her guide.

She was the last to see him alive. When the owner of Haughton Castle rode past at eight o'clock all was in darkness and the *Newcastle Chronicle* hazarded, no doubt correctly, that by this time "the horrid deed" must have been committed.

Next morning Herdman, on his way to work, found the cottage closed and silent and a pair of old clogs lying on either side of the lane, opposite a path that ran down towards the river and Wall Mill across the stream. He mentioned this at work but took no further action, even when on the Friday he found the cottage still shut and marks of blood on the door. This rather strange lack of imagination on Herdman's part was later deemed suspicious and led to his arrest, though the *Chronicle*'s final judgment, which it delivered "on the highest authority" was that "there is not a shadow of just suspicion on Herdman".

On the Saturday afternoon the cottage door was at last forced open and the body of the quilter found "in a small dark inner room", his head and face "dreadfully mangled", blood everywhere, a garden hoe "with many appalling marks of its having been used as the instrument of death" lying across his breast.

It was an age that liked strong reporting, and the *Chronicle* pulled no punches in its description of this scene of carnage or in its reconstruction of the old man's last desperate struggle for life against his murderers—for there were probably two of them—through the doorway and the "slip of a garden", across the lane and into the dark wintry fields where they hunted him down. As the *Chronicle* wrote—and it makes the tragedy live for us still—

The clock face is broken. The bed tester has been violently torn down. ... His geraniums in the window, all withered and dead, and which he used to tend with so much care, likewise tell an affecting tale. But perhaps the most touching memorial of poor old Joe is his cat, still roaming round his now cold, desolate and bloodstained hearth, wild and

47

disconsolate-like, and as if seeking the hand that will never feed nor caress it more.

The murderers were never found, though the Mr Leadbitter of the day offered a reward of £100, which his enemies said he could never pay, and many years later a confession which no one believed was made by a dying man. Before Joe's time the cottage where he lived had been a resort of smugglers, and it was said that Joe himself had harboured, just such dangerous men, two of whom were reported near Homer's Lane on the day of the murder "as if laying in wait for blood".

Buried by public subscription, the quilter lies now under the chancel of Warden Church. Of his cottage, no more than a few stones remain on the sloping ground under Warden Hill, and even his ghost seems at peace, though at one time it was supposed to haunt the spot, hopping on one leg on dark nights in search of a missing clog. It is a pleasantly macabre story and somehow fitting to the crime and the place. Only rationalists will be pleased to know that the sole recorded appearance of the phantom—to a High Warden man of the last century on his way to a tryst with a maidservant at Walwick Grange—turned out in the cold light of day to have coincided with the arrival in the district of the newfangled black and white cattle, one of which had strayed on to the road in the night.

Why should we believe in rationalists, though, any more than in ghosts. They are not half such fun. They are not poetic—

> Thus oft from Warden Paper Mill
> He'd toiling climb the weary hill,
> Tho' bed and supper with good will
> Were pressed on Joe the Quilter.
>
> Pause infidel—think sovereign love
> Will thus its martyred servants prove
> To fit them for their crowns above:
> So be it with Joe the Quilter.

His is not the sole spectre our favoured and hospitable neighbourhood can boast, as is made clear in a hunting poem of the early nineteen-hundreds, *Stirrup Cup* by Frederic Palmer, which shows us the countryside on a winter's day with the Haydon pack running—

> Scarce half way up the hill he's got
> Before out of a shepherd's cot
> A barking sheep-dog makes him turn
> A frightened mask for Newbrough burn;
> Down through the churchyard then he hurries
> Past Newbrough Lodge, across the Park;
> He knows the earth in Fourstones quarries,
> And brighter glows hope's flickering spark;
> Then in and out of Murder Lane,

Across some fields of stubble where
The black game come for winter fare,
Through the low end of Meggie's Dene,
Where once a witch had her abode.
They say her ghost is sometimes seen,
In her own cottage up the road,
Behind a broken window pane.

The verses would have recalled to many alive at the time a local
John Peel with the illustrious name of Robert Bruce, huntsman for
thirty-two years, some part of it on an "old grey horse, rather kittle
on three legs and not very sure on the fourth" which bore its master
faithfully for many a long day till he was buried at last to the sound
of a "Gone Away" in Warden Churchyard.

In the same poem the theme of continuity, of the "oneness" of
history, is there too, bred in the bone of Northumbrians:

So the whole motley cavalcade
To action now once more is stirred,
They cross the road the Romans made,
Where once the Tungrian cohorts spurred . . .

After all, if we allow a span of twenty five years, it is still only sixty
generations ago that the legions left and seventy-two since Hadrian
came to the Tyne.

NORTHUMBERLAND HISTORY AND DIRECTORY, 1886:

Description of Fourstones Paper Mill and its surroundings

WARDEN PARISH

Superficial extent, 3,122 acres; gross estimated rental, £9,282; rateable value, £8,337

This parish occupies a tongue of land between the North and South Tyne, extending from the latter river northward to the Roman Wall; but the ecclesiastical boundaries embrace a wider area, and include the chapelry of Newbrough, and at an earlier period that of Haydon Bridge was also within its jurisdiction. The soil is generally fertile, and in a high state of cultivation. Patches of woodland are plentifully scattered, enhancing the beauty of a diversified landscape by their sylvan charms. The principal landowners are John Clayton, Esq., The Chesters; Messrs Benson, Allerwash House; the heirs of John Errington, Esq.; Major J. Graham Leadbitter, Warden House; and the Rev. Canon Cruddas. The parish has no dependent townships, but for highway purposes it is divided into High Warden and Walwick Grange, Low Warden, Fourstones, and Walwick.

Warden was one of the many manors given by Edward II to Anthony, Lord Lucy, sheriff of Cumberland, in reward for his services in capturing Andrew de Harcla, who, for his gallant conduct against the Scots at Boroughbridge the year before, had been created Earl of Carlisle, and was now suspected of being in league with the enemy. Harcla was tried at Carlisle, and condemned to suffer in all its rigour the death of a traitor. Anthony, Lord Lucy, died about the year 1344, leaving by his wife Joane an infant daughter, who died the following year, and Maud, Anthony's sister, succeeded to the estates. She married for her second husband Henry Percy, first Earl of Northumberland, and settled the honours and estates on him and his heirs male, on condition that they should bear the arms of Lucy quarterly with their own. The Earl fell in the battle of Bramham Moor, in 1408, whilst fighting against Henry IV, whom he had been mainly instrumental in placing upon the throne. His honours were forfeited under attainder, but were subsequently restored to his grandson, the only son of the valiant Hotspur.

The VILLAGE of Warden occupies a delightful situation, near the junction of the North and South Tyne, two miles NNW of Hexham, and was, some twelve centuries ago, the favourite retreat of St John of Beverley. To the north-west rises a ridge of lofty eminences, whilst to the south stretches the vale of the Tyne. The *Church*, dedicated to St Michael, is a cruciform stone structure of considerable antiquity, but was almost entirely rebuilt in 1765. It was re-seated and internally restored in 1868, at a cost of nearly £1,000. The style of architecture is that known as the Early English. A new organ was presented in 1885, by the Rev. Canon Cruddas, the patron of the living and also the vicar of the church. The incumbency was valued in the time of Henry VIII at £8 16s 3d per annum; but the gross income is now about £620. In the church are preserved an ancient Roman altar, bearing a figure supposed to represent Victory, and two small stone coffins, said to have been found during the restoration in 1765. The parish register commences in 1695.

The Primitive Methodists have a chapel on the road side, about half a mile west of the church, erected in 1851. In appearance it resembles a barn rather than an ecclesiastical edifice, and it is to be hoped, the funds will soon be forthcoming to rebuild it in a style more in harmony with the revival of architectural taste, so conspicuous in the religious structures erected during recent years.

Nether Warden House is an elegant mansion, the property and residence of the Rev. Canon Cruddas. It was erected in 1867, and occupies a pleasant situation on the west bank of the North Tyne, overlooking the vale.

Hardhaugh is a hamlet in this division, about three-quarters of a mile west of the church, and chiefly occupied by the workmen of the South Tyne Paper Mill. The parish school is situated here. It was erected about the year 1850, and superseded one built by subscription in 1820. A classroom was added in 1881, and a house for the master is now in course of erection. Average attendance about 94.

A short distance from the village is the South Tyne Paper Mill, established in 1762 by the Rev. Mr Rumney, of Hexham, and now in the occupancy of Mr D. Brown. The buildings cover a considerable area, and numerous improvements have been effected during the past few years. The curious visitor to the works, during a stroll through its several departments, may witness the whole mystery of papermaking, from the sorting of the rags until their final conversion into a continuous web of beautiful white paper. About sixty-three "hands" are constantly employed, and the paper manufactured is that used for newspapers and book work.

HIGH WARDEN is a hamlet situated about half a mile north of the church. "On an eminence called Castle Hill is an ancient fort, including an area of more than two acres, and was formerly surrounded by a rampart of unhewn stone, which was further strengthened by ramparts of earth, with their corresponding ditches. The entrance to this fortification appears to have been on the east, and the approach to it was flanked by stone ramparts. The remains of buildings may yet be distinctly traced within the lines, where several hand-mills, or *querns*, have been discovered. This camp commands an extensive view of the North and South Tyne," with all the principal villages and buildings that dot the vale. Behind the vicarage house at Warden are the traces of another military station, called also Castle Hill. There is a neat mansion in the village, the residence of Jasper M. Richardson, Esq.

FOURSTONES is another hamlet, two miles north-west of Warden, at which there is a station on the Newcastle and Carlisle Railway. It has evidencly received its name from the presence of four stones, but by whom they were erected, and their purpose and origin, are alike unknown. One writer supposes them to have marked the boundaries of the place, and to have had on their tops a cavity for the reception of holy water. But according to others they were Roman altars, and there is a story current in the neighbourhood that one of them was called the "Fairy Stone", because in the rebellion of 1715, the focus of this altar was formed into a square recess, with a cover, to receive the correspondence of the rebel chiefs, and that a little boy clad in green came in the twilight of every evening to carry away the letters left in it for Lord Derwentwater, and deposit his answers, which were spirited away in a similar manner by the agency of some of his friends.

Coal, lime, and freestone are plentiful in the parish, and are extensively worked by Messrs Benson, of Allerwash House. Stone of very superior quality is obtained from the quarries at Prudham, which is sawn and dressed on the spot by powerful machinery. This stone has been largely used in the erection of several important buildings in London, Edinburgh, Glasgow, Newcastle, and other large towns. About 200 men are constantly employed in the colliery, limekilns, and quarries.

At West Boat there is an elegant suspension bridge, which was erected in 1826 at a cost of £5,000. In 1877 it gave way beneath the weight of a steam thrasher which was passing over, and was restored the following year.

Professor Peter C.G. Isaac

FOURSTONES PAPER MILL: THE DOCUMENTS SPEAK

As is very well known, papermaking was not introduced into England until one and a half millenia after its invention in China, and it was a further two centuries after its first manufacture by John Tate near Hertford before the industry reached the north-east. At least two mills seem to have been in operation south of the Tyne around the end of the seventeenth century, but the earliest paper mill in Northumberland is the subject of this chapter, Fourstones (MAIDWELL, 1959; SHORTER, 1957 and 1971).

This mill, which even today seems buried in the Northumbrian countryside, possesses an almost complete set of deeds from its establishment in April 1763. This chapter is the story told by these deeds. It starts in the days of handmade paper, passing through the heyday of papermaking in the north-east, and brings us to the current decline in machine-made papermaking in England.

Even the turgid circumlocutions of the scrivener and lawyer cannot totally obscure the human stories in this valuable collection of documents. What comes over clearly is that the owners of the paper mill at Warden, on the River South Tyne, were short of working capital during the first two centuries of production. The deeds allow us to trace the changes of ownership, and the expansion in machinery and equipment over those years. It is a fascinating tale.

An outline of this tale may be obtained simply by reading the details of the documents listed in the Appendix.[1] William Charnley, the Newcastle bookseller and prime-mover in setting up the mill, was bankrupt ten years after its foundation. On the other hand the Rumney/Crawford family remained associated with the mill for some ninety years. It remained leasehold property for more than a century, and so one sees the Kirsopp family, the local landowners, mentioned again and again over those years.

It is possible to trace also the several changes of name of the mill. In 1763 it is the Warden Paper Mill, and remained so until the late 1860s, when it became called the South Tyne Paper Mill. Finally, on its incorporation as a limited company in 1907, it took its present name of the Fourstones Paper Mill.

Two other general impressions arise from a perusal of the documents that may be of interest at this stage. The first is that, although monetary inflation was relatively slow over these two centuries, the financial needs of the papermakers steadily rose, especially after the mill's conversion to machine papermaking in the middle of the nineteenth century. The second may be drawn from the legal descriptions of the parties to the various deeds; the description "gentleman" or "esquire" became commoner for our protagonists as time passed. No doubt this was partly because they joined the more prosperous portion of the community, but, even then, the now headlong rush to egalitarianism was starting.

Going through the documents line by line, however, is like travelling through a very dense wood; it is possible to divine the nature of the country over which one is journeying, but much of the shape of the wood is obscured by the trees. And then one comes into a clearing, when interesting details are illumined by the sunshine of a schedule attached to an otherwise solid indenture (eg documents 16, 41, 62).

EARLY DAYS

The late A.H. Shorter[2] puts forward inconclusive evidence suggesting that there might have been a paper mill in Newcastle upon Tyne from the 1760s or even earlier. Except for this, Fourstones is the earliest mill in Northumberland, although there were several earlier in County Durham.[3] This, together with the facts that William Charnley was an established bookseller in Newcastle[4] and that his name appears before that of the Rev Peter Rumney in the first two documents (1 and 2), supports the view that he was the moving force in setting up the new paper mill at Warden in the valley of the River South Tyne, just west of its confluence with the North Tyne. One notes, also, that Peter Rumney, who became Master of the Free Grammar School of Queen Elizabeth at Hexham and perpetual curate of Hexham Abbey (less than four miles downstream), is described in the original lease (1) as of Kirby Hill in the County of York, a village just north of Boroughbridge on the old Great North Road, but as of Hexham in the assignment for the loan from John Waller of Kirkby Stephen, in Westmorland (2), two years later.

The little history of the Grammar School (THOMSON, 1965) shows that Peter Rumney was appointed Master on the 17 June 1765; it was in the same year that he was appointed curate of Hexham Abbey. It seems, therefore, that it was not for two years after the establishment of the mill that Rumney actually lived in its neighbourhood. This lends credence to the suggestion of WALLIS (1981) that Elizabeth Rumney was William Charnley's sister. In 1791, twenty years after Peter Rumney's death, the Governors of the School, in writing to the Archbishop of York, who appears to have acted somewhat in the manner of a university's Visitor, said

It must be owned that the School was a good School during the Time Mr Brown and Mr Rumney were Masters tho it rather declined the latter end of Mr Rumney's Time he was Curate of Hexham as well as Master of the School but those two offices unite by Experience have been found to be prejudicial to the School for as Parochial Duty is very weighty it often interferes with the Duty of the Master. . . .

The fact that the Governors critically mention only Rumney's parochial duties suggests that he was not an active partner in the mill.[5]

The original lease from Wilkinson Kirsopp was for a very small piece of ground, some twenty yards square, and the annual ground rent was ten guineas per year. This lease allowed the lessees to cut stone from a quarry on Kirsopp's land free for the first year, and thereafter at a royalty of 5d for every 20 *fothers* (or waggon-loads). They were also permitted to construct a small conduit across the landlord's land to bring water from a spring there, but it is not clear that this was ever necessary. The lease was for twenty-one years from the 12 May 1763, and the lessor covenanted to renew it on request every twenty-one years at the same rent.

The plot leased to the papermakers seems to have been too small from early days, as is demonstrated by the first renewal of the lease (9/10) by Thomas Kirsopp, nephew of the first lessor. This shows that Elizabeth Rumney, widow of the Rev Peter Rumney, had constructed a staircase to reach an upper floor and also a "necessary house"[6] on adjoining land of Thomas Kirsopp. (She and her son Robert, who was then running the mill, covenant to remove the stairs and "netty" before the 12 May 1794.)

The mill cannot have been long constructed before its owners had to raise capital—£400 from John Waller of Kirkby Stephen, Gentleman. This is the first of many mortgages that we find among the 68 documents, and is unusual (for the present time, at least) in containing a bond by the borrowers to secure the repayment of the principal and interest in the penal sum of £800.

Various further loans were made over the next eight years and corresponding bonds entered into or mortgages made. The last three loans were made in December 1772. It may be that the later loans were to replace the earlier. The deed of 15 January 1773 is a second mortgage[7] of the mill by William Charnley and Peter Rumney's widow, Elizabeth, to the Rev Samuel Lowthion, a Dissenting Minister of Newcastle, who was guarantor of the penal bonds given to the several lenders.

One important document in these early days is missing, but can be reconstructed from later deeds—a lease by Sir Ralph Milbank, of Halnaby in the County of York, assigns to Charnley and Rumney the weir that they had built across the South Tyne from his land on the opposite bank. The annual rent was one shilling (4 and 5).

William Charnley's bookshop was on the old Tyne Bridge joining

55

Gateshead to Newcastle upon Tyne, and was destroyed in the great flood of November 1771.[8] This must have hit him hard, and in the same year he advertised for sale his share of the Warden Mill.[9] It seems to have taken some time for him to recover from this mishap, and he was declared bankrupt on the 22 January 1773 (5). All his stock was sold, his circulating library being bought by Richard Fisher.[9]

By an indenture of assignment of 1 March 1773 Charnley's commissioners in bankruptcy turned over the paper mill and other premises and personal estate of his to Samuel Lowthion and Robert Harrison (5). They, in turn, assigned Charnley's moiety of the mill to Robert Rumney, Peter Rumney's son, who is described as a bookseller in the deed (5). Robert Rumney had bid £820 for this moiety at auction on the 15 July 1773, the vendors intending it to be free of mortgage. Since the mill was mortgaged to Richard Lacey for £600, Robert Rumney was permitted to retain one-half of this sum, paying £520 for the moiety (5).

It seems that Robert Rumney had bought the mill in trust for the Rev Samuel Lowthion and George Watson, described as of Warden Paper Mill Gentleman (6), and who was manager of the mill at an annual salary of £40, which he seems to have left in the business. He was also a partner, although the partnership deed was never signed (7). By the assignment of 2 July 1774 Robert Rumney is paid the £520 purchase money by Lowthion and Watson, and assigns his moiety of the mill to them (6). In consequence each of the two owned one-quarter of the mill, and Elizabeth Rumney one-half, the deed rehearsing the fact that the three of them had been carrying on the papermaking business in copartnership since 1 September 1773.

THE RUMNEY/CRAWFORD DYNASTY

If, as WALLIS (1981) suggests,[10] Elizabeth Rumney was William Charnley's sister, the Charnley family continued to have a gradually diluting interest in the mill, even after William's bankruptcy and withdrawal from Warden Mill. (It must be said here that he was back in business as a bookseller in rebuilt premises in Newcastle by December 1773. In the 1780s and 1790s he was one of the largest booksellers in the City, issuing many printed catalogues.[11]) The descendants of the redoubtable widow, Elizabeth Rumney, moreover, operated the mill into the middle of the nineteenth century. The last of her descendants are named in the renewal of lease of the 31 October 1850 (23D), but it seems likely that they continued to operate the mill for two or three years longer.

The Rev Peter Rumney died on the 16 February 1771 intestate. Letters of administration were granted to his widow by the Prerogative Court of the Archbishop of York, and, in the terms of the original copartnership, she took over his interest (4). The deeds show that she owned half of the mill until between 12 May 1784, when she and her son, Robert, renewed the lease from Thomas Kirsopp (9 and 10), and 2 October 1804, when Robert alone renewed the lease from William Kirsopp (13). As a memorial tablet to Peter Rumney, in the Choir of Hexham Abbey, shows Elizabeth Rumney died on the 7 November 1795, aged 79.[12]

Meanwhile Samuel Lowthion had died, leaving his wife Ann as residuary legatee. His will was proved in the York Prerogative Court, and his quarter share in the mill was sold by Ann to Henry Gibson, surgeon of Newcastle, on trust to pay off her husband's debts. By a memorandum of agreement of 21 June 1779 Robert Rumney had paid Samuel Lowthion £157 9s 9d for his quarter share, and this was formally transferred to him by the tripartite agreement of the 5 February 1782 (8).

George Watson, whom we met earlier as a partner and salaried manager, had left the business before the 1 May 1777, and moved to Middle Temple Lane in London. By the tripartite indenture of that date he was to be repaid what he had lent the partners and his retained salary, and in consideration of this he transferred his share to Elizabeth Rumney and Samuel Lowthion (7).

The next deed (14) is twenty years later, and Elizabeth's name, not unexpectedly, no longer appears on it.[12] In 1812 the landowners of Nether Warden wished to enclose two tracts of common land, a short distance southeast of the mill and known as Low and High Hardhaugh, with a total area of some 25 acres. They appointed William Donkin, a landowner in nearby Sandoe, who allocated, by an award of 25 April 1814, the various sections, and made orders about fencing and the construction of highways. Although Robert Rumney held the mill in leasehold he was awarded the freehold of 1 acre and 32 perches of the enclosure. Thereafter the deeds cover both leasehold and freehold estate.

Robert Rumney's will (15), dated 17 October 1815 and proved in the Prerogative Court of Canterbury on the 25 November 1816, suggests that he was a bachelor, because, at the time of his death, he was living with his sister, Lydia, and because the only legacy to a child is £200 to a natural daughter, Ann. The will tells us that Robert Rumney was a man of substance. Apart from legacies to sisters and nieces, he also owned a house in Charlotte Square, New-castle, and a freehold close in Hexham, Middle Hoodshaw. In addi-tion he owned a fourth share in St Anthony's copperas (ferrous sulphate) works in Newcastle, and a similar share in the acid and coal-tar manufactory at Derwenthaugh (to the southwest of New-castle). These and Warden Mill were left to his two sisters, who were appointed his executrices.

It is an interesting commentary on the education of the time to note that his signature to the will was witnessed by two papermakers at the mill, Jacob Atkinson and Joseph Graham, who made their marks with crosses.

By the 25 November 1823 Elizabeth Crawford had evidently died, and her share of the mill had been inherited by her son, Peter Rumney Crawford. On that date Lydia sold her share to her nephew for £4 385 (16).[13] The brief schedule at the end of the assignment reads as follows:

> The Machinery consisting of Water, pitt, Fly and other wheels; Two Engines [beaters]; Three Vatts; Four Stuff and Size Chests; Seven Metal Screwpresses; With all the other utensils now in the said paper Mill.

At that time a three-vat mill was of no great size, but it is almost another twenty years before we find the beginning of the next spate of borrowing.

Peter Rumney Crawford became a churchwarden, and on the 10 May 1825 he and his aunt gave a small plot of land on trust for the establishment of a village schoolhouse.[14] The deed (17) laid down

> That the instruction to be given at the said School shall extend and be confined to Arithmetic and penmanship and to the reading and grammatical knowledge of the English language.

(Shades of the current emphasis on relevant education!)

When the lease came up for renewal again, on the 17 December 1839, Peter Rumney Crawford was dead,[15] and his widow and executrix, Ann, was carrying on the business (18). She was soon to be assisted by her four sons, Rumney, Joseph, John and Robert Rumney. On the 5 February 1842 they mortgaged the mill to the Newcastle Shields and Sunderland Joint Stock Banking Company[16] to secure an overdraft of £5 000 (19).

Later deeds (20 and 23) recite the conditions of a mortgage of the 1 June 1840 when Ann Crawford and her sons had borrowed £2 100 from the Friendly Benefit Building and Investment Society in Gateshead (25). This mortgage was transferred to the Bank by the assignment of 23 September 1852, and this indebtedness seems to have dragged on for a long time. In 1850 Robert Rumney Crawford patented an air-drier, which would have been useful only for machine-made paper.[17] It seems likely that the first papermaking machine was installed in the mill in the 1840s; these large loans were, therefore, probably made to meet the cost of the machine, which must have been considerable for a small mill.

All was not well with the Bank, however, and we see from a notice published in the *Newcastle Chronicle* of the 9 July 1852 that a John Teather, of Alstonby in the Parish of Kirklinton, Cumberland, had petitioned for the dissolution and winding up of the Bank.[18] The petition was granted by the Master of the Rolls on the 31

January 1853 (21), Official Managers being appointed by the Court on the 21 February 1853 (25G) and on the 18 January 1855 (22).

OWNERSHIP CHANGES

The assignment of the 27 February 1857 (26), discussed below, records that an agreement was made with Thomas Fordyce on the 19 July 1854. The stable and relatively prosperous papermaking Rumney/Crawford dynasty must have come to an end at about that time. Mr Mandl suggests that this was due to overproduction and consequent price-cutting resulting from the installation of too many paper machines.

The Official Managers of the Bank sold the mill to Thomas Fordyce on the 27 February 1857. Fordyce is shown in the deed as of Warden, Paper Manufacturer (26). Neither HUNT (1975) nor WALLIS (1981) relate this Thomas Fordyce to the man of the same name, brother to William, the active Newcastle printer and bookseller, but one is tempted to identify them. Fordyce paid the Bank £3 400 for the mill (26), but had to borrow £3 000 of this on mortgage from Frederic Horn, of Bishopwearmouth (27). A month later he took out a second mortgage with John Pollock, of 27 Budge Row in the City of London, Paper Agent, to secure a loan of £1 500 (28). Another loan of £1 500 from Pollock was secured by a further charge in December of the same year (30).[19]

Fordyce was in financial straits from the start; he took out yet a further mortgage with James Hudson, a papermaker of Newcastle, on the 21 October 1859 to secure a loan of £3 000 (recited in 32), and on the 4 October 1862 James Hudson agrees to sell the mill to John Pollock, subject to the latter also paying the £3 000 mortgage debt (32). Two years later, Frederic Horn transfers his mortgage debt of £3 000 to George Mackrell and George Hindes Smith, of London, and Henry Hughes, of Maidstone; all are described as gentlemen, but may have had some connexion with the paper industry (33). The three of them immediately mortgaged the property to James Tompsett, of East Peckham, to secure a loan of £2 500 towards the payment of £3 000 to Horn (34).

Our next Fourstones papermaker is Alexander Adam, to whom Pollock and Hudson sold the mill on the 18 April 1865 for £2 000 (35), and he seems to have mortgaged it immediately back to James Hudson (36). Adam had discharged his debt to Hudson by the following year, as is attested by the reconveyance of the property by Hudson to Adam on the 9 July 1866 (37). Alexander Adam was clearly determined to make a go of the mill, for only a year later he had also paid off the mortgage to Tompsett, Mackrell and Hughes (38). And then, after more than one hundred years, the Warden mill became the property of the papermaker in fee simple, when

Adam bought the freehold from William Kirsopp on the 27 March 1868 for £825 (39).[20]

Alexander Adam, who was a bachelor (39), became a lunatic shortly before the 30 November 1875 (43), having already agreed to sell the mill to John McPherson, of Lasswade in Edinburgh. Indeed, McPherson in October 1872 entered into a contract with Adam, who was then living in Aberdeen, for the purchase of the mill and other hereditaments with the appurtenances for £12 000 (43). By the end of November 1872 McPherson had paid £6 000 and the valuation of certain furniture and chattels, and had entered into possession of the mill. Over the next three years the rest of the purchase money had been paid or deposited. McPherson had to go to the High Court to get an order to Lauchlan McKinnon the younger, Adam's *curator bonis*, and Henry Reid, his guardian, to convey the property; this order was made on the 14 February 1879 (42). The conveyance was executed on the 5 June 1879 (43).

McPherson was the owner of the mill, but clearly continued to live in Edinburgh (40 and 41), and left the management of the mill to others. On the 6 May 1874 he leased the mill and equipment to John McPherson and Company, at an annual rent of £900. This Company was a partnership of McPherson with Duncan McGillivray, papermaker of South Tyne Mill, and David Brown, papermaker of Markinch (40).

DAVID BROWN AND THE SOUTH TYNE PAPER MILL

The company was dissolved on the 31 March 1877 (41), and the mill was then let to David Brown, described in the lease of the 23 December 1876, as of South Tyne Paper Mill (41). David Brown was the last of the great Fourstones papermakers in the nineteenth century, and he remained in control of the mill until just before the incorporatioon of The Fourstones Paper Mill Co Ltd in 1907, although in his later days he was in continual financial trouble.

The annual rent to be paid by Brown to McPherson was £900. It is interesting to note that David Brown's signing and sealing of the indenture was witnessed by David Low, papermaker of the South Tyne Mill. David Brown was required to take over the premises, equipment, stock in trade etc at valuation. This was to be carried out by David Matthew Watson, papermaker of Bullionfield, Dundee, on behalf of McPherson, and by James Thrift Smith, papermaker of Markinch, on behalf of Brown.

The indenture is accompanied by a marvellously detailed and valued schedule of property (running to fourteen large pages), dated the 7 July 1877, and signed by Robert Douglas and D C Mudie, of Edinburgh. The schedule refers to the position at the 2 April 1877, the first working day after David Brown formally took possession of the mill.

The schedule indicates that the lawyer's plan on the lease is no more than a general one and does not show the then existing state of the mill buildings and other premises, the total value of which is given as £6 422 14s 0d. This did not include the value of the land, nor of the sluices, head and tail races, culvert to the river, dams and pond; these were taken over as in good condition.

The minute details of the machinery and other plant show that the mill was well equipped. The total value was £7 074 10s 3d. Several interesting facts may be gleaned from a study of the plant schedule.

There were four esparto boilers, and as Mr Mandl shows Fourstones produced esparto papers for very many years.[21] A clay mixer is mentioned, and shows that the mill was using china clay to opacify the paper. There were six beaters in all, of various sizes.

The 56-inch paper machine was valued at £875. It had two couch rolls, the upper being of 17 inches diameter and made of mahogany, the lower of 12 inches diameter and constructed of plane. There were two sets of cast-iron press rolls, 18 inches diameter at the top and 11 inches below with brass shell. These were followed by six drying cylinders, each 38 inches diameter, and two cylinders 48 inches diameter, with two intermediate rolls of 12 inches diameter. The two sets of calenders had three rolls each, the two lower rolls being of 14 inches diameter and the upper 12 inches. The machine was equipped with a revolving strainer for the stuff, sump, three vacuum pumps, and a saveall.[22]

Although steam power was used in the mill, a waterwheel, of 9 feet diameter and 6 feet wide, and valued at £45, suggests that water power was still used for pumping.[23] There is a guillotine and a revolving paper cutter. David Brown was certainly taking over a completely equipped paper mill.

The South Tyne Paper Mill was only one of John McPherson's investments: he also owned the Cone Paper Mill in Lydney,[24] Gloucestershire, and other property and farms in that county (46 and 47), and had to borrow widely. On the 1 October 1879 he mortgaged the South Tyne Mill to Edward Charles Maltby, of Croft on Tees near Darlington, to secure a loan of £8 000 (44), and on the 20 July 1880 there was a further charge on the mill to Maltby to secure a further £2 000 (45).[25] These mortgages remained in existence until the 18 July 1907, when Gerald Rivers Maltby, E C Maltby's half-brother and residuary legatee—E C Maltby had died on the 21 October 1903—finally sold the mortgaged property to John Edward Davidson, of Tynemouth, and Alexander Gemmell Barr, of Newcastle, who were among the seven original shareholders of the new limited company (57 and 58).[26]

On the 23 July 1883 John Macpherson, who was then living in

Gloucestershire, was adjudicated bankrupt at the Monmouthshire County Court at Newport. A fortnight later Samuel Augustus Tylke, an accountant of Cardiff, was appointed Trustee of his property, and three London merchants and paper agents were appointed as his Committee of Inspection. On the 14 January 1884 they mortgaged the South Tyne Paper Mill (subject, of course, to the existing mortgages to Maltby) to James Richard Upton, of 14 Austin Friars in the City of London, to secure a loan of £3 000 (46).

In turn, the mortgagees sold the mill to David Brown, the "sitting tenant", on the 14 August 1888 for £4 500, subject to the Maltby mortgages (47), which, on the following day, he covenants to pay. At some time in the five years since he had been declared bankrupt Macpherson had emigrated to Invercargill in New Zealand, and, though still a bankrupt, was there carrying on business as a merchant and commission agent (47).

The absence of mortgages for the next fourteen years suggests that David Brown, like Peter Rumney Crawford before him a churchwarden, was reasonably prosperous for a decade, although it seems that he was receiving loans from the local vicar, the Rev George Cruddas (50, 52 and 54).[27]

On the 9 May 1902 David Brown executed a deed of assignment for the benefit of his creditors (49). John Martin Winter, a chartered accountant of Newcastle, was his Trustee, and the Committee consisted of Robert Paton Herbert, an esparto merchant of Glasgow, and Edward Thompson, a Hexham bank manager. Again, the schedule of creditors illustrates those with whom David Brown was doing business. As may be expected from the constitution of his Committee, the principal debts were to Lambton & Co, the Hexham bankers, for £9 180 16s 0d, and Morris & Co (presumably esparto importers from the identity of their address and Herbert's) for £3 723 0s 9d. The other creditors, all for amounts of less than £200, include The United Alkali Co Ltd (now ICI), the United Wire Works Ltd of Edinburgh, Goodall Bates & Co (still refining oil on Tyneside) and H D Pochin & Co Ltd (presumably for china clay) (49).

Nevertheless, David Brown was able to carry on papermaking, and his friends agreed to lend him £2 500 to buy and fix new machinery—two double-flue boilers, a horizontal compound engine of 450 hp, and a horizontal jet condenser (53). This loan was guaranteed by the Rev George Cruddas, and E C Maltby agreed not to call in his mortgage for three years (50), subject to the assignment to him of the new plant when installed (53).

By May 1903 David Brown seems to have weathered the first crisis, for in that month, the mill is reconveyed and reassigned to him by his Trustee and Committee (51). Two years after this, however, his business was again ailing, and he made a second assignment for the benefit of his creditors, J M Winter once more acting as his Trustee (54). This time no bank was creditor, but the Rev George Cruddas was, to an extent unspecified in the schedule, in which several of the former creditors again appear.

In December 1905 David Brown owed Cruddas a total of £12 969 7s 8d in principal and interest, and it was estimated that the value of the paper mill and premises was insufficient to secure this. Taking account of the still outstanding mortgages to G R Maltby, the Trustee agreed to sell the mill, premises, plant and tools, stock in trade, goodwill and book debts, together with the mill's money on deposit at Lambton & Co's Bank of £1 475 8s 4d, for a consideration of £1 171 7s 2d. At the same time the Vicar agrees to make no claim for dividend against David Brown's estate (55).

The accompanying schedule of 44 debtors, for a total of £1 891 6s 2d, is interesting in showing how widely Fourstones paper was supplied. It includes such well-known names as Blackie, de la Rue, Waterlow, Dickinson and Spicers (55).

This is a sad end to the almost forty years' reign of a distinguished papermaker.

THE LIMITED COMPANIES

On the 31 August 1907 the memorandum and articles of association of The Fourstones Paper Mill Co Ltd were registered with seven initial shareholders, including Davidson and Barr, and with Alexander Annandale, whose wife, Annie, was also an initial shareholder, as Managing Director (58).[28] The company was set up with a nominal capital of £20 000, divided into 2 000 £1 cumulative preference shares and 18 000 £1 ordinary shares. Davidson and Barr transferred the mill to the company on the 24 September 1907 (59), at which time the Rev George Cruddas was repaid for his loyal support of the mill over the years, with a cash payment of £3 000 and an allotment of 1 172 preference shares. Davidson and Barr, in their turn, received a debenture for £4 550 at 4.5% p.a. (For the apportionment of stamp duty the 'goods chattels moneys and other effects capable of manual delivery' were valued at £4 172 10s 0d.) (59).

On the following day G R Maltby conveyed the mill to Davidson and Barr, and to the Company for £4 500 (60). The mortgages are, at last, discharged, after almost thirty years.

Formal documents throw no light on the next seventeen years,[29] but the Company went into voluntary liquidation on the 31 May 1924, James Edward Wilson, a chartered accountant of 24 Basinghall Street in the City of London, being appointed liquidator (62).

The memorandum and articles of association of the new company, The Fourstones Paper Mill Company (1924) Limited, were registered

63

on the 11 June 1924 (61). The names of the two original shareholders, with addresses in Camberwell and Wembley, were nominees of the large Becker Group and show that the centre of gravity of the mill had now passed out of the northeast. The reconstituted company bought the mill, goodwill, book debts etc for £40 608 7s 9d; these book debts totalled £11 194 16s 0d (62). Once again the schedule of debtors is very illuminating. These number 71, and include Van Gelder and two other companies in Amsterdam and one in Copenhagen. Several of the companies mentioned earlier, in connexion with David Brown's financial problems, appear again together with, for example, Grosvenor Chater, Spalding & Hodge, Tullis Hunter, Phillip Son & Nephew, The Darien Press, Jarrolds, Gordon & Gotch, Somerville and Samuel Jones (62). It must have been a continual struggle, for, on the 17 December 1925, the reconstituted company issued a debenture to Lloyds Bank to secure all its debts to the Bank (63).[30] On the 10 April 1931 this debenture was transferred by Lloyds Bank to Samuel Hird Milne, of Edinburgh (64). At that time only £5 000 of the principal was still owing and, in an endorsement dated the 26 June 1931, on the original debenture, Milne acknowledges that this has been repaid with interest (63). This appears to have required a new loan from Milne, for, on the same date, the company issues a second debenture in his favour to secure £4 500 (65). This, the last of the formal documents studied, brings us almost to the bicentenary, because the affixing of the company's seal to this debenture was attested by, amongst others, Mina Mason, who succeeded her father as Managing Director, and figures prominently in Mr Mandl's history.[31]

CONCLUSION

These sixty-eight documents have allowed us to live briefly through the first two centuries of the Fourstones Mill, and to trace it fortunes. Now one of the oldest paper mills in the country, still in production, it has always made a major contribution to employment in a rural area of the northeast, which, even now, is fairly isolated. For almost its first century its owners were northeasterners. In the second half of the nineteenth century Scots, with their long tradition of papermaking, made their contribution, and in the twentieth century the paper mill at Warden became first part of a national group, and now of an international papermaking concern. It is a fascinating cameo of papermaking history.

REFERENCES

BROCKETT, J T (1846) *A Glossary of North Country Words*. Third edition. Newcastle upon Tyne, Emerson Charnley.

The Charter and Rules of the Incorporated Company of Upholsterers, Tinplate-Workers and Stationers of Newcastle upon Tyne. (1817) Newcastle upon Tyne, E. Humble.

CHESTER, C A (1976) *History of Ford Paper Mills: the Introduction of Esparto Grass for Papermaking*. Newcastle upon Tyne, History of the Book Trade in the North. Working paper PH26.

DUNN, R K (1984) Personal communication.

HUNT, C J (1975) *The Book Trade in Northumberland and Durham to 1860*. Newcastle upon Tyne, History of the Book Trade in the North.

MACKENZIE, E (1827) *Descriptive and Historical Account of the Town and County of Newcastle upon Tyne*. Newcastle upon Tyne, Mackenzie and Dent.

MAIDWELL, C F (1959) *A Short History of Paper Making in the North-East*. Newcastle upon Tyne, School of Printing.

MANDL, G T (1984) Personal communication.

PHILLIPS, Maberly (1894) *A History of the Banks, Bankers and Banking, in Northumberland, Durham, and North Yorkshire*. London, Effingham Wilson.

RENNISON, R W (1979) *Water to Tyneside*. Newcastle upon Tyne, Newcastle and Gateshead Water Company.

SHORTER, A H (1957) *Paper Mills and Paper Makers in England 1495–1800*. Hilversum, Paper Publications Society.

SHORTER, A H (1971) *Paper Making in the British Isles*. Newton Abbot, David and Charles.

SMITH, Barry (1984) Personal communication.

THOMSON, Sheila D (1965) *Education in Hexham from 1294*. Northumberland County Record Office.

WALLIS, P J (1981) *The Book Trade in Northumberland and Durham to 1860*. A Supplement to C J Hunt's Biographical Dictionary. Newcastle upon Tyne, History of the Book Trade in the North.

WELFORD, Richard (1895) *Men of Mark 'Twixt Tyne and Tweed*. London and Newcastle upon Tyne, Walter Scott.

NOTES

1. Superior figures refer to these notes, and figures in parentheses, eg (21), refer to the documents listed in the Appendix.

2. SHORTER (1957) pp 222–3.

3. SHORTER (1957) pp 160–3.

4. William Charnley was born in Penrith in 1727 and was apprenticed to Martin Bryson, a Newcastle bookseller, on 28 January 1742. He was admitted to the freedom of the Newcastle Company of Upholsterers, Tinplate-Workers and Stationers by servitude on the 25 January 1749; see HUNT (1975) and *The Charter and Rules of the Incorporated Company of Upholsterers, Tinplate-Workers and Stationers* (1817). WELFORD (1895) gives a disappointingly brief life of William Charnley.

5. I am grateful to the present Headmaster of the Queen Elizabeth County High School, Mr Patrick Eavis, for this reference.

6. No doubt the origin of the common Northumbrian word 'netty' for privy. Brockett's (1846) glossary is too genteel to give either word.

7. Richard Lacey still held the first mortgage for his loan of £600.

8. HUNT (1975) p 21, and MACKENZIE (1827) vol 1, p 61.

9. HUNT (1975) pp 21–22.

10. p 40.

11. p 22.

12. A memorial tablet in the Choir of Hexham Abbey records that Elizabeth Rumney died on the 7 November 1795, aged 79.

13. Shown in a later abstract (25B) as £4 085.

14. The original school was replaced by a larger building next door in 1850 (SMITH, 1984). This later school was in operation until 1965, when it was sold by auction and converted into a private dwelling house (MANDL, 1984).

15. He died in April 1829.

16. This bank was founded in 1836, its business being for a time suspended in 1847, and was purchased by Woods & Co in 1859 (PHILLIPS (1894) pp 320-6.

17. Mr Mandl still has the Letters Patent and the accompanying drawings (MANDL, 1984).

18. There are echoes here of George Hudson, the railway king. The order (21) mentions an affidavit of service of the petition on 'Joseph Mather, Esq., Chief Clerk of the said Railway Co', and the same document notes the undertaking of the Bank 'to protect Mr Teather ... against the proceedings of Mrs [so] Hudson'.

19. The firm is still in existence in London under the name of Pollock and Searby (MANDL, 1984).

20. Adam also bought two other small parcels of land from William Kirsopp (37a and 39a).

21. Following the pioneer experiments on alternatives to rags as papermaking furnish by Matthias Koop in the early nineteenth century, the first commercial use of esparto grass for this purpose was at Ford Mill in Sunderland in 1860. This advance was made by Thomas Routledge (CHESTER, 1976). Fourstones adopted esparto very soon after this, as Mr Mandl shows in his history.

22. This paper machine was in operation until 1975. It is now preserved as the oldest paper machine in the UK on its original site. A small museum is being created around it and other old papermaking equipment (MANDL, 1984).

23. This is still in place but inaccessible.

24. There is still a connexion between Fourstones and Lydney: non-woven tissue for the hospital pads made at Fourstones is purchased from James R. Crompton & Bros Ltd of Lydney Paper Mills.

25. His surname from now on is spent Macpherson in the deeds.

26. See the next section of the paper.

27. Probably of the same family as the George Cruddas (1788-1879), who was one of the founders in 1845 and first Joint Managing Director of the Whittle Dean Water Company (now the Newcastle and Gasteshead Water Company). He was a linen draper and shipowner, and was active in many Newcastle undertakings (RENNISON, 1979).

28. WALLIS (1981) lists seven Annandales as papermakers in Northumberland and Durham, starting with Alexander Annandale senior, who at some stage after 1796 took over the Haughton Castle Paper Mill, Northumberland, with his brother John (SHORTER (1957) p 222). This mill, because of its rather wild isolation was selected, under its previous owners Magnay and Smith, by William Pitt's government to manufacture the special paper required for producing large quantities of forged *assignats* to flood the Continent and damage the economy of the French revolutionary government (MAIDWELL (1959) p 6). The coincidence of occupation and Christian name suggests that the twentieth-century papermaker descended from the first-mentioned Alexander Annandale.

29. The present group has the minute book of the Board from 1907 to 1924. This shows that the mill did very well over these years, producing esparto antiques (laid and wove), blottings etc at about 30 tons per week. Large profits were made during and after the war, but the depression set in in 1923 when the mill was sold to the Becker Group (MANDL, 1984).

30. In 1929 or 1930 the company was insolvent following the bankruptcy of the Becker Group. The mill was sold to David Mason, whose family sold it to Mr Mandl in 1962, just before its bicentenary (MANDL, 1984).

31. It is interesting to learn that Mina Mason and her sister, who married Mr R K Dunn, both studied at the local school, originally given to the community by the papermaker Peter Rumney Crawford (DUNN, 1984).

APPENDIX
List of documents consulted

1   21 April 1763
Indenture of Lease—Wilkinson Kirsopp to William Charnley and Rev Peter Rumney

2   3 July 1765
Assignment of Premises at Neather Warden by William Charnley and Rev Peter Rumney to John Waller to secure loan of £400 and interest

3   19 December 1766
Tripartite Indenture—John Waller, William Charnley and Richard Lacey

4   15 January 1773
Assignment of Lease by William Charnley and Elizabeth Rumney to Rev Samuel Lowthion

5   1 July 1774
Assignment of a Moiety of a Paper Mill and Utensils by the Assignees of William Charnley to Robert Rumney

6   2 July 1774
Assignment of a Moiety of a Paper Mill and Utensils by Robert Rumney to the Rev Samuel Lowthion and George Watson

7   1 May 1777
Tripartite Indenture—George Watson, Rev Samuel Lowthion and Elizabeth Rumney

8   5 February 1782
Tripartite Indenture—Henry Gibson and William Charnley, Elizabeth Rumney and Robert Rumney

9   12 May 1784
Lease by Thomas Kirsopp to Elizabeth Rumney and Robert Rumney

10   12 May 1784
Lease by Thomas Kirsopp to Elizabeth Rumney and Robert Rumney [counterpart of document 9]

11   28 August 1795
Will of Thomas Kirsopp

12   10 December 1797
Codicil to Will of Thomas Kirsopp

WILLIAM CHARNLEY
Newcastle Bookseller
1727–1803
Founder of Fourstones Paper Mill

SCOTTISH PAPER MANUFACTURERS
1866

Showing David Brown of Fourstones

ALEXANDER ANNANDALE (Beltonford)

D. M. WATSON (Bullionfield)

W. S. ANNANDALE

CHARLES ANDERSON (Fettykil)

J. H. BEILBY (Woodhall)

HILL (Balerno)

JAS. T. SMITH (Auchmuty and Rothes)

CHAS. W. COWAN

DAVID BROWN (Balbirnie) now Fourstones

DAVID CHALMERS (Katesmill)

DAVID CRAIG (Portobello)

ROBT. PHILIP (Bridge of Allan)

THOMAS CHALMERS (Lochmill)

HUGH SOMERVILLE (Dalmore)

H. BRUCE (Kinleith)

A. F. SOMERVILLE (Kevock)

WM. TOD (Sanctuary)

WM. TULLIS (Auchmuty)

ALEX. ANNANDALE (Polton)

WM. TOD (St. Leonards)

MR. HILL (Balerno)

RBT. CRAIG (Newbattle Moffat)

DR. SCOTT (Mossie Mill)

JOHN POLLOCK.
Partner in Fourstones Paper Mill
1857–1865

ROBERT A. HORSBURGH. Mill Manager Fourstones 1894–1899.

Rev. Canon GEORGE CRUDDAS, Vicar of Warden, who owned Fourstones Mill 1900–1907

JOHN ROWLEY 1867–1964 of Ludgate Hill London, Agent for Fourstones 1900–1924

Sir FREDERICK BECKER
1872–1936

DAVID MASON with daughter MINA outside Fourstones Mill in 1935

13   2 October 1804
Renewal of Lease by William Kirsopp to Robert Rumney

14   25 April 1814
Copy of Award on Division of Low and High Hardhaugh in Nether Warden

15   17 October 1815
Will of Robert Rumney [Endorsed 'Extracted by Geo Buckton Proctors Commons—Duty 220*l.*']

16   25 November 1823
Assignment of a Moiety of Paper Mill and Stock in Trade by Lydia Rumney to Peter Rumney Crawford

17   10 May 1825
Declaration of Trust with a Small Plot of Land on Hardhaugh [for a schoolhouse]

18   17 December 1839
Renewal of Lease by William Kirsopp to Ann Crawford

19   5 February 1842
Assignment on Mortgage of Leasehold Premises at Warden for securing floating balance on current account at Newcastle Shields and Sunderland Joint Stock Banking Company

20   23 September 1852
Assignment of a Leasehold Paper Mill etc by Trustees of the Friendly Benefit Building and Investment Society to Trustees of the Newcastle Shields and Sunderland Joint Stock Banking Company

21   31 January 1853
Order of the Master of the Rolls Dissolving the Newcastle Shields and Sunderland Joint Stock Banking Company

22   19 January 1855
Order of the Master of the Rolls Appointing Official Managers for the Newcastle Shields and Sunderland Joint Stock Banking Company

23   1855
Abstract of Title to Paper Mill at Warden belonging to the Official Managers of the Newcastle Shields and Sunderland Joint Stock Banking Company
  A Abstract of document 18
  B 1 June 1840 Abstract of Assignment by Ann Crawford, Rumney Crawford, Joseph Crawford and Robert Crawford to George Hawks, John Abbott and Ralph Wylam
  C Abstract of document 19
  D 31 October 1850 Abstract of Lease by William Kirsopp to Ann Crawford and her four sons, and George Hawks, John Abbott

and Ralph Wylam, and John Galloway, George Gamsby and John Atkinson
  E Abstract of document 20

24 1855
Additional Abstract—abstracting Orders of the Master of the Rolls (documents 21 and 22) and an earlier order of 21 February 1853 appointing Official Managers for the Newcastle Shields and Sunderland Joint Stock Banking Company

25 1857
Abstract of Titles to Paper Mill at Warden
  A Abstract of document 18
  B As 23B
  C Abstract of document 19
  D As 23D
  E Abstract of document 20
  F Abstract of document 21
  G 21 February 1853 Abstract of Order of the Master of the Rolls appointing Official Managers for the Newcastle Shields and Sunderland Joint Stock Banking Company
  H Abstract of document 22

26 27 February 1857
Assignment of Warden Paper Mill and premises by the Official Managers of the Newcastle Shields and Sunderland Joint Stock Banking Company to Thomas Fordyce

27 28 February 1857
Mortgage of Warden Paper Mill to secure £3000 by Thomas Fordyce to Frederic Horn

28 27 March 1857
Second Charge on Warden Mill by Thomas Fordyce to John Pollock to secure a loan of £1500

29 1857
Additional Abstract of Title to Warden Paper Mill and premises
  A Abstract of document 26
  B Abstract of document 27
  C Abstract of document 28

30 21 December 1857
Further Charge on the Equity of Redemption of Leasehold and Freehold Tenements at Nether Warden to secure £1500 by Thomas Fordyce to John Pollock

31   1858
Abstract of Deeds and Writings to the title to a parcel at Warden belonging to Thomas Fordyce but now in Mortgage to Frederic Horn for securing £3 000 and interest

  A Abstract of document 14
  B Abstract of document 18
  C As 23B
  D Abstract of document 19
  E As 23D
  F Abstract of codument 20
  G Abstract of document 21
  H Abstract of document 26
  I Abstract of document 27

31a   21 October 1859
Transfer of Mortgage of £1 000 by John Pollock to James Hudson

32   4 October 1862
Contract for sale of Warden Paper Mill by James Hudson to John Pollock

33   24 October 1864
Transfer of Mortgage of Warden Paper Mill to secure £3 000 and interest from Frederic Horn to George Mackrell and others

34   24 October 1864
Mortgage to secure £2 500 and interest from George Mackrell and others to James Tompsett

35   18 April 1865
Assignment and Conveyance from John Pollock and James Hudson to Alexander Adam

36   19 April 1865
Mortgage by Alexander Adam of Warden Paper Mill to James Hudson subject to £3 000 and interest to secure £1 000 and interest, and Covenant by John Pollock for payment of the money

37   9 July 1866
Reconveyance of Mill by James Hudson to Alexander Adam [on back of second skin of document 36]

37a   12 January 1867
Conveyance of a Parcel of Land at Nether Warden by William Kirsopp to Alexander Adam

38   24 October 1867
Reassignment and Reconveyance of Leasehold Paper Mill on discharge of mortgage for £3 000 by James Tompsett and others to Alexander Adam

39   27 March 1868
Purchase of Freehold by Alexander Adam from William Kirsopp

39a   19 November 1872
Conveyance of a Parcel of Land at Warden by William Kirsopp to Alexander Adam

40   6 May 1874
Lease of the South Tyne Paper Mill, Engines, Machinery etc for five years from 1 July 1874 by John McPherson to John McPherson & Co

41   23 December 1876
Lease of South Tyne Paper Mill by John McPherson to David Brown [This deed is accompanied by a detailed schedule and valuation of all the equipment of the mill]

42   14 February 1879
In the High Court of Justice, V C Malins, Between John McPherson, plaintiff, Lauchlan McKinnon the younger and Alexander Adam, a lunatic out of the jurisdiction of this Court, by Henry Reid, his Guardian, defendants

43   5 June 1879
Conveyance of Mill to John McPherson

44   1 October 1879
Mortgage of South Tyne Paper Mill for £8 000 by John McPherson to Edward Charles Maltby

45   20 July 1880
Further Charge for securing £2 000 by John Macpherson[so] to Edward Charles Maltby [on reverse of second skin of document 44]

46   14 January 1884
Mortgage of South Tyne Paper Mill to secure £3 000 by Samuel Augustus Tylke, John Ewart, William Richard Dewdney and Thomas Dunster to James Richard Upton

47   14 August 1888
Sale of South Tyne Paper Mill etc to David Brown

48   15 August 1888
Deed of Covenant to secure payment of £8 000 and £2 000 with interest by David Brown to Edward Charles Maltby

49   9 May 1902
Deed of Assignment for the Benefit of Creditors by David Brown to John Martin Winter

50 31 October 1902
Agreement Supplemental to Mortgage of 1 October 1879—David Brown and others to Edward Charles Maltby

51 27 May 1903
Reconveyance and Reassignment of Mill by John Martin Winter and others to David Brown [on last skin of document 49]

52 28 May 1903
Mortgage of South Tyne Paper Mill by David Brown to Rev George Cruddas

53 24 October 1904
Assignment of Machinery and Plant in the South Tyne Paper Mill by David Brown to Gerald Rivers Maltby

54 5 May 1905
Assignment for the Benefit of Creditors by David Brown to John Martin Winter

55 1 December 1905
Conveyance of the Equity of Redemption of South Tyne Paper Mill, together with goodwill and book debts, by John Martin Winter to Rev George Cruddas

56 17 July 1907
Power of Attorney by Gerald Rivers Maltby to Ralph Daubeny Upton

57 18 July 1907
Agreement for Sale of Fourstones Paper Mill by Gerald Rivers Maltby to John Edward Davidson and Alexander Gemmell Barr

58 31 August 1907
Memorandum and Articles of Association of The Fourstones Paper Mill Company Limited

59 24 September 1907
Agreement by John Edward Davidson and Alexander Gemmell Barr to convey mill to The Fourstones Paper Mill Company Limited

60 25 September 1907
Conveyance of Paper Mill and other premises at Fourstones by Gerald Rivers Maltby and Others to The Fourstones Paper Mill Co. Ltd

61 11 June 1924
Memorandum and Articles of Association of The Fourstones Paper Mill Company (1924) Limited

62 3 July 1924
Assignment of Book Debts by The Fourstones Paper Mill Co. Ltd and Another to The Fourstones Paper Mill Company (1924) Ltd

63   17 December 1925
Debenture by The Fourstones Paper Mill Co. (1924) Ltd to Lloyds
Bank Ltd

64   10 April 1931
Transfer of Mortgage by Lloyds Bank Ltd to Samuel Hird Milne

65   26 June 1931
Second Debenture by The Fourstones Paper Mill Co. (1924) Ltd in
favour of Samuel Hird Milne to secure £4 500

G. T. Mandl

FOURSTONES PAPER MILL

BICENTENARY SPEECH AT
STATIONERS' HALL, LONDON, ON
19 APRIL 1963

The 200th anniversary is certainly a date worth celebrating, particularly in our case, where it represents uninterrupted continuity of papermaking on the same premises, which I believe to be unique even amongst the oldest paper mills in existence today.

It gives me particular pleasure to hold this celebration in this historic Hall of the Stationers' Company, in the presence of the Master, Clerk and a number of the Livery, which has celebrated its quart-centenary in 1957 and is therefore more than twice our age. The original Stationers' Hall was destroyed in the Great Fire of London in 1666, but it is gratifying to know that the present Hall was in existence exactly as we see it today almost 100 years before the foundation of our Mill, and therefore provides a suitably historical setting for our bi-centenary dinner.

I should now like to give you a brief account of the Mill's history, as far as it can be ascertained. Our research in this sphere continues, and we hope to publish a book on Fourstones history of which you will be receiving a copy.

Early papermakers were notoriously secretive about their methods and production. No trade directories were published until about 1850.

Very little information therefore exists about the activities of the Mill from its foundation on 21 April 1763 until the middle of the last century. I am greatly indebted to Mr C. F. Maidwell of the College of Art and Industrial Design in Newcastle for research on this subject, published in his excellent booklet *A Short History of Paper Making in the North-East*, from which I am quoting several passages.

Our main sources of information are conveyances of leases and title deeds, giving only names of successive owners, and entries in the local Parish Rates Book.

The original title deed of Fourstones Paper Mill is fortunately preserved and exhibited here tonight. The two founders of the mill were the Rev. Peter Rumney, perpetual curate of Hexham Abbey and Master of Hexham Grammar School, and Mr William Charnley, a Newcastle bookseller.

The local historians' Table Book describes Mr Charnley as: "Father of the trade in the town of Newcastle; justly respected for his literary and professional talents, his strict integrity and moral worth. His view of human nature was enlarged and liberal, and the natural dignity of his mind was tempered with the purest urbanity."

I can only hope that future historians will be equally kind, if not necessarily accurate, when describing the present owners.

The original title deed★ is a lease from which I should like to quote the opening paragraph:

> This Indenture made this twenty-first day of April in the third year of the reign of our Sovereign Lord, King George 3rd, by the Grace of God of Great Britain, France, and Ireland, King, Defender of the Faith and in the year of our Lord one thousand seven hundred and sixty-three Between Wilkinson Kirsopp of Hexham, in the county of Northumberland, Gentleman, of this one part, and William Charnley of the town and county of Newcastle-upon-Tyne, Stationer, and the Reverend Peter Rumney of Kirby-Hall in the county of York, Clerk, of the other part.

This building lease provides the assignment of land in the village of Nether Warden together with water rights of the River Tyne for the purpose of erecting a paper mill, at an annual ground rent of Ten Guineas for a term of 21 years. It also provides for the right to obtain stone for building the mill from Mr Kirsopp's quarry free of charge during the first year of the term, and the price of 5d per every 20 weighing loads taken in subsequent years.

The Rev. Peter Rumney died in 1771, aged 56 years, and Mr Wm. Charnley in 1803, aged 76 years. The mill then remained in possession of the Rumney family for about 90 years.

It finally passed into the hands of the widow of Mr Peter Rumney-Crawford, under whose ownership the mill ceased to prosper and was entered in the Rate Book as not working in 1839. This was most probably due to competition from the new fangled paper-making machine, built by Donkin to Fourdrinier's design, costing about £1,250, which was far out of reach for most of the small hand-made mills, numbering over thirty in the district of Newcastle in the early 1800s. The first papermaking machine was installed at Fourstones in the 1840s.

By 1862 only twelve paper mills out of the original thirty-two in the district were in existence, possessing between them nineteen machines, ten on whites and nine on browns, producing an average of 8 tons a week per machine.

★ Full text of the foundation deed of 21 April 1763 is given on page 85.

Fourstones Paper Mill Bicentenary Dinner at Stationers' Hall on 19 April 1963

Fourstones Bicentenary Dinner
from *l. to r.:* Arne Therkildsen (Fourstones Agent in Denmark), R. R. Rudd
(Iping Paper Mills), Miss M. M. Winterton (Samuel Jones), R. K. Dunn
(Fourstones), Mrs J. B. Dunn (Fourstones), G. T. Mandl, John Pitts (Trew's
Weir Paper Mills, Exeter)

Fourstones Bicentenary Dinner
from *l. to r.:* R. S. W. Bailey (NAPM), D. E. Blow (Bradbury & Smith), A. G. W.
Freeman (Ihlee & Sankey), D. M. Mason (Fourstones), Andrew Gibson (President
NAPM), G. T. Mandl, G. St. P. Wells (Clerk, Stationers Company), John Betts
(Master, Stationers Company), A. H. Bruce (Inveresk)

Fourstones Bicentenary
Party 21 April 1963
l. to r.: Mr RUPERT
SPEIR, MP for Hexham,
G. T. MANDL,
EDWARD GRIERSON,
Author

Fourstones Bicentenary
Party
l. to r.: A. C. CRANKSHAW
(Pembertons Gateshead),
R. A. PATTERSON (Team
Valley Paper Mills),
A. E. CRANKSHAW
(Team Valley Paper
Mills), P. P. Wilson
(Pembertons Gateshead),
D. M. MASON (Fourstones),
I. E. DAVIDSON (Hendon
Paper Mills), J. T. ARTHUR
(Fourstones),
G. T. MANDL

Fourstones Paper Mill Bicentenary Party on 21 April 1963 in the Mill Salle

Telegram from Windsor Castle dated 21 April 1963: The Fourstones Paper Bicentenary on 21 April 1963 coincided with the Queen's Birthday

The MG Wadding Machine arrives at Fourstones from Southalls Birmingham in 1964. The after-dryer on the right was not installed. In centre R. K. DUNN

The Press Pate House at Fourstones being demolished to make way for the new MG Machine, 1964

Foundations for the new MG Machine in 1964 with the original Stuff Chests for the Press Pate in the background, which are still in use

First wadding comes off the MG Machine at Fourstones in 1965

The new MG Wadding Machine 240 cm wide at Fourstones Paper Mill in 1982

The Hospital Disposables Converting Dept at Fourstones Mill 1982

George Mandl:"At the time when you wouldn't expect a bank to help, the Midland helped me."

George Mandl is Chairman of the Fourstones Paper Mill at Hexham, Northumberland. A company founded over two hundred years ago and doing very nicely at the moment, thank you.

But back in 1962, when Mr. Mandl acquired the majority shareholding of the mill, things were nowhere near as rosy.

"The company really was in a bad state", says Mr. Mandl, "it had been making a substantial loss for some time.

"But all the same, I thought I could make a go of it—with some pretty strong help from the Bank.

"I went along to the Midland. They judged I'd be able to make a success of things, and what's more they were prepared to back their judgment. They lent me the money to get the company back on its feet.

"And since then, the company's gone from strength to strength. Needless to say, I'm very impressed with what the Bank has done for me".

The Midland would like the chance to help you too.

Your nearest Midland manager will be pleased to discuss any problem *you* may have—without obligation, of course.

Almost certainly, the Midland can help.

Midland Bank

A GREAT BRITISH BANK
meets any financial need . . . anywhere

Advertisement of the Midland Bank in the National and Regional Press 1972

Consumption of coal then equalled nearly $4\frac{1}{2}$ tons per ton of paper produced. In those days the best browns were made entirely from rope and inferior sorts were made from old tarpaulins, oil–cloth–cuttings, old wagon covers, doormats and other refuse, and I need hardly say that even during this period Fourstones was always a white mill. At the beginning of the 1860s esparto began to be used as a papermaking material and Fourstones was one of the earliest mills to install an esparto plant under the ownership of Mr Alexander Adam.

Within a few years, local esparto grass imports rose from 2,000 to 18,000 tons a year and nearly all newspapers, including *The Times*, were using esparto paper. Only a cheap penny newspaper would still be printed on an inferior rag furnish.

This development also coincides with the final abolition of the famous Paper Tax in 1860, which was originally imposed by William and Mary in 1696 and fixed at the rate of 1s 6d per ream of demy fine by Queen Anne in 1711. In 1803 it was revised to 3d per lb for white papers and $1\frac{1}{2}d$ for browns.

Mill numbers originated with this tax but are not always a reliable guide to a mill's age, as they were frequently transferred to new paper mills as old ones closed down. They were issued geographically. Local numbers in the north-east appear to have fallen into two groups, nos. 71/100, in which Fourstones Paper Mill bears no. 100, and nos. 230/245. The famous no. 1 was Dartford, one of the first white mills in this country, which kept its number, although it ceased to operate in 1739. When it started up in 1862 the tax had already been repealed. No. 2 was at Pickford in Hertfordshire with which Samuel Jones was indirectly connected. In 1839 the tax was amended to $1\frac{1}{2}d$ per lb, irrespective of quality, and the Customs Law allowed a variation of 5% up or down for paper of L.P. 20 lb and up, and 10% for paper below L.P. 20 lbs. (L.P. = Large Post).

It is not surprising that papermakers took advantage of the permitted variation to make the paper slightly underweight, thus saving 3d per ream in tax, and it is probable that L.P. 18 became a standard substance by established precedent after the abolition of the tax in 1860 and has remained so to this day.

Many papermakers endeavoured to evade payment of duty altogether on their paper, and it is recorded in Newcastle that in 1825 out of a dozen or more papermakers in the district, only two were actually out of prison.

There appears to be nothing new in the paper trade. Already in 1800, eight stationers in Newcastle formed a society for the purpose of regulating prices of stationery, particularly paper, which had at that time greatly risen in price, but after 20 years they again began price-cutting, according to contemporary records.

Work in the early machine mills of the 1860s and 1870s was often arduous and dangerous to health. The rags were not thoroughly boiled then, bleach and vitriol doing most of the job, the rag boilers were flat, others were just open pans, and all rag, rope, etc., was manhandled at each stage, right up to the beater. When a beater was emptied into the Chest, a large handbell was rung vigorously to warn the machineman to put on more water. The early machines ran at between 10 and 30 feet per minute with wooden couch rolls, one set of press rolls, usually three drying cylinders, and five little calanders less than 4″ in diameter. Records exist of one mill in the district, which had 63 separate steam engines and some or other of them were always breaking down. If the mill engineer of today feels under the weather sometimes, let him ponder on the lives of his predecessors.

Mr Alexander Adam prospered as a papermaker at Fourstones and a plan of the mill buildings made in 1874 shows little difference to the present position. In 1876 it passed into the hands of Mr David Brown and an extract from the *Northumberland History and Directory of 1886* describes the mill as follows:

The buildings cover a considerable area, and numerous improvements have been effected during the past few years. The curious visitor to the works, during a stroll through its several departments, may witness the whole mystery of paper making, from the sorting of rags until their final conversion into a continuous web of beautiful white paper. About 63 hands are constantly employed, and the paper manufactured is that used for newspapers and book work.

A further reference to Mr David Brown is made in the *Hexham Courant* on the occasion of his marriage to Miss Bell in October 1883 when he entertained his employees to the number of 66 at dinner at the Royal Hotel, Hexham, in honour of the occasion, and Mr Low, the manager of the works, presided. The bride had been presented with a handsome gold necklace by the employees. The Browns were deservedly popular in the neighbourhood and Mr Brown was Church Warden for many years. In the last years of his ownership, the mill however ceased to prosper for the second time in the century and was saved from closure by the Rev. George Cruddas, Vicar of Warden, who supported the mill financially and finally took it over so as to save it from being closed down.

Apart from its many ups and downs during its long history, the mill has weathered many a flood, commencing with the great flood of 1771, the year in which the founder of Fourstones Paper Mill died. Then again in 1881 when the mill dam broke for the first time and in 1904 and 1910. In 1916 the water again reached the high mark of 1771 and the mill dam burst again, never to be repaired. An account of the flood on 10 November 1929 tells us that

Armistice Sunday dawned on scenes of household desolation, and the Paper Mill Authorities showed their sympathy in a most practical way by presenting the sufferers with coal. The school had to be closed for a week and hundreds of pounds worth of damage was done to the stock of paper at the Mill.

Even tons of the best Blotting Paper could not absorb all the moisture. The Mill was last flooded on January 10th, 1955, and the paper machine was under 2 ft. of water. New banks were built jointly by the Riverboard and the Mill during the same year, 2 ft. above the highest flood level ever recorded and it is now most improbable that the Mill will ever suffer again.

In 1907 a joint stock company was formed to carry on the business at Fourstones Paper Mill, headed by the Mill Manager, Mr Alexander Annandale as managing director with Mr Alexander Barr, coal exporter of Newcastle, and Mr John Edward Davidson as principal shareholders. Several well-known papermaking names appear in Fourstones history at about this time, commencing with Mr R. A. Horsburgh, who preceded Mr Annandale as Mill Manager from 1894 to 1899 and whose son we are very happy to have amongst our guests this evening.

Mr D. M. Mason came to the Mill from Pennycuick in 1905 and was successively employed first as machineman, then as foreman and finally as papermaker, which position he held until 1922 when he took up position as papermaker with Reed & Smith in Devon.*

In 1908 Mr Annandale resigned as managing director in order to take up position with Trotters Paper Mill in Scotland and the mill remained under the management of the Davidson family, first under Mr John Davidson and his son, Alfred, and finally under Mr Percy Davidson, until they sold their interest in 1922 and Mr Percy Davidson took up management of Hendon Paper Works. This period also marked the mill's greatest prosperity and during several years a dividend of 30% was paid on its share capital of £20,000 after excess Profits Duty of over £10,000 per annum had been paid to the Inland Revenue.

From 1924 to 1929 the mill was associated with the Becker Group of Companies with Mr William Harrison, as Chairman and with Mr G. R. Hall-Caine and Mr E. B. Montesole as directors.†

---

* He was the brother-in-law of William Tweedy who later became chairman of the Reed & Smith Group. They soon had violent disagreements which culminated in Mr Mason's departure from Silverton in 1927 and purchase of Fourstones Mill for £1,250 following the bankruptcy of the Becker Group in 1929. The purchase was initially financed by Jas Milne & Son the Edinburgh Paper Engineers in the hope of selling a new machine to Fourstones but the debts were later assigned. One third of the share Capital was held by nominees of J.J. Hetherington, secretary of Weir's Mill, Kilbagie until the sale of Fourstones in 1962.

† A summary of Sir Frederick Becker's career published on the occasion of his fiftieth birthday in *The Paper Maker* on 2 January 1922 is reproduced on page 101.

In this period a part of the shares was owned by the Westfield Paper Co. Ltd, of Bathgate, Scotland, and here again we are very happy to have Mr A. M. Bruce, the present chairman of Inveresk, with us this evening, whose connection with Fourstones goes back well over 40 years. Gordon & Gotch Ltd in London also held an interest in the mill during the twenties. The longest surviving connection with the mill is no doubt held by Mr John Rowley (1867–1964), who at present lives in retirement at Barnet, 96 years of age. He first became agent for Fourstones at the turn of the century and was appointed to the Board. He continued in that capacity for almost 30 years. During the last decade before his resignation in 1930, he was assisted by the then very junior, Mr George Pizzey, whom we are very happy to have amongst us tonight.

In the depression of 1929 the mill had to close, together with many other industries and its survival today is undoubtedly due to the courage and enterprise of Mr D. M. Mason, who returned from Devon in order to take over the management and finally the ownership of the mill. It continued as an esparto mill, specialising in featherweight and other esparto papers during the thirties, and in line with many other paper mills in this country used some extra-ordinary raw materials for papermaking, mainly for the production of the notorious Blackout paper, during the war. Mr Mason died in 1948 and was succeeded by his daughter Mina, whom many of you have known for many years, first as very able assistant to her father and in later years as the only lady managing director of a paper mill in this country.* The news of her premature death in 1960 was sadly received by her many friends in the paper trade and I should like to call on Mr Christopher Savory, whose family have been connected with Fourstones Paper Mill and the Mason family for over 30 years, to pay a tribute to her.

I believe it is traditional on bi-centenary meetings for the Chairman to give an account of the company's activities and progress not only over the past 200 years but also to give a forecast on the prospects for the coming century or so.

Let us therefore look for a moment at the growth of paper production over the past 100 years. In 1862 about 100,000 tons of paper were produced in Britain, of which 8,000 tons were made in the district of Newcastle. This figure has risen 40-fold to 4 million tons by 1962 in spite of the fact that there were many more recessions than boom years during this period, mostly due to overproduction.

Dare we think of a corresponding increase over the next 100 years? This would bring the British annual production of paper to 160 million tons a year of which over 13 million tons would be produced

* At one of her early stunning appearances at the Scottish District Paper Makers' meetings in Edinburgh a member's exclamation "Jesus Christ" was corrected by the chairman: "It is not, it's Miss Mason."

in the district of Newcastle. We could certainly rely on a more than buoyant future for Fourstones on that score alone. I hope that my friends from Bowaters, present here tonight, will forgive me for having borrowed their slogan. Fourstones would then be able to undertake the unpopular 10 ton making orders, which would be too uneconomical for the other mills to make and I presume that extra carriage for smalls will then be charged on lots of less than $3\frac{1}{2}$ tons.

I hasten to assure our very junior but much larger colleagues in our industry, however, that the only craft we ever think of at Fourstones is spelt with a capital C and the last newsprint order was delivered some 80 years ago.

Just as there is a place for the bicycle in the age of jet aircraft and rockets, so there is a place for the small speciality mill, running side by side with the huge enterprises which have grown out of the paper industry in the present day.

After an interval of almost 100 years, our mill has reverted from esparto to rag and we now produce our own rag pulp for our production of blottings. Our slow-running 65-inch paper machine, capable of running not more than 160 feet per minute, is ideally suited for the production of specialities, such as blottings, imitation mould-mades and absorbent industrial base papers in special specifications, requiring only small quantities per making. The re-organisation is still in progress and I am happy to say that according to figures for the last six months, the mill is at last beginning to pay its way, after having suffered continuous losses under the severe trading conditions which have prevailed in the paper trade during the last few years.

This achievement would not have been possible without the loyalty, enthusiasm and very hard work of all the people at the mill, and I should like to take this opportunity to pay a special tribute to those present here tonight, Mr John Arthur, Mr and Mrs R. K. Dunn, Mr David Mason and Mr J. F. Thompson.

Now we stand on the threshold of the third century, once again as a rag mill, though no longer hand-made. I should like to quote here an old and popular saying quoted in this book by our fellow bi-centenarians, Evans & Adlard: "Rags make Paper, Paper makes Money, Money makes Banks, Banks make Loans, Loans make Beggars, Beggars make Rags, Rags make Paper."

FOURSTONES PAPER MILL NOW

There does not remain a great deal to relate of the history of Fourstones after reprinting Mr G. T. Mandl's speech at the Bicentenary Dinner, for which a great deal of historical research was done at the time. It is undoubtedly one of the oldest mills still working on its original site and one whose history reflects much of the development of papermaking in the British Isles.

In 1851 Mr Robert Rumney Crawford, a direct descendant of one of the founders, registered a patent, fully reproduced on pages 92–97, for what has subsequently become known as the air drier, originally used for the tub sizing of paper but subsequently for many other applications. It was probably the first mill to install an air drier unit on its tub sizer in connection with the installation of a Fourdrinier machine and it was also certainly one of the oldest Esparto Mills in the British Isles with a capacity of some 1,500 tons under Mr Alexander Adam.

The decline started in the last decade of the century with installation of very much larger machines and consequent over-capacity, which has been the major problem of the paper industry in general.

Whilst its capacity remained static at the level of 1860 and it had gone through all imaginable grades of paper from Newsprint to filter paper, its fate would undoubtedly have been sealed in the series of depressions culminating with the greatest depression of all in 1975 if it had not been for the diversification into a completely new product through the installation of the Cellulose Wadding machine in 1965. In his report to the Rural Industries Bureau, Dr Julius Grant described the investment in November 1963 as follows: "This is an old Mill in poor condition and the present project is a courageous attempt to make it profitable. Technical difficulties are bound to be experienced before the Mill is running smoothly and efficiently on Cellulose Wadding and I feel that the cost of some of these have been under-estimated." (A full report is on page 112.)

The subsequent ten years proved Dr Grant's assessment to be absolutely correct and the ultimate commercial success could only be achieved after completion of the vertical integration into the production of hospital disposables.

The wadding machine had been purchased from Southalls in 1963 at a price of £3,000, equal even in those days to virtual scrap value. It had been constructed by Wagner in Warmbrunn in 1930, in a part of Germany that now belongs to Poland, and was one of the earliest wadding machines installed in the UK, with a width of 220 cm and a maximum speed of 220 metres per minute. Compared with the ancient Fourdrinier machine it was certainly very modern but a long way from modern tissue machines capable of speeds up to 2,000 metres per minute.

Papermaking skills, which must have existed in the locality, disappeared gradually with the advent of the two World Wars and intermediate and subsequent depressions. High unemployment in the North-East, as well as the remoteness of the mill, made industrial relations extremely difficult and caused a great strain on the management since its integration within Thomas & Green Holdings Ltd.

The original plan to sell market wadding and thus remain in the traditional area of papermaking had to be abandoned when the Fourdrinier programme became more and more unprofitable due to structural problems and full vertical integration into hospital incontinence pads was commenced in 1969 and completed by the end of 1972.

After the transfer of the Fourdrinier programme to Thomas & Green the old machine had a brief revival in the manufacture of ticket papers, Middles and corrugating paper during 1974, when a new building with a modern rewinder and a completely new stock preparation plant had been added.

In the autumn of 1975 the Fourdrinier machine had to be finally closed down. The mill now operates as a fully integrated unit in the hospital disposables field as one of the market leaders. The recession of 1975 witnessed its return to full profitability and it was able to make a welcome contribution to Group results.

In 1978–79 a new cellulose wadding machine was installed replacing the one installed in 1963. This was done in stages in order to reduce the loss of production to a minimum. During the Christmas shut of 1977 the MG Cylinder was replaced and a new hood installed. During the Summer shut of 1978 the wet end, flowbox and suction press were installed thus completing the installation.

In September 1978 a very serious fire broke out on the cellulose wadding slitter due to ignition of accumulated dust. The violent explosion destroyed the entire slitter house. The machinehouse roof, housing the new machine, was also destroyed but fortunately only minor damage occurred to the new machine. Subsequent to the fire the layout of the mill was completely changed and a new building housing two new slitters was erected adjacent to the machine house.

In order to strengthen the vertical integration of hospital incontinence pads through the Wardens Dressing Company, a wholly owned converting subsidiary at Fourstones Mill, the business of Kattan Disposables in Stockport, Greater Manchester, was acquired in 1977 with its entire labour force and plant and converted a part of the increased cellulose wadding capacity produced on the new machine.

The old Fourdrinier machine installed in 1860 is being preserved as a museum. It is the oldest Fourdrinier in the British Isles and the first to be purchased by the G. T. Mandl Group of Companies in 1962.

In 1982, the production of Kattan Disposables was transferred from Manchester to a new factory at Haltwhistle,* very close to the mill. This very modern unit now converts an increasing portion of the cellulose wadding output and provides work in one of the worst unemployment black spots in the North-East of England.

* See page 128.

Early drawing of Fourstones Paper Mill and House (left) about 1826 (from a Woodcut published with the "Joe the Quilter ballad"

Aerial view of Fourstones Paper Mill 1958 with the Esparto Pulp installation still intact. Roaster chimney on right, with Evaporators in black shed

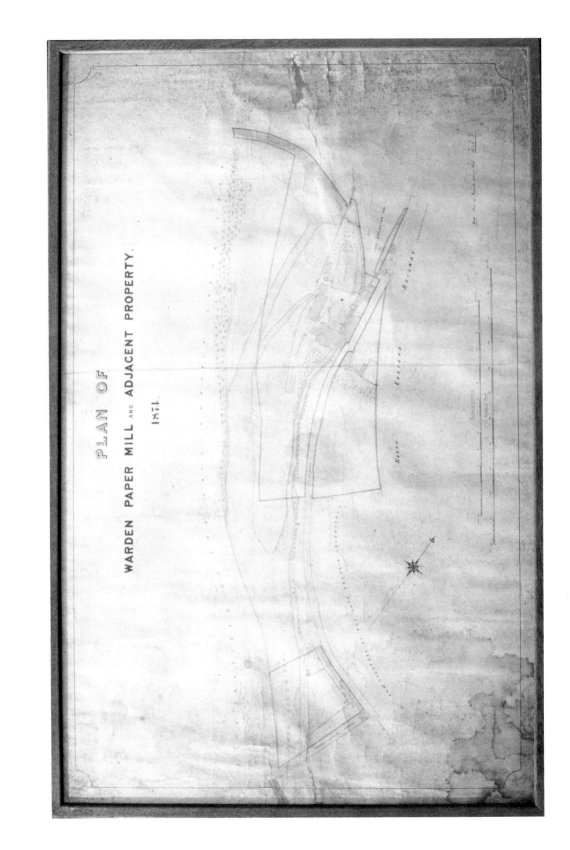

PLAN OF

WARDEN PAPER MILL AND ADJACENT PROPERTY.

1871.

Fourstones Mill Beater floor with Esparto Pulp Breakers & Washers 1908

Digging out the Esparto from Vertical Grass Boilers at Fourstones Mill 1955
(*l. to r.*: NORMAN STOKOE and GORDEN REAY)

Fourstones Mill Paper Machine 1908. D. M. MASON on extreme left with cap

Fourstones Mill Cutting House 1908

The Fourstones Mill Finishing House workers about 1910. 3rd and 4th from right
are David Mason's half sisters ANNIE and ELISABETH MASON

Esparto Pulp Presspate in operation in 1955. The space is now occupied by the
MG Wadding Machine

The family of DAVID MASON
l. to r.: R. K. DUNN, Mrs J. B. DUNN, Mrs MASON with granddaughter GILLIAN, D. M. MASON. In garden of the Mill House in 1944

Fourstones Paper Mill had remained practically unchanged for 100 years from 1874 to 1974

Foundation Deed of
Fourstones Paper Mill of
21 April 1763

Commemorative Tablet of
the Rev. PETER RUMNEY
founder of Fourstones Paper
Mill at Hexham Abbey

M. S.
Rev.di PETRI RUMNEY de Hexham.
Qui ob. 16. Feb. 1771. Æt. 56. et
Eliz.ta Uxoris ejus. quæ ob. 7. Nov. 1795. Æt. 79.
Grata et pia Proles
Hoc Monimentum
poſuit.
1796.

ORIGINAL FOUNDATION DEED
DATED 21st APRIL 1763

This Indenture made twenty-first day of April in the Third Year of the Reign of our Sovereign Lord George the Third by the grace of God of Great Britain France and Ireland King Defender of the Faith and soforth And in the Year of our Lord One Thousand Seven Hundred and Sixty Three Between Wilkinson Kirsopp of Hexham in the County of Northumberland Gentleman on the one part And William Charnley of the Town and County of Newcastle upon Tyne Stationer and the Reverend Peter Rumney of Kirby Hill in the County of York Clerk of the other part Witnesseth that the said Wilkinson Kirsopp for and in consideration of the Yearly Rent and Covenant hereinafter reserved and mentioned which on the part and behalf of the said William Charnley and Peter Rumney their Executors Administrators and Assigns are to be paid done and performed Hath demised granted and to farm letten and by these presents Doth demise grant and to farm let unto the said William Charnley and Peter Rumney their Executors Administrators and Assigns All that messuage or tenement piece or parcell of land adjoining the same which said piece of land contained by estimation twenty yards square and the said messuage and parcell of land within the Township Village or Hamlet called Nether Warden in the said County of Northumberland and the North Side of the Kings High Road leading from Hexham aforesaid to Newbrough in the said County of Northumberland and bordered on the South by the said Road and on the East North and West by the other lands of the said Wilkinson Kirsopp at Nether Warden aforesaid And also all that other parcell of ground within the said Township Village or Hamlet of Nether Warden lying on the South side of the said Road leading from Hexham to Newbrough and which is bordered on the North by the said Road and on the South by the River Tyne and on the East and West by the Land of Mr. Matthew Leadbetter all which said provisions are a part of the allotment of Warden Hills alloted upon the Divisions to the late Cuthbert Heron deceased and which were since purchased by the said Wilkinson Kirsopp of the Heirs of the said Cuthbert Heron and another lying and coming within the said Township Village or Hamlet of Nether Warden in the Parish of Nether Warden aforesaid Together with Liberty Lease and Licence for them the said William Charnley and Peter Rumney their Executors Administrators or Assigns to erect build and make a Paper Mill and make other Erections and buildings as they shall think proper upon the said premises or any part thereof And also all privileges of using the River as far as the Liberties of the said Wilkinson Kirsopp extend And also full and free liberty of making a conduit or conduits and bringing the water of any of the Springs in the adjoining land of the said Wilkinson Kirsopp through the said adjoining land and to the said Paper Mill when so erected they the said William Charnley and Peter Rumney their Executors Administrators and Assigns conveying the said water through a conduit or conduits shall not exceed six inches in breadth at the bottom and the top of which shall lye ten inches at least under the surface of the earth Provided they the said William Charnley and Peter Rumney do as little damage to the said land of the said Wilkinson Kirsopp in laying the said conduit as maybe and pay reasonable satisfaction for any Spoil of Ground which shall be Occasioned thereby And also full and free Liberty of winning working getting and bringing from a Quarry now open belonging to the said Wilkinson Kirsopp any quantity of Stones for the erecting building making and repairing the said intended Paper Mill and other erection to the said intended Paper Mill and other erection through the lands of the said Wilkinson Kirsopp along the Road or way now used from the said Quarry to the Ground by the River where the said Paper Mill is intended to be built for and during the First Year of the said Term without paying or making any satisfaction for the winning working or leading the same they the said William Charnley and Peter Rumney their Executor Administrators and Assigns paying unto the said Wilkinson Kirsopp his Heirs and Assigns five pence for every twenty wagon loads or ffothers of the said stone which shall be lead from the said Quarry to the said Paper Mill after the expiration of the said first year of the Term hereby granted Together with allways paths passages water and watercourses and Appurtenances whatsoever to the said messauge Tenenent and pieces or parcells of Ground hereby owned belonging or in anywyse appertaining To have and to hold the said messuage or Tenement and pieces or parcells of ground and premises Liberties privileges power and Authority with their Appurtenances and every part and parcell thereof in and by these presents demised unto the said William Charnley and Peter Rumney their Executors Administrators and Assigns from the Twelfth Day of May next ensuing the date hereof for and during and unto the full end and Term of Twenty One Years from thenceforth next ensuing fully to be complete and ended Yielding and Paying therefore Yearly and every Year during the said Term and to the said Wilkinson Kirsopp his Heirs and Assigns the Yearly Rent or Sum of Ten Pounds and Ten Shillings of Lawful money of Great Britain at those days or times in the Year (That is to say) the Twenty second day of November and the Twelfth day of May in every year by even and equal portions The first payment therof to begin and be made at or upon the

Twenty second day of November now next ensuing Provided always
nevertheless and it is the true intent and meaning of their presents
That if the said Yearly rent of Ten Pounds and Ten Shillings or any
part thereof shall be in arrears and unpaid by the space of fforty days
next after any of the said days or time of payment whereon the same
ought to be paid as aforesaid That then and from thenceforth without
making any demand thereof it shall and may be lawful to and for
the said Wilkinson Kirsopp his Heirs and Assigns into all the said
demised premises and every or any part thereof in the name of the
whole to reenter and the same to have again repossess and reenjoy
in his and their first and former Estate anything herein contained to
the Contrary thereof in anywise not withstanding And the said
William Charnley and Peter Rumney do hereby for themselves
jointly and severally and for their joint and severall Heir Executors
and Administrator Covenant Promise and Agree to and with the said
Wilkinson Kirsopp his Heirs and Assigns in manner following that
is to say that they the said William Charnley and Peter Rumney or
the one of them their or one of their Executors Administrators or
Assigns shall and will well and truly pay or cause to be paid unto
the said Wilkinson Kirsopp his Heirs or Assigns the said Yearly Rent
of Ten Pounds and Ten Shillings in and by those presents resolved
at the depositions hereinbefore mentioned for the payment thereof
And also shall and will pay and discharge all and all manner of tax
or Assessments which during the said term hereby granted shall
become due or payable for the said premises hereby demised or
which shall or maybe Taxed Charged or Imposed upon the same or
upon the Erection or Building to be made thereon or upon the said
Wilkinson Kirsopp his Heirs Executors Administrators or Assigns for
or in respect thereof And also shall and will lay a good and efficient
conduit or conduits for conveying the said water from the same
springs to the said Paper Mill through the Grounds of the said Wilkinson Kirsopp which said conduit shall not exceed six inches in
breadth at the bottom and the top of which shall be laid ten inches
at least from the surface of the earth And also shall and will in laying
and placing the same do as little damage to the ground of the said
Wilkinson Kirsopp as maybe and pay a reasonable satisfaction for
any unnecessary Spoil of Ground which shall be occasioned thereby
And also shall and will bring the stones which they shall use from
the aforesaid Quarry along the Road or Way now used from the
said Quarry to the ground hereby demised where the said Paper Mill
is intended to be built as aforesaid And also shall and will pay or
cause to be paid unto the said Wilkinson Kirsopp his Heirs or Assigns
Five pence for every twenty wain loads or ffothers of the stones
which they shall lead from the said Quarry after the expiration of
the First Year of the Term hereby Granted And also that if the said
William Charnley and Peter Rumney their Executors or Adminis-

trators shall at any time during the Term hereby granted be aminded or desirous to assign or dispose of this lease or the premises hereby demised and their Estate and Interest therein then and in such case the said Wilkinson Kirsopp his Heirs and Assigns shall have a right of preemption and a preference to become purchaser or purchasers of all the said premises and the remainder of the said Term which shall be then to come and unexpired before all other persons in case the said Wilkinson Kirsopp his Heirs or Assigns shall offer to give and pay at and for as good a price for the said premises and the then remainder of the Term so to be assigned with the Appurtenances as any other person or persons shall really and bona fide offer and be willing to give or pay for the same And the said Wilkinson Kirsopp for himself his Heirs and Assigns doth covenant promise and agree to and with the said William Charnley and Peter Rumney their Executors Administrators and Assigns by these presents in manner and form following (that is to say) That it shall and maybe lawful to and for the said William Charnley and Peter Rumney their Executors Administrators and Assigns they paying the Rents and performing the Covenants herein before reserved and contained on their parts to be paid done and performed peaceably and quietly to have hold and occupy possess and enjoy all and singular the said demised premises for and during the said Term hereby granted with such the Lot Suit Trouble Denial Hinderance or Disturbance of him the said Wilkinson Kirsopp his Heirs or Assigns or any person or persons whatsoever lawfully claiming or to claim by from or under him them or any of them And also that he the said Wilkinson Kirsopp his Heirs or Assigns shall and will at the end or expiration of the Term of Twenty One Years hereby granted and also at the end of every Twenty One Years thereafter on the request of the said William Charnley and Peter Rumney their Executors Administrators or Assigns for that purpose to be made and at their charge and expense renew a Lease or Leases of the hereby demised premises to the said William Charnley and Peter Rumney their Executors Administrators or Assigns for the like Term of Twenty One Years and under the like Rents and Covenants which are hereinabove mentioned on the Lessees part to be paid done and performed They the said William Charnley and Peter Rumney their Executors Administrators or Assigns paying unto the said Wilkinson Kirsopp his Heirs or Assigns the sum of One Pound and One Shilling upon every renewal of the said Term over and above the said Annual Rents hereby reserved and Existing and delivering the counterpart of every subsequent Lease thereof to be granted as aforesaid to the said Wilkinson Kirsopp his Heirs or Assigns being the intention of those presents and of the parties to the same That the said Wilkinson Kirsopp his Heirs or Assigns shall at the end or expiration of every Twenty One Years next after the Commencement of this present

88

Lease for ever thereafter renew or grant a New Lease to the said William Charnley and Peter Rumney their Executors Administrators or Assigns of the said Premises for Twenty One Years then next after and upon the like Rents and Covenants as in this Lease and without paying any other or further consideration for the same save only One Pound and One Shilling for each renewal aforesaid and the charge and expenses of every subsequent Lease and Counterparts thereof to be granted of the premises hereby demised as aforesaid In witness whereof the said parties to these presents Interchangeably have set their hands and seals the day and Year first above written

Wilkinson Kirsopp   William Charnley   Peter Rumney

LETTER FROM Dr A.H. SHORTER

Geography Department,
Queen's Building,
University of Exeter,
Exeter,
Devon
19th May 1969

Dear Mr Mandl,

In the article on Fourstones in the *World's Paper Trade Review*, 1963, it is stated that there is very little information about the activities of the mill from its foundation in 1763 until the middle of the last century. When you kindly called on me here, I promised to go through my notes and let you have any information relating to that period. I append the scraps of information—which you probably know already!

Carrying on from the references I gave in *Paper Mills and Paper Makers 1495-1800*, and first giving a fuller reference to the item for 1773:

1773 Assignees of William Charnley advertise Moiety of all that large and commodious Paper-Mill, now carrying on to great advantage, situate and being upon the River Tyne, about two miles from Hexham, called Warden Paper Mill. 2 water wheels, 2 engines, 2 vats, 4 presses with iron screws, 1 sizing press, 1 glaze, 1 pair iron rollers. Building 89 feet in front, the wings 38 feet each, the whole fabric 20 feet wide. 3 stories high, the top a very commodious drying room. Held by lease for 21 years (ten only just expired). Mrs Rumney is the owner of the other Moiety.
The Newcastle Courant, 15th May 1773

1816 Elizabeth Crawford and Lydia Rumney, paper makers of Warden, insured their water paper mill for £1 500, and their stock and utensils in a warehouse in the Old Flesh Market, Newcastle.
Sun Fire Insurance Policy 924679. 6th December 1816

1816 Robert Rumney, paper maker, Warden.
Excise General Letter. 1816

1823   Lydia Rumney and Peter Rumney Crawford.

                             ......do......,   1823

1825 Peter Rumney Crawford   ......do......,   1825

1832 Ann Crawford   ......do......,   1832

1851 Warden Mill: 6 beating engines at work, 1 silent.
House of Commons Papers, 1852

1852 Ann Crawford, paper manufacturer of Warden, bankrupt.
London Gazette, 24th August 1852
(Her dividend was to be declared. *Morning Chronicle*, 10th May 1854)

1853 Dissolution of partnership: John Alexander Cockburn of Barrasford and Thomas Fordyce of Warden, paper manufacturers.
Morning Chronicle, 8th January 1853
(It is interesting that at times the names of Rumney and Fordyce occur in the references to Haughton Mill: *1857* Robert Rumney, Charles and William Fordyce, paper manufacturers of Haughton, bankrupt. *Morning Chronicle*, 21st February 1857)

1860 Thomas Fordyce, Warden. Printings.
Paper Mills Directory, 1860

1866 Alexander Adam, South Tyne Mill. News and printings. ......do......, 1866

I hope the above is of some interest.

With reference to my next book★ on *History of Paper Making in the British Isles*, I am beginning to think about the illustrations, and I am wondering whether you would agree to the inclusion of a photograph of Fourstones Mill. Perhaps an aerial view would be better than the photograph in the *World's Paper Trade Review*? As an old-established mill, originally a vat mill in a rural setting, Fourstones is a very good example for one of my plates (I am allowed only 16!) I should be most grateful for your advice.

With best wishes and kind regards,
Yours sincerely,
Alfred Shorter

★ The book was subsequently published by David & Charles Ltd, Newton Abbot, after Dr Shorter's death and edited by Mrs Shorter and G. T. Mandl.

A.D. 1850 . . . . Nº 13,171.

SPECIFICATION

OF

ROBERT RUMNEY CRAWFORD.

DRYING PAPER.

LONDON:

PRINTED BY GEORGE E. EYRE AND WILLIAM SPOTTISWOODE,

PRINTERS TO THE QUEEN'S MOST EXCELLENT MAJESTY:

PUBLISHED AT THE GREAT SEAL PATENT OFFICE,

25, SOUTHAMPTON BUILDINGS, HOLBORN.

Price 1s. 8d.   1857.

A.D. 1850 . . . . Nº 13,171.

Drying Paper.

CRAWFORD'S SPECIFICATION.

TO ALL TO WHOM THESE PRESENTS SHALL COME, I, Robert Rumney Crawford, of Warden Paper Mill, in the County of Northumberland, Paper Maker, send greeting.

WHEREAS Her present most Excellent Majesty Queen Victoria, by Her
5 Royal Letters Patent under the Great Seal of the United Kingdom of Great Britain and Ireland, bearing date at Westminster, the Tenth day of July, One thousand eight hundred and fifty, in the fourteenth year of Her reign, did, for Herself, Her heirs and successors, give and grant unto me, the said Robert Rumney Crawford, my exōrs, admōrs, and assigns, Her especial
10 license, full power, sole privilege and authority, that I, the said Robert Rumney Crawford, my exōrs, admōrs, and assigns, or such others as I, the said Robert Rumney Crawford, my exōrs, admōrs, or assigns, should at any time agree with, and no others, from time to time and at all times during the term of years therein expressed, should and lawfully might make, use,
15 exercise, and vend, within England, Wales, and the Town of Berwick-upon-Tweed, my Invention of "AN IMPROVEMENT IN DRYING PAPER;" in which said Letters Patent is contained a proviso that I, the said Robert Rumney Crawford, shall cause a particular description of the nature of my said Invention, and in what manner the same is to be performed, by an instrument in
20 writing under my hand and seal, to be inrolled in Her said Majesty's High Court of Chancery within six calendar months next and immediately after the date of the said in part recited Letters Patent, as in and by the same, reference being thereunto had, will more fully and at large appear.

93

NOW KNOW YE, that in compliance with the said proviso, I, the said Robert Rumney Crawford, do hereby declare that the nature of my said Invention, and in what manner the same is to be performed, are fully described and ascertained in and by the following description thereof, reference being had to the Drawings hereunto annexed, and to the figures and letters 5 marked thereon, that is to say :—

My Invention comprises a new mode of drying paper chiefly after it has been sized, and this object I effect in the various ways herein described. The plan which I adopt for drying paper in the web or in long lengths consists of a series of flat tubes, through which the paper conducted by tapes 10 is passed, and in its progress through these tubes it is subjected to a stream of air (warm air I prefer) which is forced through the tubes by a fan or other machine which is or may be used for blowing air or for exhausting air. Figure 1 represents a side elevation of the machinery I have found to answer the purpose ; Figure 2, a front elevation of the same ; Figure 3, a longitudinal 15 section ; Figure 4, a cross section at A, B, on Figure 3. a, a^1, a^2, a^3, a^4, a^5, a^6, a^7, a^8, a^9, a^{10}, a^{11}, Figure 3, are rollers of wood for conducting the paper and tapes through the tubes. b, b^1, b^2, b^3, and b^4, Figure 3, are the tubes (which I prefer made of sheet zinc) supported by wood framing stiffened by ledgers shewn at c, c, c, c, c, c. d, d, Figure 3, represent the air boxes for 20 feeding the tubes, and e, e, the trunks for conveying the air from the blowing machine to the air boxes d, d. Motion is given to the rollers a, a, by the driving shaft A and band wheels C and D, Figures 1 and 2. A crossed strap is passed partly round the pully or band wheel D and drives the roller a^9 by passing round the pulley E. A pulley L is keyed concentric with the pulley 25 E and drives by a strap the pulley G which is keyed upon the spindle of the roller a^5. This roller drives the roller a^1 by a strap passing round the pullies F and H. The pulley C drives by an open strap the rollers a^7, a^3, and a^{11}, by the pullies placed upon their spindles in a similar manner to the above. k, k, k, k, Figure 4, are throttle valves placed on each side of the machine at 30 the mouths of the air boxes d, d; their use when closed is for preventing the air from passing from the air trunks e, e, into the air boxes d, d, until the paper is fairly introduced into the tubes. These valves are then opened, and the air enters the air boxes, and from these boxes it passes into the tubes travelling in the same direction as the paper. The paper (represented by the 35 blue line) to be dried is passed into the machine between the roller a and a^2, Figure 3, and the tapes (represented by the red line) firstly closing the throttle vales at the mouth of the air box belonging to the tube b until the paper has passed the apertures for the air at the points f, f, in tube b, and

when it has so passed, the throttle valves are opened and the air is forced on both sides of the sheet in the direction the paper is travelling, taking up and carrying off the wet and moisture in the form of vapour and discharging it at the end of the tube b at g, g. When the paper reaches the roller a^1, it is
5 passed beneath it into the tube b^1, and the tape h is passed round the roller a^{11} and returns to roller a. The paper in the tube b^1 has the air thrown on both sides of the sheet, and the vapour is expelled at the end of the tube b^1 at i, i. The paper is then passed into the tube b^2 round the roller a^4, and the tape j returns into the tube b round the roller a^2. This process is
10 repeated until the paper is passed through all the tubes of the machine and the paper is dry. In drying thin papers it may be found unnecessary to use all the tubes, as the paper may be found dry after it has passed through a certain number of them, when the paper may be taken off and wound upon a reel or passed through a cutting machine at pleasure. Hand-made papers
15 and papers that are cut into sheets before they are sized are after sizing generally hung upon lines in rooms or lofts and dried in summer by the natural atmosphere, and in winter by dry air warmed by steam pipes, &c. This mode is very expensive, and occupies a great deal of time; it also requires a considerable space to dry in. To obviate this I have invented
20 certain methods of drying paper of this description by machinery, as herein-after described.

My first plan is by using a machine constructed as before described, but although I have dried such papers with the tapes passing round the rollers, yet I prefer using nets or other reticulate or open sheets for conducting the paper
25 through the machine, and when the machine is used for drying paper in the sheets the throttle valves are always open.

My second plan for drying paper in sheets is by using a series of reels round which the paper passes between tapes, cords, nets, or reticulate sheets to conduct it from reel to reel. Air, heated by steam pipes or any other
30 well-known means, rises against the surface of the paper and dries it. Figure 1 (Sheet 2) represents a longitudinal sectional elevation of the machinery I have used for drying paper in sheets, and Figure 2 is a transverse sectional elevation of the same. A, Figures 1 and 2, is a pulley which may be driven by the strap B from any prime mover. This pulley is keyed upon the
35 spindle of the roller C. D, D^1, D^2, D^3, D^4, D^5, and D^6, Figure 1, are reels or drums. E, Figure 1, is a tightening roller; and F, F^1, and F^2, are guide rollers for conducting the tapes, cords, nets, or porous sheets through the machine. G, G, Figures 1 and 2, are steam pipes for warming the air; or the air may be warmed by cockles, flues, or any other well-known means used

for that purpose, and which need not be particularly described. Motion is given to the reels D, D¹, and by the endless tapes, cords, nets, or porous sheets represented by the brown lines *a, b,* Figure 1, passing partly round them and the roller C, which roller is driven by the pulley A and the strap B worked by some prime mover. The paper *c, c* (represented by the blue line) 5 to be dried is placed between the conducting tapes, cords, nets, or porous sheets at the roller E, and when the paper reaches the reel D it is held between the tapes, cords, nets, or porous sheets which conduct it over the reel D¹, under the reel D², over D³, under D⁴, over D⁵, and under D⁶, when the endless tapes, cords, nets, or porous sheets separate, *a* passing over the guide 10 rollers F², F¹, and F, and *b* passes over and beneath the rollers C and E to bring through more paper, and the dried paper is taken off the machine at the roller C. During the time that the paper is passing through the machine, it is subjected to the warm air from the steam pipes G, G, and the vapour rises out of the top of the machine and is discharged into the atmosphere through 15 openings made for that purpose in the roof of the building. Although up to this stage I have only spoken of drying sized paper, yet I have used the machines thus described for drying water-leaf or paper before it has been sized, and I find the paper so dried approaches more nearly in quality the character of such papers when dried in lofts.   20

My third method of drying paper in sheets after they are sized is by using metal cylinders heated by steam instead of using the reels or drums just described in my second method of drying paper in sheets. In this case I prefer coating all or some of the cylinders with felt cloth, wooden slips placed a short distance apart, or with any material that is not a good conductor of 25 heat, which prevents the size drying too rapidly on the surface of the paper; but some paper of an inferior quality may be dried in coming in contact with the metallic surfaces, excepting so far as it may be separated by the endless tapes, cords, nets or sheets, which I always use with the metallic cylinders for conducting the paper. Although the cylinder just mentioned may be driven by 30 the tapes, cords, nets, or porous cloths, yet I prefer driving them by a train of wheelwork in the same manner that the cylinders of the well-known drying machine is driven, and which machine is used for drying papers in long lengths, and is generally placed at the end of the paper-making machine.

My fourth method of drying paper in sheets after they are sized is, by using 35 a single reel or drum of large diameter. This drum is turned at a slow rate. The paper [is kept to the surface of the reel by endless tapes, cords, nets, or open sheets, and warmed air is allowed to rise against the surface of the paper to dry it. Instead of using the large reel just described, a heated metallic cylinder can be used, the paper being retained upon its surface by the endless tapes, cords, nets, or sheets; and whether the reel or the cylinder is used the endless tapes, cords, nets, or porous sheets may be returned by guide and conducting rollers in a similar manner to the tapes and guides of a printing

5 machine, or as described in the tubular machine in my first method of drying papers.

In witness whereof, I, the said Robert Rumney Crawford, have hereunto set my hand and seal, this Tenth day of January, in the year of our Lord One thousand eight hundred and fifty-one.

10 ROBERT RUMNEY (L.S.) CRAWFORD.

AND BE IT REMEMBERED, that on the Tenth day of January, in the year of our Lord 1851, the aforesaid Robert Rumney Crawford came before our said Lady the Queen in Her Chancery, and acknowledged the Specification aforesaid, and all and every thing therein contained and

15 specified, in form above written. And also the Specification aforesaid was stamped according to the tenor of the Statute made for that purpose.

Enrolled the Tenth day of January, in the year of our Lord One thousand eight hundred and fifty-one.

MOWBRAY.

LONDON:
Printed by GEORGE EDWARD EYRE and WILLIAM SPOTTISWOODE,
Printers to the Queen's most Excellent Majesty. 1857.

JOHN POLLOCK

Notes on the connection of John Pollock (son of the founder of the present company Pollock & Searby Ltd) with Fourstones Paper Mill 1857 to 1865

The original John Pollock traded in paper in Edinburgh under the name of Pollock and Naismith.

Following the building of the Edinburgh to London railway he moved to London in 1836 and set up as a paper mill agent for Alexander Cowan of Penicuik. He is first recorded in London in 1839 and died about 1855.

His son, also John Pollock, may well have lent money secured on the mortgage of Warden Mill in return for the sales agency in London, which was then extended into an outright purchase of the mill in 1862.

The business could not have been very lucrative as it is unlikely that he would have had to re-mortgage the mill within such a short space of time, leading to the ultimate sale to Alexander Adam in 1865.

John Pollock continued to trade as John Pollock and Son with the agency of Alexander Cowan. In the latter part of the nineteenth century the company ceased to act as paper agents and started a paper merchanting business. After John Pollock's death the company was converted into a limited company in 1914 by his son, also John Pollock, under the style John Pollock and Son Ltd.

The present John Pollock, the great grandson of the one connected with Fourstones is still actively engaged in the trade as Chairman of Pollock and Searby Ltd, of Mill Lane, Alton, Hampshire, fulfilling an unbroken record of five generations in the same business.

ROBERT A. HORSBURGH

*Some notes on the closely connected families of Johnston and Horsburgh
and their almost three centuries' connection with the paper industry—by
Mr G. B. C. Johnston concerning Robert A. Horsburgh, Mill Manager at
Fourstones Paper Mill 1894–99*

Robert Horsburgh, obtained early in his life, the job of Salle Foreman at Carrongrove. This was a 12-hour-day job with the understanding that if the manager (his brother-in-law) wanted him, he had
to come back to the mill after 6.00 p.m. In due course he left to
become manager at Fourstones Paper Mill in Northumberland and
then went on to the Albuheira Mill near Lisbon, Portugal.

His next move was to the Bengal Paper Mills at Runnygunge,
about 100 miles from Calcutta. He was managing director when he
retired to England. Not satisfied in doing nothing he acquired an
interest in the Swiftbrook Paper Mills at Saggart in Eire, with which
he remained connected until he died.

While at Fourstones he had married Jean Hepple. There were two
daughters and two sons, Roy and John, who both entered the paper
trade. Roy went to the Papeterie de Mandeure to learn some French
and to get some knowledge of papermaking. He then spent some
time with a firm of chartered accountants in London and finally
joined Wiggins Teape. He went first to Hele and then to Stoney-
wood before becoming assistant manager at Withnell Fold. On his
father becoming connected with Swiftbrook he left W. T. and became manager there and retired a few years ago when he held the
position of managing director.

The second son John was trained at Swiftbrook and then spent
some time with Backhouse and Coppock before joining the Dartford
Paper Mills where he remained until he retired.

TELEGRAMS:
"PAPER, FOURSTONES."

SOUTH TYNE MILL,
FOURSTONES, NORTHUMBERLAND.

The
Fourstones Paper Mill Co. Ld.
MILL No. 100.

July 14th 1915

My dear Father,

I have a letter from Mr Milne today, saying he will not be back at his office till the middle of next week. & will write me again as soon as he can conveniently see me.

Mr Richardson returned on Monday Evening. & did <u>not</u> see Mr Milne. He saw Mr Bruce & Mr Lister. & he says they both intend to stick to the advanced price, irrespective of what Mr Wallace does.

I have spoken to Mr Mason "re Output". & I can assure you we will do everything in our power to make at least 33 Tons weekly.

There are several things quite beyond our control, that keeps down output such as, thin weights. Bad sizes for our machine, Having to change from one quality to another owing to being so busy etc.

We expect a much better week this week, as we are going out Blottings tonight.

Have written away for the price of Scrap Platinum. & will sell the crucible if the price is good.

I am going to Prestwick on Saturday of June, so cannot play golf.

I remain, Your affectionate Son. Percy

---

* Letter from Percy Davidson, Mill Manager at Fourstones, to his father dated 14 July 1915.

SIR FREDERICK BECKER

A brief sketch of his business career

Reprinted from "Paper Maker" 2 January 1922
(Fourstones Mill was part of the Becker Group from 1924 to 1929)

It is but justice to state that today Mr F. E. R. Becker, JP, is one of
the most outstanding figures in the British pulp and paper trades,
and on the occasion of the commemoration of his fiftieth birthday
it is not inappropriate that a brief sketch of his career, which, like
most of those of men who have risen from the ranks, is not without
an element of romance, should be given.

Mr Becker began his business life as a clerk in the chambers of Mr
(now Sir) C. F. Gill, the well-known barrister, but it was not long
before he yielded to the call of commerce by associating himself with
the Norwegian firm of Messrs Chr. Christophersen & Co., of 39
Lombard Street, E.C., then under the successful management of Mr
Felix Seyfert. Gifted with great ability, energy and strong determination, Mr Becker, however, in the year 1893 began business for
himself as a wood pulp merchant at small offices at 115 Cannon
Street, London, E.C., under the style and title of Becker & Co. The
new firm's success was immediate, and as agents for some of the
leading mills in Scandinavia the company's operations attained to
such proportions that in 1896 the offices were removed to more
extensive premises at 64 Cannon Street. Three years later Mr Becker
opened a branch office at 34 Royal Exchange, Manchester, under the
management of Mr W. H. Grimshaw, who had represented the firm
in Scotland for four years previously. About this time some attempt
was made to boycott the firm by the Norwegian mechanical pulp
manufacturers, but the only result was the strengthening of Mr
Becker's position in the trade. It was to this that he would probably
attribute the development of his interest in Canada, to which Dominion he made his first trip in that year. He was one of the first to
recognise the potentialities of the Canadian wood pulp industry, and,
greatly to the satisfaction of those who believed that the Scandinavian
pulp manufacturers were attempting a combination of their mills
with a view to increasing prices, he formed important business connections with the Chicoutimi Pulp Co., of Chicoutimi, Quebec; the
Acadia Pulp and Paper Co., of Halifax; the Nova Scotia Wood Pulp
Co., Ltd, and the Maritime Sulphite Fabric Co., Chatham, New
Brunswick. With an enterprising spirit always characteristic of him,
large steamers were chartered by Mr Becker, and it was not long
before considerable cargoes of Canadian pulp began to arrive at
British ports. As a matter of fact, Mr Becker's firm may be said to
have had the monopoly of 90% of the imports of the Canadian

101

wood pulp in the United Kingdom. Early in 1901 Mr Becker's firm were appointed the sole agents in the United Kingdom for the Chicoutimi Pulp Co., and in due course many large and important cargoes arrived from Canada in this country.

Among the early charterings was that of the *Norfolk*, carrying 2,500 tons of wood pulp and four voyages every season from Chicoutimi to Queenborough, commencing in the spring of 1903 and continuing until 1908. The largest charter, however, was that of the *Manchester Engineer*, in 1902, which carried 6,300 tons to Manchester. It may also be mentioned that a contract between the Chicoutimi Co. and Edward Lloyd, Ltd, called for the supply daily of 100 tons of dried spruce pulp over a number of years, while a later contract with the latter was for 50,000 tons of ground wood yearly for a period of 10 years.

In 1908 the business was formed into a limited company, and it may be said that the confidence inspired by the fact that the foundations of the undertaking had already been successfully laid has been more than justified in each succeeding year. The company was formed with a capital of £100,000 in deferred and preferred shares of £1 each, and an issue was made of £35,000 7% cumulative deferred ordinary shares, which were over subscribed. In addition, there was an issue of £50,000 5% first mortgage debenture stock. The balance of the 15,000 deferred ordinary shares were issued in 1908 and were speedily taken up.

Such was the commencement of a new era in the history of what has now become incontestably the largest pulp selling concern in the United Kingdom, if not in the world. From the first four years, when 7% was paid on both the preferred and deferred shares, the annual dividends have been such as to arouse envy among the investing public, especially during the last few years, when dividends of 15% free of income tax have been declared. The record of the firm has, indeed, been remarkable, and we recall that at the annual meeting in 1913 Mr Becker was able to make the astonishing announcement that "up to 1924 the position of the company was already assured, and there were few companies in any trade, and especially in the pulp trade, who could say that profits of upwards of £120,000 were already earned". During the first three years of its existence the company sold 13,000,000 tons of pulp, with orders on its books to the extent of 1,884,737 tons, while at the last annual meeting in June Mr Becker stated that they had a working capital of £300,000, liquid assets of £900,000, and a turnover, so far as the English office was concerned, of £6,715,000, mostly with Scandinavia. If the business done at the New York and Paris offices were included the total turnover was more than £10,000,000. Having regard to the turnover mentioned, the profit on volume of business done was very small, this being in pursuance of the policy which has characterised the firm of treating their customers with the consideration these difficult times demand. As a matter of fact, Mr Becker was able to point to the fact that not only had the mills with which he himself was identified, but many others with which he was in no way concerned, relied upon the company for the bulk of their supplies.

This leads us to make reference to Mr Becker's wide interests in the paper-making industry. His association, as executor of the late Mr James Marsden, with the group of paper mills included in the estate, led him to do all he could to place the company upon a sound basis, and since his acceptance of the position of chairman of the company, modernised mills and increased production have been the result. Additional mills have also been purchased—the Lintzford mills in 1917, the Ramsbottom paper mill in 1918, and, later, the Irish paper mills at Clondalkin, near Dublin, while a controlling interest has been acquired in the Northfleet paper mills. Mr Becker is also the chairman of the Donside Paper Co., Ltd, Aberdeen, and a director of the Empire Paper Mills, Ltd, Greenhithe. In the French Paper Stock Paper Co., Ltd, and the Sissiboo and Clyde Mills in Canada, Mr Becker exercises an important influence, while the formation of the Ha! Ha! Bay Sulphite Co., Ltd, and the completion of the works at Port Arthur, Quebec, were largely due to Mr Becker's energetic direction of an enterprise to which the British paper-makers and newspaper publishers looked as likely to safeguard supplies without being entirely dependent upon Scandinavia. Mr Becker is chairman of the company, the capital of which is £500,000, whilst the Board of Directors is practically one of British paper-makers.

Another of the allied companies of Becker & Co., Ltd, and one which plays an important part in the operations of the firm, is the Preston Steam Navigation Co., Ltd, which has had a uniformly successful career under the management of Mr Becker. Shipments of pulp are regularly coming to this country from Canada, and even during the war, when all the company's ships were requisitioned by the Government, supplies did not cease. At the close of the war the company had only three ships, seven having been lost by enemy action and one lost at sea. A steady increase is to be reported in the company's earnings, one dividend amounting to 25% free of tax.

As illustrating the keenness of Mr Becker's business instincts, it may be recalled that about 1912 he sent Mr G. Buchanan, a director of the company, to Roumania with a view to investigating the possibilities of doing business in pulp. Mr Buchanan's mission was so far successful that a steamer was loaded at Braila with a large cargo of Delta grass pulp and sulphite pulp. This, we believe, was the first shipment of purely industrial products from the Danube, and Messrs Becker & Co., Ltd, are to be credited with having made the initial attempt to develop Roumanian export trade in paper pulp.

Other commercial undertakings with which Mr Becker is associated are Spanish and African Exports Company, Limited, and Woodpulp Transport Company, Limited.

During the war, when the paper trade was harassed by restrictions, regulations, embargoes, and other awkward phenomena, Mr Becker was to the forefront in rendering valuable service not only to the paper-making industry, but also to the country. The stringency experienced with reference to supplies of wood pulp became so serious at one period that the utilisation of sawdust and waste paper was resorted to. Mr Becker placed at the disposal of the Government the resources over which he had command for experimental purposes required by the Paper Controller, and at the Donside Mill was produced paper upon which an issue of *The Times* was made principally from sawdust. Messrs. Becker & Co., were also responsible for providing wood pulp to the value of £3,000,000 for the British, French and Italian Governments. This was supplied without any profit whatever. He was also a member of the Admiralty Arbitration Committee. Mr Becker's personal interest in the 900 men at the front, drawn from the various businesses with which he is associated, was as generous as it was keen. Indeed, his relations with members of the staff of Becker & Co. have always been of the most cordial nature, and it was not without pride that at one annual meeting of the shareholders Mr Becker, referring to his staff, said "Once with Becker's, always with Becker's." Certainly the record of long service with the firm of several gentlemen who are still in harness, some on the directorate, is an enviable one.

As an indication of the appreciation and respect in which they are held, the silver wedding of Mr and Mrs Becker on 2 June 1916 was not allowed to pass unheeded by members of the paper and allied trades. A complimentary dinner at the Hotel Cecil, and the presentation of a solid silver loving cup and a mahogany cabinet of table cutlery were the outward and visible tokens of deep regard entertained for the "happy pair". The staff at the head office also made a handsome presentation. Another feature of Mr Becker's varied career is that he is a keen Freemason, holding London rank, and being a founder of the "Papyrus" Lodge, of which he was W.M. in 1899. In public service he is a magistrate for the county of Middlesex, and, finally, he is esteemed by his friends and acquaintances as "a jolly good fellow".

KNIGHTHOOD FOR MR BECKER

The New Year Honours List contains the name of Mr F. E. R. Becker, upon whom a Knighthood has been conferred. It need scarcely be said that the announcement has been received with great satisfaction by his numerous friends in all quarters of the world.

ESPARTO PAPER MILLS, LIMITED.

DIRECTORS:

SIR FREDERICK BECKER, J.P. GORDON RALPH HALL CAINE, C.B.E.

EDWARD BERNARD MONTESOLE. CONDIE SANDEMAN, K.C.

WILLIAM MORGAN WALLACE, *Managing Director.*

REPORT and ACCOUNTS for the year ended 31st October, 1923.

The Directors beg to submit herewith the Balance Sheet of the Company as at 31st October, 1923, duly certified by the Company's Auditors.

After maintaining the Mills and Machinery in an efficient condition and providing for Depreciation, Corporation Profits Tax, Directors' Fees and Managing Director's Remuneration, there remains a net Profit for the eight months trading of £43,699 1 1

Deduct Debenture Interest	...	...	...	...	8,431 8 2
Leaving available ...	...	...	...	...	35,267 12 11

There has been paid :—

The fixed Dividend on the Preference Shares for the period from the dates of payments of instalments to 31st October, 1923 ... ... 8,700 12 5

Leaving available 26,567 0 6

Your Directors recommend :—

The payment of a Dividend on the Ordinary Shares of 6d. per Share (less tax) ... £5,000 0 0

To carry to Reserve Fund 5,000 0 0

10,000 0 0

Leaving to be carried forward, subject to Income Tax, a balance of ... £16,567 0 6

The Directors draw attention to the fact that the preliminary expenses and the discount on the Debenture issue have been written off from reserve, and the balance of reserve has been carried to Depreciation Account.

Trading conditions have been extremely difficult during the period under review, and at present there is no indication of much improvement. The Directors, however, have confidence in the future, having regard to the efficient state of the works and to the extensions now in hand.

The extensions which are now proceeding provide for the coating of paper for special purposes. This policy has been in contemplation for several years and has received the most careful consideration.

Mr. E. B. Montesole retires by rotation from the Board, and, being eligible, offers himself for re-election.

Messrs. Mackay Irons & Co., C.A., the present Auditors of the Company, also retire, and, being eligible, offer themselves for re-election.

By Order of the Board,

A. CARTER,
Secretary.

BLACKFRIARS HOUSE,
NEW BRIDGE STREET, E.C. 4.

Dated this 30th day of November, 1923.

ESPARTO PAPER MILLS, LIMITED.

BALANCE SHEET, 31st October, 1923.

LIABILITIES.

	£	s.	d.
SHARE CAPITAL—			
Authorised :			
500,000 8 per cent. Cumulative Preference Shares of £1 each	500,000	0	0
1,000,000 Ordinary Shares of £1 each	1,000,000	0	0
Issued and fully paid :			
200,000 8 per cent. Cumulative Preference Shares of £1 each	200,000	0	0
200,000 Ordinary Shares of £1 each	200,000	0	0
	400,000	0	0
6½ PER CENT. FIRST MORTGAGE DEBENTURES	300,000	0	0
DEBTS DUE BY THE COMPANY ...	46,267	17	8
PROFIT AND LOSS ACCOUNT—			
Balance at Credit	35,267	12	11

There is a contingent liability of £5,000 on partly paid Shares held by the Company.

£781,535 10 7

ASSETS.

	£	s.	d.	£	s.	d.
PROPERTY ACCOUNT—						
Heritable Property, Buildings, Water Rights, Fixed and Moveable Machinery and Plant	587,304	14	10			
Less Depreciation	13,698	13	11			
				573,606	0	11
DEBTS DUE TO THE COMPANY ...				74,419	16	4
STOCK-IN-TRADE				39,271	19	9
INVESTMENTS				33,112	1	0
CASH IN BANK AND ON HAND ...				61,125	12	7

WILLIAM M. WALLACE } *Directors.*
E. B. MONTESOLE }

£781,535 10 7

REPORT OF THE AUDITORS TO THE SHAREHOLDERS OF ESPARTO PAPER MILLS, LIMITED.

In accordance with the provisions of The Companies (Consolidation) Act, 1908, we beg to report that we have audited the Books and Accounts of Esparto Paper Mills, Limited, for the period ended 31st October, 1923, and have found them to be correct; that we have obtained all the information and explanations we have required, and that, in our opinion, the foregoing Balance Sheet is properly drawn up so as to exhibit a true and correct view of the state of the Company's affairs as at 31st October, 1923, according to the best of our information and the explanations given to us and as shown by the Books of the Company. The Stock-in-Trade has been certified by the Managing Director of the Company.

DUNDEE,
28th November, 1923.

MACKAY IRONS & CO., *Chartered Accountants,*
Auditors.

200 YEARS OF PAPER MAKING—
FOURSTONES CELEBRATES
BI-CENTENARY

(Reprinted from *The World's Paper Trade Review*, 9 May 1963.)

Two hundred years of paper making on the same site was celebrated recently by The Fourstones Paper Mill Co. Ltd, whose Mill No. 100 is at Hexham, Northumberland. There was a dinner, attended by representatives of various sections of the paper and board industry in the United Kingdom and on the Continent, at the Stationers' Hall in London on 19 April and this was followed by functions at the mill on 21 April, the exact anniversary of the mill's foundation.

Mr G.T. Mandl, chairman of The Fourstones Paper Mill Co. Ltd, presided at the dinner in London and first read a number of letters and telegrams of congratulations and good wishes.

The toast to Fourstones Paper Mill was proposed by Mr L.S. Humphries, who said that the occasion they were marking that evening was one of the big events in the paper industry. Two hundred years on one site was a period which very few mills had enjoyed.

Mr Humphries then went on to recall some events of 200 years ago and points from the mill's long history. He concluded: "We wish Fourstones Paper Mill every success in the future."

Mr Mandl, who replied, said that it gave him particular pleasure to hold the celebration in the historic Hall of the Stationers' Company, in the presence of the Master, Clerk and a number of the Livery. (His speech is reproduced in full on page 75.)

Mr R.R. Rudd, who proposed the toast to the guests, first welcomed the Master and Clerk of the Worshipful Company of Stationers and Newspaper Makers; Mr S. Ingvarsen, of the United Paper Mills of Denmark; Mr Jean Thiry, of the paper making machinery firm of Thiry and Cie, Belgium; Mr J. Odink, of the paper making felt manufacturers, Haaksbergen, Holland; and Mr A. Therkildsen, the company's agent in Denmark.

"We very much welcome the paper makers of this country and abroad. Stora Kopparbergs existed as a company in 1288 and we are glad to see Mr G. Parsons with us representing the company in 1963. Also Mr A.H. Bruce, chairman of Inveresk, whose Wookey Hole Mill made paper in 1610; Messrs S.I. Martin, J.R. Vaudrey and R.T. Stagg, from Spicers (Edward Spicer first made paper in 1645); Mr Adlard, of Evans Adlard, paper makers for well over 200 years; Mr J.R. Sedgwick, of Allnut and Thomas and Green, paper makers in

1686; Mr J.M. Horsburgh, of Wiggins Teape, paper makers since 1761; Mr H. Lewis Ward, chairman of Olives; and Mr J. Pitts, chairman of John Pitts and Sons, of Exeter."

Mr Rudd also welcomed Mr J.W. Bates, director of contracts, H.M. Stationery Office; Mr F.H. Llewellyn-Thomas, representing the B.P. & B.M.A.; Mr Humphries, Mr P.C. Fells, president of the Association of Paper and Board Exporters of Great Britain; Mr Andrew Gibson, president, and Mr S.R.W. Bailey, of the N.A.P.M.; and the Press.

The response was by Mr Andrew Gibson, president of The National Association of Paper Merchants, who said that it made little difference whether an industry was large or small or whether the firms within that industry were groups or smaller units. There came a time, as it had come to the paper trade today, maker and merchant alike, when they had to re-think and re-plan if they were going to have continued prosperity in the future. The small unit had an important and profitable role to fill, just as the larger combine must also make its mark and prove its usefulness to the trade and its customers alike.

Proposing the toast at the mill on 21 April, Mr Rupert Speir, M.P. for Hexham, said that with a chequered career over the first 200 years he hoped the mill would continue to go from strength to strength in the future. Mr Mandl replied.

Tribute was paid to Miss Mina Mason, former managing director of the company, by Canon H.B. Richardson, vicar of Warden.

During the evening Mr Mandl presented inscribed gold watches for long service to three employees. They were Mr Norman Stokoe (46 years), Mr J.T. MacMillan (45 years), and T.H. Philipson (40 years' service).

A silver fruit dish was presented to Mr Mandl on behalf of the office staff and workpeople by Mr J. Irving.

Among the guests at the celebrations at the mill were Mr R.A. Patterson and Mr A.E. Crankshaw, Team Valley Paper Mills Ltd; Mr I.E. Davidson, Howard Smith Hendon Ltd; Mr A.C. Crankshaw and Mr P.P. Wilson, Pembertons (Gateshead) Ltd.

MILL NUMBER 100

The Fourstones Paper Mill Co. Ltd.

Est. 1763

South Tyne Mill
Fourstones
Hexham
Northumberland

Bi-Centenary Dinner

at Stationers' Hall, Ludgate Hill, London, E.C.4.

on Friday, April 19th 1963

at 6.45 for 7.30 p.m.

R.S.V.P. to London Office.
1-9 Ludgate Hill.
London, E.C.4.

Evening Dress

110

1:01:1963.

PRICE LIST

BLOTTINGS

		Smalls	3½ cwts.	1 ton	2 tons	5 tons
No. 1 Rag	per lb.	2/-½d.	2/-¼d.	2/-d.	1/11½d.	1/11d.
No. 2 Rag	,,	1/10½d.	1/10¼d.	1/10d.	1/9½d.	1/9d.
Pink Interleaving	,,	2/3½d.	2/3d.	2/2d.	2/1½d.	2/-d.
White Warden	,,	1/2¼d.	1/2⅛d.	1/2d.	1/1¾d.	1/1½d.

Pink Warden is ¾d. per lb above the White price.
All the above Blotting Prices are subject to Purchase Tax extra.

DUPLICATORS

			Smalls	3½ cwts.	1 ton	2 tons	5 tons
Hard-Sized Esparto s/o L'Post 18 lbs.	White	per lb.	1/2⅞d.	1/2⅜d.	1/2¼d.	1/2⅛d.	1/2d.
	Tints	,,	1/3¾d.	1/3¼d.	1/3⅛d.	1/3d.	1/2⅞d.
Hard-Sized	White	,,	1/1⅞d.	1/1⅜d.	1/1¼d.	1/1⅛d.	1/1d.
Warden Woodfree s/o L'Post 18 lbs	Tints	,,	1/2¾d.	1/2¼d.	1/2⅛d.	1/2d.	1/1⅞d.

Reduction for making L'Post 19 lbs and up, ⅛d. per lb.
Extra for making thinner substances s/o L'Post 17 lbs, ⅜d. per lb.
" " " " " 16 lbs, ⅝d. per lb.

			Smalls	3½ cwts.	1 ton	2 tons	5 tons
Warden Airmail		per lb.	1/5d.	1/4¾d.	1/4½d.	1/4⅜d.	1/4¼d.
Warden Duplicator	White	,,	1/3d.	1/2¾d.	1/2½d.	1/2¼d.	1/2d.
Board	Tints	,,	1/3¾d.	1/3½d.	1/3¼d.	1/3d.	1/2¾d.

For all Duplicators : Extra for cutting to small size 1/3 per ream.

IMITATION MOULD MADE

		Smalls	3½ cwts.	1 ton	2 tons	5 tons
White and Toned .. .. Deckle Edged	per lb.	1/5¾d.	1/5½d.	1/5⅛d.	1/5	1/4¾d.

The above can be supplied with plain edges for minimum quantities of 10 cwts at ¼d. per lb less.

		Smalls	3½ cwts.	1 ton	2 tons	5 tons
Bright White .. .. Plain Edge	per lb.	1/6d.	1/5¾d.	1/5¼d.	1/5⅛d.	1/4¾d.

The above can be supplied with deckle edges for minimum quantities of 10 cwts. at ¼d. per lb. extra.

THE FOURSTONES PAPER MILL Co., Ltd.

SOUTH TYNE MILL

HEXHAM

NORTHUMBERLAND

Telephone Hexham 30

London Office :
1 - 9 Ludgate Hill
London, E.C. 4.
Telephone CITy 7228

Manchester Representative :
C. D. McFarlin & Co. Ltd.
29 Minshull Street
Manchester 1.
Telephone CENtral 4885

Printed on Fourstones Bond s/o L. Post 18 lbs.

Details available for making quantities of 10 cwts or over on request.

REPORT BY DR JULIUS GRANT

HEHNER & COX, LTD.

DIRECTORS:
DR. JULIUS GRANT, M.Sc., F.R.I.C.
G.W. AYLEN.
C.H. ROBINS, B.Sc., F.R.I.C.
PUBLIC ANALYST
—

ANALYTICAL & CONSULTING CHEMISTS.
UNION INTERNATIONALE DES
LABORATOIRES INDEPENDANTS
—

Telephone:- Royal 3538.
Telegrams:- Hehner, Royal 3538.

The Laboratories,
107, Fenchurch Street,
London, E.C.3.

OUR REF.   JG/MR/25517X

YOUR REF.   GS.50/EDP/CL

19th November, 1963.

Rural Industries Bureau,
35, Camp Road,
Wimbledon Common,
S.W.19.

Dear Sirs,

Fourstones Paper Mill Co., Ltd

As instructed in your letter of the 23rd October, I visited the South Tyne Mill of this Company on the evening of the 11th November, returning on the evening of the 12th November, 1963. The objective of the visit was to obtain material to enable me to report on the proposed manufacture of cellulose wadding at this mill as a qualification for a loan of £5000 from the Rural Industries Bureau.

I was accompanied by Mr Holmes of your Newcastle office, and received every co-operation from Mr G.T. Mandl (Chairman), Mr R. Dunn (Secretary) and Mrs Dunn, and Mr J. Arthur (Director and General Manager).

It is convenient to discuss this matter under the headings as follows:

Background of Fourstones Mill

This mill was founded in 1763 as a hand-made mill. A paper machine was installed subsequently, followed by an esparto pulp making plant and, in 1907, a soda recovery plant. It is safe to say there has been no major technical improvement or alteration since the latter date. The mill has experienced many vicissitudes, culminating in serious financial losses of approximately £10 000 per year in 1961, when it was purchased by Mr Mandl. By making economies and improving efficiency under Mr Mandl's direction, the rate of loss (so he told me) has been halted, and during the last 6 months the mill has been running at a small profit. This is despite the fact that it is working only at approximately 50% of its normal capacity, i.e., making 20 tons instead of 40 tons of paper per week.

This underproduction is due to lack of orders for the papers normally made by the mill, which are blotting papers of various kinds, imitation mould-made writings and printings, duplicator papers and boards, and cover papers. This transition from a large loss to a small profit has been achieved without appreciable capital expenditure.

The mill has at present one small paper machine, 66 inches deckle, with beater stock preparation plant. The raw materials are imported wood pulp, good grades of waste paper, and cotton pulp which is prepared at the mill from second-grade cotton linters using the digesters which are no longer used for esparto pulp. The soda recovery process is also closed down, and is virtually derelict. Consequently the waste rag cooking liquors are disposed of as described below.

The mill, as might be expected, is in a poor condition structurally and mechanically. However, the paper qualities are good, and most of the deficiencies are of a nature that can be rectified in the course of time as finance becomes available without dislocating production. The present payroll is approximately 50 persons, all drawn from the local area.

The Cellulose Wadding Project

Mr Mandl has purchased from Southalls (Birmingham) Ltd, who are cellulose wadding manufacturers, a fourdrinier M.G. paper machine with a new spare drying cylinder, complete with drive, for £3 000. It was built to make M.G. papers, but by omitting two presses (which were not included in the sale) it can be used for and has made cellulose wadding. The machine has been dismantled and is in pieces at Fourstones. From what I could see of it on the site, and from the drawings which were shown to me (which were however, incomplete), I am prepared to agree that it is suitable for the purpose. However, to re-erect it may well be more expensive than the quotation of £1 400 already received.

The cylinder is 10 ft. in diameter and has been tested at 90 lb. per sq. in. for 45 lb. per sq. in. operation. The surface is in poor condition and will have to be reground, and possibly plugged. Its permissible working pressure after this depends on the amount of grinding involved, but unless unsuspected faults are discovered, this should be adequate.

113

Cellulose wadding is made up of layers of thin paper having a deep crepe, and is usually made from bleached or unbleached wood pulp. The bleached grades are used chiefly for sanitary pads, baby diapers and for surgical work; and the unbleached grades for packing purposes. A maximum production of 30 tons per week is envisaged from this machine and this seems reasonable if, as stated, the machine is capable of running at 450 ft. per minute, making tissue of 12 grams per square metre substance (before creping), in a width of 92 to 94 inches corresponding with the 99-inch face of the cylinders. This production seems reasonable if the stated speeds and deckles can be obtained. I am informed by Mr Mandl that the present selling price of the bleached wadding is £130 per ton; my own subsequent enquiries have led to a figure nearer £125 per ton, and this is used in present Report. Production is scheduled to start in March, 1964 and full production to be achieved by May, 1964.

Technical Aspects

My inspection of the mill disclosed the following points relevant to the present enquiry.

Water.—I estimate that another 1 500 000 gallons per week will be required in addition to the present consumption. At present the water is drawn from a small reservoir on the mill premises, which is fed by a stream consisting mostly of surface water from the surrounding hills. This overflows into the former water-turbine alley and flows into the South Tyne River which forms one boundary of the mill. When the reservoir water is inadequate, and this appears to happen fairly frequently (including the time of my visit when it was actually wet weather) it is replenished from the River Tyne for which purposes there are two pumps. I am informed that the water rights enable unlimited supplies to be drawn from the river in this way. The water is filtered at present through one of two Bell filters; these may be inadequate to cope with the full production of the existing and proposed machine.

Effluent.—There is at present an effluent from the cotton linter digestion plant, although this is small because of the small quantity of linters at present being boiled. This effluent is disposed of by allowing it to trickle through an earth channel, during the course of which it soaks away into the ground without reaching the river. While the quantity of liquor remains small this method is adequate. The effluent from the paper machine however, passes through a backwater tank to a primitive saveall, and thence to the river. This plant appears to be most inadequate both on grounds of fibre economy and water pollution, and will undoubtedly have to be improved upon whether the cellulose wadding project materialises or not.

114

Pulp Preparation.—At present there is one spare 1 200-lb. breaker-beater; and 4 600-lb. beaters, of which three at the most are in use at one time. The surplus beaters and the breaker-beater could cope with the extra tonnage for the cellulose wadding machine. In addition there is space in the beater house for one or two more such beaters. A Fraser refiner is available for the existing machine, but another will probably be necessary for the new machine if full production is to be maintained in all parts of the mill. Machine chests and pulp handling facilities are also adequate; but further screening facilities will have to be provided.

Buildings.—With the exception of the two-floor stock building, which was rebuilt after a fire in 1939, these are generally in poor condition; in any case the stock room is likely to be small for the bulky material (reels of cellulose wadding) it is proposed to make. The installation of the new machine involves structural alterations which are at present in hand. Apart from the roof, which is in poor condition and is not included in the present building programme, these building alterations should be satisfactory for the new paper machine and the finishing house.

Steam and Power.—Electricity is purchased, and steam for drying the paper and space heating the mill is available from three Lancashire boilers operating at 80 lb. per square inch pressure. The mill formerly used its own water power with steam engines as prime movers, and now that these have been discontinued in favour of purchased electricity, only one boiler is required leaving ample steam-raising capacity for the new machine. The machine will be erected by the same company that dismantled it at Southall's, and the erection and start-up will be supervised by a Czechoslovakian engineer in association with the Swedish company who are supplying the finishing equipment on a long-term credit loan basis (see below).

Transport.—The mill has a siding from the main Newcastle–Carlisle railway line. Under the Beeching Plan this line, and the station at Hexham $2\frac{1}{2}$ miles away will remain open, although the local station at Fourstones ($1\frac{1}{2}$ miles away) will be closed. This will not affect the utilisation of this facility by the mill. The mill is approximately 25 miles by road from Newcastle to which much of the imported Scandinavian pulp is shipped; the freight rates from Newcastle to the mill are 10/- per ton per road and 22/- per ton by railway. The latter is often preferred because the price includes $2\frac{1}{2}$ days' demurrage; owing to the restricted staff this is convenient for unloading purposes.

Capital Cost

This has been estimated as follows:

	£
Machine and drive, as purchased	3 000
Dismantling and removal of above to mill	1 140
Re-erection of machine at mill	1 400
Repairs to cylinder	500
Building	2 500
Finishing (sheeting and cutting plant)	5 000
Contingencies	6 460
Total	20 000

In order to allow for contingencies a round figure of £20 000 has been estimated by Mr Mandl.

It is proposed to finance this as follows:

	£
Ordinary shares	5 000
Cumulative Redeemable Preferance shares	5 000
Loan from Swedish company (see above)	5 000
Loan from Rural Industries Bureau	5 000

There are bank overdraft facilities of £38,000, only half of which have been taken up; however Mr Mandl does not wish to use this for capital expenditure purposes.

My own view is that £20 000 may well prove to be an underestimate even allowing for the approximate £6 500 given above for contingencies. The above items do not take into account such expenditure as water and effluent treatment plants, screens, and refiner, and I think that the estimates for the building and the machine erection are also low. I would prefer to add £5 000 to the estimated total cost, making £25 000 in all.

Market Considerations

The Present Position. Cellulose wadding is at present made in Britain only by the following Companies:

Robinson & Sons Limited, Chesterfield	6 000 to 7 000	tons per annum
Southalls (Birmingham) Ltd	6 000 to 8 000	tons per annum
Charles Turner & Co. Ltd, Bolton	2 500	tons per annum
Total (say)	16 000	tons per annum

The above are bleached and unbleached grades. The above figures were given to me by Mr Mandl who apparently knows the mills through his paper agent activities. My independent source of information gave a total of approximately 21 000 tons per annum for 1962. Robinsons & Southalls are also converters, that is to say, they convert the creped tissue paper as produced on reels by the paper

116

machine into the layers of wadding, and thence into the final product, in particular sanitary pads. Southalls are associated in this business with Messrs Smith, Son & Nephew, and both Southalls and Robinsons sell to other converters, but only in relatively small amounts because of their own converting activities. The other converters are therefore mainly dependent on Turners, who are themselves not converters; however they are comparatively small producers of the creped tissue. The machine to be used at Fourstones was purchased from Southalls who disposed of it when installing a newer and larger machine. They have therefore at present two old machines and the new machine. Robinsons, although they have a relatively large production, make this on comparatively old and small machines.

No statistics are issued specifically for cellulose wadding, but the Board of Trade figures mention "Household, toilet papers and tissues" as one item and, as a separate item, "Other tissues". It has been ascertained that cellulose wadding is included under the former heading. In 1962 the production in this category by the British mills was nearly 127 000 tons, of which 21 250 tons were cellulose wadding. In 1962 also, the ratio of production to capacity for all tissues and special papers (including cellulose wadding) was 105%. It is noteworthy that this was the only category of paper which showed a figure exceeding 100% in that year or in the immediately preceding years. The overall average ratio for all paper and board was 91% for 1962, and the runner-up (vegetable parchment, greaseproof and glassine, which are also specialties) was only 96%. Since the capacity data are based on normal working hours, excluding overtime, it would appear that with tissue and speciality papers there is and has been an unsatisfied or barely satisfied demand. Stocks of all tissues held at mills remained fairly constant at approximately 5 800 to 6 900 tons between December 1961 and December 1962.

In 1962 there were also imports of 18 000 tons of tissues of all kinds. However it is unlikely that these included much cellulose wadding, as owing to its bulky nature it is relatively expensive to transport.

It seems reasonable to assume therefore, that the production and consumption of cellulose wadding in the United Kingdom were approximately 21 000 tons in 1962, and that the demand is slightly in excess of the supply.

Mills other than the above three are also capable of making bleached cellulose wadding, but they do not normally do so. This applies especially to mills making facial tissues and similar papers most of which have high production units. While these are fully occupied with their present production it is unlikely that they will

117

turn to a product which has to be made at a lower speed and is less convenient to handle, store and despatch for the sake of a relatively small increase in selling price. However if the demand for their present products falls off they might well fill up their machines in this way, and could then no doubt undercut the prices of the existing manufacturers of cellulose wadding paper.

It may well be that the difference between Mr Mandl's estimate of present total production of 16 000 tons per annum and mine of 21 000 tons per annum in 1962 is accounted for by such circumstances; this difference is by no means inconsiderable.

Future Prospects

These are now considered for the principal uses of cellulose wadding.

Sanitary Pads.—A simple calculation based on the female population leads to a maximum annual consumption of actual wadding of approximately 10 000 tons. It seems probable that this market is already nearly saturated, and that only a population increase can be relied upon for any future increase in consumption.

Baby Diapers.—Compared with the U.S.A. and possibly also with other countries, such as Sweden, where the paper consumption per capita is higher than in the U.K., the consumption of baby diapers is relatively low in Britain. A calculation based on the annual birth rate indicates a present maximum annual consumption of approximately 10 000 tons. At present however the cellulose wadding baby diaper does not particularly appear to appeal to the average conservative British home. Thus it may have the convenience of avoiding washing, but it has to be disposed of, and the cost (approximately 2d. each) is still a consideration.

Surgical Uses.—The use of cellulose wadding in hospital work eliminates the use and washing of bandages and dressings. From enquiries I have made I would say that the present demand is virtually satisfied and that any future increases will be due to increases in population and medical activities rather than to any present lack of appreciation of the advantages of this material. It is difficult to estimate a figure for the present consumption, but something approaching approximately 5 000 tons per annum seems reasonable.

Intensive advertising will no doubt change the above general position, but it should be noted that at Fourstones it is intended to supply only the raw material for the wadding and not the finished product, so that the onus and cost of advertising will be beyond their control. However, Mr Mandl states that certain existing converters who now have to purchase from Southalls and Robinsons are very interested

118

in this project, since it would render them independent of the inter-mittent surpluses of Southalls and Robinsons who themselves are converters. Indeed he feels that he could place some 20 tons per week of this production at once. Of course I have no means of verifying this.

The following figures show some approximate per capita con-sumptions per annum for 1962.

U.S.A.	–	438 lb.
Canada	–	250 lb.
Sweden	–	200 lb.
U.K.	–	156 lb.

The big difference between the figures for the U.K. and U.S.A. (and the latter is still increasing) is an indication of the potential increase in consumption of paper of all kinds as the standard of living rises.

It seems therefore, that future increases in the consumption of bleached cellulose wadding in Britain must come from increases in population and an increased use of cellulose wadding baby diapers. This assessment takes no account of the unbleached grades, which sell at a lower price. These grades could however, be used to fill gaps in the order book of the new Fourstones machine if the project materialises.

Production Costs

Below are given estimated production costs for cellulose wadding assuming full production (i.e., 30 tons per week, or 1,500 tons per annum); or half production (i.e., 750 tons per annum). The calcula-tions assume that the mill will break even by running at half pro-duction on its present papers, i.e., as it has been doing during the last six months. The calculations below are therefore based on the material, labour, power and overhead cost items associated specifi-cally with the cellulose wadding, without regard to the present general overheads etc. of the mill.

The cost items are numbered for ease of reference to the explan-atory notes given below.

	Production	
	£	£
Production (tons/annum)	1 500	750
1. Wood pulp	97 000	48 500
2. Labour	7 200	7 200
3. Fuel & power	15 000	8 000
4. Wires & felts	1 000	500
5. Maintenance materials	2 000	1 000
6. Overheads	3 000	3 000

	£	£
7. Carriage outward	10 000	5 000
8. Sales costs	4 700	2 500
9. Total	139 900	75 700
10. Sales	187 500	93 750
Profit:		
per annum	47 600	18 050
per ton	32	24

Notes:

(1) The imported bleached sulphite wood pulp consumption is based on an 85% yield, with wood pulp at £55 per ton delivered to the mill.

(2) The labour charges are based on 12 additional workers at a total inclusive pay averaging £600 per annum.

(3) Steam and electricity costs are combined and based on a consumption equivalent to 1·5 tons of coal per ton of paper.

(4) & (5) These are based on general papermaking experience.

(6) This item is based on depreciation at 5% and interest at 6%, plus the small additional overheads involved by the extra process.

(7) Carriage outward is an average figure for deliveries over the whole country, although it is anticipated that most of the market will be in the North-East and in the south of Scotland. From a transport point of view Fourstones is more favourably situated with regard to these areas than are the existing manufacturers, who are in the Midlands or Lancashire.

(8) & (10) Sales costs are taken at $2\frac{1}{2}$% of the selling price which is taken at £125 per ton.

It will be seen from the above figures that even if orders can be obtained for only 750 tons per annum (i.e., half of the potential production of the machine) a profit can still be made. It is apparent also that in the event of a shortage of orders of this magnitude, unbleached cellulose wadding (selling at £115 to £120 per ton) could be used to fill up the machine capacity, and a small profit would still be made.

Summary

(1) This is an old mill in poor condition and the present project is a courageous attempt to make it profitable.

(2) Technical difficulties are bound to be experienced before the mill is running smoothly and efficiently on cellulose wadding, and I feel that the cost of some of these have been under-estimated.

(3) On the market side much depends on future demand and prices for cellulose wadding, since the present demand appears to be virtually satisfied. This calls for a sales effort in which Mr Mandl's

existing sales organisation can be used to advantage, although it is at present largely unfamiliar ground.

(4) On the other hand it seems that the mill can make a profit with its existing and proposed machine both running only at half production.

(5) The project will give employment to only approximately 12 additional persons. However since the mill is doing little more than breaking even at present it will make secure the jobs of the 50 existing workers should present selling conditions continue.

(6) On balance, if the Rural Industries Bureau loan of £5 000 means that the project will be put into operation, then the granting of the loan would appear to be desirable.

Mr Mandl asks me to request that the information given in this Report as to his future plans for the manufacture of cellulose wadding be regarded as strictly confidential.

Yours faithfully,

pp. Hehner & Cox Limited.

J. GRANT

THE FOURSTONES PAPER MILL CO. LTD SHOWS THE WAY ...

(Reprinted from *The World's Paper Trade Review*, 2 February 1967.)

BOOK PRINTINGS SUPERSEDED BY ABSORBENT SPECIALITY PRODUCTS

An outstanding example of how a small, privately owned British paper mill has adapted itself to meet the future in a free market is provided by The Fourstones Paper Mill Co. Ltd, whose mill near Hexham, Northumberland, has recently been converted to produce absorbent speciality products in place of book printings, for which it was well known for many years.

The history of Fourstones goes back for more than 200 years, but its more recent development dates from 1962 when a majority interest in the company was acquired by Mr G.T. Mandl, who is now chairman and managing director. A year later, a substantial rebuilding and modernisation scheme started with the purchase of a second paper machine.

The new machine, which produces bleached and unbleached highly creped surgical cellulose wadding, has a trimmed width of 90 inches and a top speed of 600 feet per minute. It has a single felt lick-up, a suction roll, and an MG cylinder 10 ft. in diameter and 100 inch face. Originally of German origin, the machine was re-built at Fourstones with the technical assistance of one of Sweden's leading manufacturers of cellulose wadding.

The new manufacturing unit is housed in a new building, specially designed and built largely of transparent plastic material to afford the maximum amount of light.

Stock preparation plant at the mill, which serves both machines, is located above and between the new machine and the existing Fourdrinier unit. It consists of three bleaching breakers, five beaters and a new Bolton-Emerson "Triple Attack" pulper, which has a capacity of approximately 20 tons per 24 hours. There are only two of these pulpers in the United Kingdom.

Raw material used at Fourstones is principally high alpha sulphate and other speciality short and long fibre pulps.

The Fourdrinier machine has a trimmed width of 63 inches and a top speed of 180 feet per minute. There is a suction box on the wire in place of a couch roll, and the first press has a creping device. A second reverse press precedes the dryers. A smoothing press is followed by three stacks of machine calenders. Each section of the machine has an individual electric drive.

Lancashire coal boilers have been replaced by a new Steamblock oil–fired package boiler.

Fibre recovery plant has been installed for both machines and a final second stage water cleaning plànt for effluent treatment will be installed.

The evaporator and roaster section of the old Esparto pulp mill has been converted into storage sheds and a new engineers' and carpenters' shop.

Changes made to the various floor levels at the mill have enabled easy flow of raw materials with fork lift truck and overhead crane to replace the previous method of manhandling and transport by lift. A new concrete floor has been laid in the beater room, which is now fully electrified. Large individual motors are now being installed to drive each unit.

Plant for the production of disposable baby nappies has been purchased from Dalmas Ltd. This will give fully integrated production for a part of the cellulose wadding capacity. The registered trade mark "Small Change", already well established in many retail outlets, has been acquired for the distribution of disposable nappy rolls.

In the new converting plant, rolls of 20 ply wadding are enclosed in 2 ply wet strength tissue and an outer covering of gauze, which is knitted at the mill. The end product is packed in a printed polythene bag.

The capacity of the mill, now about 3,000 tons a year, has been doubled since 1962, while production has been trebled. Total output has gone up from approx. 700 tons in 1963 to over 2,000 tons in 1966. The total number employed at the mill has risen from 55 to only 65 in the same period.

There has been an even more remarkable development in exports, most of which go to Scandinavia. In 1963, exports amounted to 5·5% of total output. For 1966 the figure was 20·8% of paper, other than wadding.

Concurrently with the rebuilding and modernisation programme, the manufacturing programme of the Fourdrinier machine has gradually been changed. Industrial papers, filter papers, and blottings have been further developed in place of book printings and featherweights, and the mill is now one of the largest producers of blottings in Britain. The range of coloured antique papers and boards from the Lasswade Mill of John Tod & Son Ltd was added to the existing production of imitation mould made when this mill was closed in 1965.

Other products include socking base, coarse and smooth natural ingrain, speckled, mottled papers, and creped absorbent.

The very considerable engineering and development programme was carried out under the direction of Mr G. Egermayer, who came to Fourstones from Czechoslovakia in 1963, and to a large extent by the mill's own labour force. Although the mill is in a development area, no financial assistance has been received from the Government.

Sales and purchasing have been pooled with Thomas & Green Ltd and H. Allnutt & Son Ltd, and joint sales offices operate at 1-9 Ludgate Hill, London E.C.4; 42 Tennyson Road, Birmingham 10, and 29 Minshull Street, Manchester 1.

The bi-centenary of the mill was celebrated in April 1963 and a dinner was held at Stationers' Hall, attended by a large number of representatives from the trade and other paper mills who had passed their bi-centenaries.

This, together with a detailed history of the mill, was fully reported in *The World's Paper Trade Review* at the time, but a brief outline of the mill's chequered history, spanning more than two centuries of paper making, may nevertheless be of interest.

The original title deed dated 21 April 1763, still in the possession of the company, gives the names of the two founders, the Rev. Peter Rumney, a curate of Hexham Abbey, and Mr William Charnley, a Newcastle stationer.

The mill operated as a hand-made mill for the first 100 years of its existence and remained in the ownership of the Rumney family up to the middle of the last century. One of the descendants of the founder, Rumney Crawford, was the inventor of the airdryer and the letters patent granted to him by Queen Victoria are still in the company's possession.

A paper making machine was installed in conjunction with an esparto plant with a capacity of 2 000 tons a year under the ownership of Alexander Adam, and the mill was one of the earliest and largest esparto mills in the 1860s producing printing paper and newsprint. The foundations of the present Fourdrinier machine date back to this time.

It continued as an esparto mill under various owners and many well-known paper making families such as the Annandales, Horsburghs and Davidsons were connected with the mill at one time or another.

Inveresk, as well as Gordon & Gotch, held an interest in the mill at various times until it was bought by the late Mr D.M. Mason in 1930, whose daughter, Miss Mina Mason, was the only lady managing director of a paper mill in Britain until her death in 1960.

The mill and its workers form part of a closely knit community in Northumberland and many workers have spent their entire lives in the service of the mill. A large proportion of the younger generation, who have entered the mill following its rebuilding programme, ensure continuity of the skills carried on from previous generations also for the future.

It was considered a good omen when starlings built a nest inside the MG cylinder of the new machine while it was under construction. In due time the eggs hatched and the young family prospered but showed no signs of leaving. As the start-up date drew nearer and nearer, and it became essential to complete the necessary work on the cylinder, there were many discussions as to what should be done about the birds. It is not known how the engineers conveyed their problems to their guests but almost at the eleventh hour the starling family flew away.

FOURSTONES PAPER MILL NEAR HEXHAM
£1m investment upgrades UK mill to a leading cellulose wadding producer

(Reprinted from *Paper*, 21 April 1980.)

A £1m development programme at Fourstones Paper Mill Co. Ltd, one of the oldest mills in England still working, has now elevated the operation to place it among the leaders in the production of cellulose wadding used mainly for hospital disposable incontinence pads. Capacity of the new paper machine is 4 500 tonnes a year.

The mill, near Hexham, Northumberland, was converted to produce absorbent speciality products in the early 1960s. Previously it produced book printings, for which it was well known.

The history of Fourstones, which goes back for more than 200 years, changed significantly in 1962 when the company was acquired by G.T. Mandl, the present chairman.

Shortly after he took over, a second paper machine to produce bleached and unbleached creped surgical cellulose wadding was installed. This machine, since replaced, had a trimmed width of 90 in. and a top speed of 600 ft. per minute.

In 1975 the Fourdrinier machine, then the oldest in Britain still in operation, was shut down, and thus today the mill is again a one machine unit. The Fourdrinier machine was, in fact, in continuous operation from 1860 to 1975, and during its long life produced everything from newsprint to fluting medium. It has been preserved on site as a paper museum.

The latest development in the mill's long history, involving a £1m investment in the new paper machine and stock preparation plant, was partly financed by the Government's £23m waste paper scheme, and regional area grants.

The bleached and unbleached single and multiply wadding, in an average substance of 12–13 gsm, is made entirely from various grades of waste paper.

The stock preparation system starts with a waste paper conveyor by O.K. Engineering, followed by a continuous stainless steel Solvo pulper, Escher Wyss Fiberizer, Finckh vibrating screen, Voith high density pulp cleaners and Escher Wyss deflaker.

From the machine chest the stock is pumped to a fan pump followed by a Black Clawson Selectifier feeding a Pamach hydraulic breast box. Rejects from the pressure screen are screened on a Watford vibrating screen. The consistency and flow of thick stock are controlled by Techsystems Digitrac Controllers.

The 212 cm (trim) wadding machine, which has a 300 cm diameter MG cylinder, runs at 400 metres per minute and produces 90 tonnes of wadding per week.

A new slitter section houses two mill designed slitting-plying machines which can produce 10 cm to 212 cm wide reels of any number of plys to one metre in diameter.

The new machine started up in January 1978, but a serious fire at the mill in September shut the operation for six months. In fact, it was not until last Autumn that production reached the same level as immediately before the fire. While production was suspended, the converting section was kept going by bought in material.

The mill operates continuously on a four shift system. About 80 people are employed in the mill and converting section.

About 800 tonnes a year are converted by a subsidiary in Stockport, Kattan Disposables. Converted products from the mill are marketed through a wholly-owned subsidiary, Warden Dressing Co. There is a growing export market, exports to Denmark being handled by another subsidiary in the G.T. Mandl Group of Companies.

Today, this speciality group operates a paper mill in Switzerland, two paper mills and two converting factories in England and one converting unit in Denmark, with a total group turnover of around £12m.

Its latest acquisition is the converting business of Brittains Arborfield Ltd, at Helpston, near Peterborough, which produces a range of book coverings and hospital sterilisation papers.

FOURSTONES' NEW EXTENSION

(Reprinted from *Paper Technology and Industry*, January/February 1983.)

A new converting factory for hospital disposables was opened in December on the new industrial estate at Haltwhistle, Northumberland.

The official opening was performed by Sir Rupert Speir QC, former Conservative MP for Hexham; Sir Rupert referred to Fourstones' bi-centenary celebrations (which he attended as then Member of Parliament almost 20 years ago) and expressed pleasure that Fourstones Mill had been able to expand so successfully under extremely difficult conditions, to permit a new factory to be opened "in one of the worst unemployment black spots in the North East".

Chairman Mr George Mandl recalled that, when he first came to Fourstones 20 years ago, the mill was the smallest of six in the area, making only 1 000 tonnes out of 60 000 tonnes being made in the district. It was not only the smallest but certainly the least viable mill, as the machine was over 100 years old and no investment had been made since 1908.

In the intervening period, he recalled, all the remaining five mills in the North East had closed down but Fourstones—which was then certainly amongst the ten worst mills out of 200 in the UK—can now "proudly classify itself amongst the *best* five of the remaining 110 mills".

The old Fourdrinier machine—now in its 122nd year—has been turned into a museum centrepiece and the new machine, completed in 1980, is kept operating on four shifts with an order book well into the second half of 1983, producing hospital disposables.

Fourstones is now part of a small, multi-national group employing some 400 people in seven units in four countries; Sir Rupert's closing remarks at the mill's bi-centenary in 1963 "are certainly a prophecy now come true—'The mill has been known as a village industry. Now its future may be going to be on a wider, more global scale.'"

Mr Mandl paid tribute to Mr George Robinson, General Manager of Fourstones during the past seven years, "without whose effort and foresight the present success story would not have been possible", and presented a gold watch to Mrs Beavers on her retirement after 35 years' service. He also welcomed to the ceremony Mr T.H. Philipson, who received the British Empire Medal in the Queen's Birthday Honours List in the summer of 1982 for 60 years' service at Fourstones Mill.

Mr James Cropper, Chairman of the Northern District of the *Federation*, congratulated the Company on its achievement on behalf of the industry.

The opening was also attended by Mr Hamish Mill, Scottish Secretary (IR) of the *Federation*. Three sets of paper educational kits, sponsored by the mill, were presented to pupils of three schools who had won the "Keep Britain Tidy" awards.

HISTORY OF
THOMAS & GREEN

L. John Mayes, FLA

(Librarian and Archivist of High Wycombe 1935–1971)

PAPER IN THE WYE VALLEY
Buckinghamshire

This brief account of paper making in the valley of the little Buckinghamshire Wye was intended to have in its title—"from 1627 to 1977", a nicely rounded period of 350 years. For a very long time the author was quite confident that the earlier figure was correct, though he always hoped to take it even further back, and now new facts have emerged which do just that—but first a short introduction to the whole subject.

The earliest firm date for a paper mill in England seems to be around 1490 when John Tate had a mill near Hertford. The English version of the work by Bartholomaeus, "De proprietatibus rerum" printed by Wynkyn de Worde about 1496 includes verses praising John Tate for making the paper on which it was printed—and the paper has a quite distinctive watermark. Royal expense accounts were usually kept with great accuracy and Henry VII's privy purse account contains an entry "For a rewarde given at the paper mylne" and that entry is dated May 25th 1496, a date when the King was known to have been nearby at Hertford. The mill seems to have been in existence only for a few years.

Later mills were established by Thomas Thirlby, Bishop of Ely, in 1554, who built a paper mill at Fenditton near Cambridge and by Sir Thomas Gresham, at Osterly, in Middlesex, around 1575. A mill was built about this time at Bennerton—but the most interesting development was due to Richard Tottyl who endeavoured, around 1585, not only to establish a paper manufactury, but also to obtain a general monopoly for the making and also a prohibition on the export of rags to foreign countries, a very sore point with early makers who were constantly worried by the competition of French paper in particular. This petition came to nothing but it probably encouraged another man to make the same sort of proposal only three years later, in 1588. This man was in an excellent position to succeed. He had the royal ear, in that he was one of Elizabeth I's court jewellers, and succeed he did. He was a German, John Spilman, and his monopoly also included the very valuable privilege of having the sole right to collect rags for paper making throughout the whole kingdom. At first his monopoly covered only white paper but, in 1597, it was extended to cover all kinds of paper.

Now comes the first tantalising reference to Bucks. In, or just before, 1600, Spilman applied to the privy council for a warrant to summon before them John Turner, Edward Marshall and George Friend who, he claimed, had erected a paper mill in Buckinghamshire and had collected rags for it in defiance of the terms of his monopoly. The three seem to have made a determined attack on his position for he specifies that they had gathered up the best of the rags, especially those most suited to the production of white paper, so that he was obliged to make brown when he would have much preferred to make writing and printing qualities. His plea succeeded in part and though Marshall was definitely allowed to continue his mill, it was only on condition that he obtained his rags from Spilman. Meantime the latter was himself in trouble for his rag gatherers were getting a very bad reputation. He was accused of employing vagrants and other poor people who not only forced their way into people's houses but were not above using the pretence of rag collecting to cover petty pilfering and the like. There is a splendid poem by Sir Thomas Churchyard concerning Spilman's ventures which includes the following description of the mill itself:

> I prayse the man that first did Paper make,
>   The only thing that sets all virtues forth:
> It shooes new bookes, and keepes old workes awake,
>   Much more of price than all the world is worth:
>
> It witnesse bears of friendship time and troth,
> And is the tromp of vice and virtue both;
> Without whose help, no hap nor wealth is won,
> And by whose ayde great workes and deedes are done
>
> The mill itself is sure right rare to see,
>   The framing is so queint and finely done,
> Built all of wood, and hollowe trunkes of tree,
>   That makes the streams at point device to runne,
> Nowe up, nowe downe, now sideward by a sleight,
> Nowe forward fast, then spouting up on height,
> As conduits colde coulde force so great a heate,
> That fire should flame where thumping hammers beat
> The hammers thump and make as lowde a noyse,
>   As fuller doth that beates his wollen cloth,
> In open shewe, then sundry secrete toyes,
>   Makes rotten ragges to yeeld a thickned froth:
> Then is it stampt, and washed as white as snow,
> Then flong on frame, and hang'd to dry, I trow:
> Thus paper streight it is, to write upon,
> As it were rubde and smoothde with slicking-stone.

But back to Buckinghamshire. No exact location for Marshall's mill has been discovered and so we cannot claim it for our valley. But what a temptation! The Wye was an ideal river on which to site a paper mill. It was full of mills even at the time of Domesday when

134

there were eighteen of them on the nine miles between West Wycombe and the Thames. The water was pure and mineral free—it already had a great reputation as a trout stream—and the fall was quite adequate for any power needs. A cloth trade developed in medieval times and several fulling mills had either been purpose built, adapted from or added to, existing corn mills. By 1600 the trade was largely at an end and there were records of derelict fulling mills even in the fifteenth century when the now still existing Hedge Mill was so described, with its wheel idle, its store houses and dye houses empty. The function of a fulling mill was to beat newly woven cloth under hammers driven by water power to thicken and shrink it—substitute mortars for the boards, on which the cloth was beaten and you had that first essential for paper making, a method for pounding rags and water into "stuff". Continuing with Hedge Mill, we know that it was a working paper mill as early as 1627. In May of that year it appears in a presentation by a jury at a Court of Survey of Bassetsbury. Within the boundaries of the Parish of Chepping Wycombe the Manor of Bassetsbury held six mills from the Dean and Canons of Windsor, and re-leased them to individuals. The Court of Survey in 1627 was held to settle a dispute over fishing rights (remember the Wye was famous for its trout). The finding of the court was that whenever the land of Bassetsbury lay against the water on either side of the stream it should be lawful for the Lord of the Manor to fish. It goes on to list the six mills, running upstream from the boundary with Wooburn Parish. The first mill is described simply as "the paper mill" and we know that it was Hedge because the other five mills were all named, Tredway, Loudwater, Bassetsbury, Chalfonts (Rye) and Bridge. Hedge is the other one of the six,. Its description as "the paper mill" suggests that it was already well known as such—what a pity we do not know the name of the tenant! The first such naming comes twenty-two years later when it is recorded as "One mill commonly called or knowne by the name of Hedge Paper Mill in the tenure or occupation of the widow Clemens". It could quite easily be that elusive 1600 mill.

Equally well it could have been that other mill that for so long was always paired with Hedge since the first mention of it by name occurs in 1627. In that year Glory Mill was leased by Richard King at the very considerable rent of £50 a year, but whether to start papermaking, or to continue it has been uncertain, but now fresh evidence has appeared. In the County Record Office at Aylesbury there is preserved the will of one Edward Isac, or Isaac, of Wooburne in the County of Bucks. The will was proved in 1612 and it contains bequests to his children. He obviously felt that quibbles were likely to occur as to exactly what was left to each legatee and so he prepared inventories.

In the mill and mill house

Stuff to make paper,
Iron crow (bar) and sledge (hammer)
pails and tankards (probably water tanks)
a poste of raggs (felts?) to work paper on
presses for paper
ffatts for paper
seven iron plates for the hammers to strike on (probably mortars)

In the drying house

twenty reams of paper, trebles, ladders and stools

Being a paper maker, the inventories were written on odd scraps of paper and one such includes the complete description of his paper mill and its contents, "Seven iron plates for the hammers to strike on", the equipment in other words, for the reducing of rags to pulp, pails, "tankards"—probably water tanks, a ffat for the stuff, "stuff to make paper"—presumably rags, a poste to work paper on, presses for paper, sledges (sledge hammers presumably), crow bars, ladders, stools—and twenty reams of paper. There is no mention of the mill itself or other premises so it is most likely that it was leased or rented. Several names are mentioned in the will, James Morecroft, Ralph Atkinson, John Brine, William Reading of Loudwater (the Readings, William and John, seem to have been the local millwrights) and Richard King. This is the really interesting name because it was to him that Edmund Waller of Beaconsfield leased the Glory Paper Mill in 1627, only 15 years later—fairly conclusive proof that Edward Isac's mill was indeed Glory and sufficiently well established in 1612 to be left as a going concern and even for the inventory to include 24 reams of paper already made. The rent of £50 which King agreed to pay was very high and may well have been the cause of his failure in the business, certainly by 1645 he was in a hopeless condition, including being six years in arrears with his rent. He had to surrender all his equipment and stocks of paper in part satisfaction. Waller then leased it to Richard Littleton, described as a bargeman, and Samuel Triplet—and this venture seems to have been even less successful. Owner and lessee were soon in litigation concerning unpaid rents and similar issues and before long Waller was offering it for outright sale at the figure of £100—just two years' rent! Before leaving these two mills, strangely enough two out of the four surviving mills, it is interesting to note that there are connections between them covering periods totalling hundreds of years. Not that the connections were always amicable, among the documents relating to Hedge there are masses concerning an attempt by the occupier of Glory to gain control of Hedge where his father had recently died and where his stepmother was continuing the business though on a rather shaky legal footing. What is very nice is that the family feud between the widow, Johanna Spicer and the stepson Ralph Spicer, led the lady to list in great detail the conditions at the mill, the necessary repairs, and the equipment and stock in trade. This was in 1763 and the legal arguments led to a sensible compromise, but by 1765 Ralph had taken over from "late widow Spicer".

By 1636 another paper mill had been established, this time at the top end of the stream in the Parish of West Wycombe. Once again the wording of the evidence suggests a going concern rather than a new venture. It comes in the form of a lease granted by the West Wycombe Estate to Leonard Greene, who is named as "the occupier of a mill called the paper mill", together with certain other property which definitely pinpoints it as the mill later known as Fryer's Mill after the family which, from 1730, held it for about two centuries. Only two years later another mill appears by name, Loudwater, in the accounts of Bassetsbury Manor. It had already figured in the 1627 fishing right's dispute, presumably then as a corn mill, but now it appears as a "paper mill called Loud Water Mill, new built, let for £50".

From individual mills to a general, and disastrous, sequence of events which happened around this time. In and around Wycombe, in 1631 and 1632, there had been a severe outbreak of the plague, accounting for almost half the deaths from all causes during those years, even in this small area the tally reached nineteen in one month. In 1636 the plague in London, Oxford, Gloucester and other big centres of population was so bad that a scapegoat had to be sought, and the paper trade was seized on. Paper was made from rags, rags collected, in the natural order of things, from the most populous places—and rags truly were rags, no clean offcuts from clothing factories, but old clothes handed down and down the social ladder until the poorest tramp would not wear them. Such rags stank, especially when stacked in damp heaps to ferment and rot before going to the beating hammers, and it was easy to assume, and declare, that the stench of them carried the germs of the plague which could be so spread abroad by the winds. Accordingly an order was made that all existing stocks of rags should be burned or buried and no more gathered within ten miles of any of the Royal residences, including Windsor Castle, which effectively meant a ban on paper making in those areas. Some of our valley mills were obviously included, and in any case, the ten mile limit appears to have been regarded as an indication, not as an absolute limit. It was recognised that such a standstill order would bear harshly on the papermasters and it was proposed to raise a special local rate to defray the expenses which would have to be met when the mills were idle and to pay the wages of the people employed, so that they would not be tempted to seek other work and so result in the loss of their skills to the trade. There was an immediate outcry—paper making was not a popular trade in the areas where it flourished most. It was said that its coming had forced corn mills out of business since the owners of such mills were turning them out and renting the mills to the paper men at grossly inflated figures, up to ten times as much as the corn men had previously paid.

The streams had been dammed up to get an increased head of water for their wheels and to maintain that head for long periods, a proceeding which had drowned out local farmers. This latter charge is easy to understand since although a paper mill required less horse-power to drive its hammers than did a corn mill to drive its stones, still the corn mill only needed its power intermittently, but the hammers needed to continue day and night for long periods, not excepting Sundays, to the great scandal of local churchgoers. An interesting light on this problem is shed by some leases in the invaluable Dashwood Collection which, in the case of a combined corn and paper mill, quite a popular arrangement, defined the "common of water" and how the main force was to be available for the stones but a continuous though smaller supply went to the hammers. The crowning objection to the levying of a special rate lay in the proposal to use part of it to pay the unemployed paper workers. These men, the objectors stated most vehemently, were mostly foreigners introduced into the locality where they rejoiced in wages roughly double that paid to other "skilled" workers and as such could surely have been expected to accumulate savings adequate to tide them over such periods of idleness. These were individual objections but a group petition was presented to the Privy Council backing them up. Their damming of the streams to unprecedented heights had destroyed farm land, and the roads had become "passages for boats, rather than highways for men and horses to travel". The continuous hammering of the rags by day and night produced "hideous noises"—and all ills were associated with the paper mills "which had been erected only about forty years previously"—further evidence for an early start.

The plague died down and work restarted and quite soon we can add another mill to our list. In the County Record Offices at Aylesbury there is a lease dated 1656 but referring to an earlier one of 1653. This concerns a paper mill and lists its premises, including rag and drying houses, and its equipment of shafts, wheels, mortars, coggs, swinging hammers, presses, ffatts, iron potts, trebles, etc. The lessors were a group of men, including George Gosnold, who although he lived in Beaconsfield, had great holdings, for which he was highly rated, in the Parish of Chepping Wycombe. The lessee was one Edward Gerrard, associated with John Reading of Chepping Wycombe, Millwright. The rent is interesting, ten shillings a year plus "thirty newe catcht and seasonable trouts" at least eight inches long "in the fish". The reason for the low rent is that the earlier lease was for the land, water courses, etc. on which stood a mill (presumably corn) "long since decayed", so it seems that John Reading most probably obtained the original lease at a nominal figure provided that he built a paper mill on it. There are other cases rather similar where a lease was granted at a low rent and increased as the lessee began to see his outlay returned. It is very tempting to think of men like John Reading as "speculative mill builders". What remains is to place the mill. It was specified in the lease as "situated at Lower Marsh, Chepping Wycombe", which limits the choice considerably but there is more evidence. The land, says the lease, formerly belonged to the "Manor of Great Missenden". A search of the charters and property registers of the Abbey of Great Missenden reveals only one mill in our area to have ever been in their possession. In the thirteenth century Elias Gynant handed over his mill to them in return for cash considerations and its position is fairly clear. Gynant's lands in Wycombe were where the present Guinions Road now runs and the mill is stated to be on the opposite side of the river to his manor house. The description continues by mentioning the bridge below the said mill. Only one mill fits all these conditions, Marsh Mill, and about the only truly conclusive piece of evidence now lacking is how the mill and its land, watercourses, etc. passed to Gosnold following the dissolution of the religious houses in the time of Henry VIII, when all the holdings of Missenden Abbey were dispersed into private hands. There is certainly no doubt in the present writer's mind that one more mystery has been solved, how was it that when Marsh Mill appears by *name* in the rate books in the early eighteenth century it was already a very valuable concern?, and one, by the end of that century, that was capable of producing a paper "Equal to the French" for the purposes of reproducing fine engravings, an achievement recognised by the award by the Society of Arts of their highest honour, the gold medal.

In 1686, more trouble came to the valley. A group of Frenchmen had in that year obtained a patent concerning the making of "all sorts of writing and printing paper". From that they went on to seek, and obtain, a charter from James II which gave them a strict monopoly of making such paper for fourteen years. The charter was confirmed in 1690 and its period extended while its limits were more clearly defined as referring to paper above the value of four shillings a ream, below this value all paper, including the coarser sorts, blue, brown, and paper made from old ropes, ex naval hammocks and the like could be freely made by anyone. The confirmation was by Act of Parliament. The immediate and forceful objections to the monopoly give useful information on the type of production at that time in our valley. The existing white paper manufacturers, calling themselves "The Ancient Paper Makers of this Kingdom" presented a petition against it. The Corporation of High Wycombe, acting for the parish, for there were no paper mills in the little borough itself, contributed information in support. There were, they said, eight mills producing white paper and supporting fifty families. Where were these eight mills? Among the signatories to the main petition appear Edward Spicer of Hedge, Jeremiah Francis of Loudwater and William Russell of Snakeley, the mill which was latterly known as Ford's, of blotting paper fame. The last mill had been in existence at any rate since the advent of rate books in 1667 but it has not been possible to confirm it as paper until 1670 when Thomas Blackwell, a paper maker, had it and he relinquished it to William Russell in 1679. Thus we are left with five mills to pinpoint. Marsh, as has been related, is an obvious one. Another West Wycombe mill, Francis, or Upper Mill End mill, the highest on the stream, was in the occupation of Thomas Murren, or Murrain, in 1687, and at his marriage three years earlier he is entered as "paper maker". Fryers was certainly one, William Turner of Tredway Mill, was making paper at that time. The eighth place has two candidates, Lords Mill; the third of the West Wycombe Parish Mills, was occupied by 1689 by William Murren, and the Murren family included at least one paper maker, and by 1716 was definitely making paper under the direction of John Butcher who is recorded as a maker in insurance policies and other documents, and Bowden's Mill, a corn mill in 1667, for that matter almost certainly one of the Domesday Mills, but though by 1674 there is reasonable supposition that a paper mill had been added in the occupation of George Wys, we cannot be absolutely sure until some time later. By the end of the eighteenth century there were two paper mills working independently, attached to this corn mill.

So, by the early part of the eighteenth century the trade, and a quality trade at that, was well established on the Wye. To all the mills so far mentioned we can now add Soho, held in 1705 by the widow of Hayden or Haydon, alternative spellings of a known paper making family. Hedsor, always referred to as two mills, was held in 1724 by one Robert Moorer, a paper maker, who insured it, or them, as paper mills in that year. In or around 1757, the Lunnon family had the mills which at that time included a corn mill and "his new mill". The family still has its place in the district. The detailed descent of Hedsor Mills cannot conveniently be traced since, unlike the other parishes, the rate books have not survived, but the family held the mills for something like a century and a half after which they went into the Jackson group. Bourne End Mills (there were two of them, a paper mill and a paste board mill), were the lowest on the stream. The two are referred to in a lease of 1736 when a piece of land was let to Francis Jefferies and on the land stood a paste board mill, lately burned down together with the paper mill new erected and built. Some mills are hard to pin down, Lower Glory, later a paste board mill, is a case in point. It appears in the rate book of 1705 as in the occupation of Widow Saunders, but the valuation is very low indeed and it is not until the last quarter of the century when the figure rises to the average for paper or board mills in the area, by which time it was in the hands of Samuel Davis, a known maker.

Around the district known as Cores End, Egham's Green and variations of that name there was a group of mills whose beginnings as paper mills are very hard to trace. One of these became known as Princes Mill, but in early days it was usually called the Fuller's Mill, possibly referring to its earlier still use as a fulling mill. By 1730 it was occupied by a Mr Revell, described as paper maker of Wooburn and earlier still it was occupied by Wm Church who was almost certainly in the trade. In recent times, 1921, the mill was making hand made board but it was closed down in 1922. In the nineteenth century, around 1810 to 1830, Princes seems to have been divided into no less than three separate paper or board mills, but by the later date it had gone back to just the one. Almost next door was Gunpowder Mill—and no trace of gunpowder manufacture has ever been traced to it, what is known is that in 1705 it was occupied by Emmanuel Wright, probably as a paper mill and in 1729, by the name of Francis Rance's mill, it certainly was one. Princes, Gunpowder and later Hedsor, all became part of the complex which the Jackson family began to set up in 1867 when J.H. Jackson took over Gunpowder, though Princes had a short period after that when it was a a half stuff mill for Soho.

Ash Mill had a complicated history too. It is the first, the highest that is, on the stream within the Parish of Chepping Wycombe. As a paper mill its first firm date is 1726 when James King was the paper maker there. Its history is probably nearest to Bowdens for certainly, at times, there were two paper mills and a corn mill, all sharing the same site. It held the melancholy distinction of being the first mill to have its machinery smashed during the riots of 1830, a subject which will be dealt with more fully later.

Of our next mill, Beech, there are no doubts at all. Not just from the cradle to the grave is its history known—we also have some ante-natal information and it continued a rather gruesome connection with the trade even after its decease as an active paper mill. The first mention is in a lease to John Crouch by the Earl of Shelburne of a piece of land in Long Acre Meadow, on the back stream, with licence to build a paper mill. Crouch got this lease in 1739 and went straight ahead with the building. As in the case of an earlier mill this seems to have been an example of a man getting ground and water power, building a suitable mill, and either sub-letting it or disposing of the lease entirely, for by the following year it appears as occupied by a well known paper man, William Goodwin, who insured it immediately. As were all mills at that time, it was a vat mill, but, unlike many others, it continued as a vat mill long after the days of

141

machines and was working up to the year 1900. Some time after that appears the gruesome business mentioned above. There was a major outbreak of smallpox in the town, allegedly traced to rags imported from Gloucester where there was an epidemic. The mill where these rags were being used was, in fact, Rye, at that time owned by the company that had owned Beech. It seems that no suitable hospital accommodation could be found for the smallpox cases and so they were put into Beech Mill which was isolated for the purpose. It is not easy to visualise a less suitable place for a "hospital"—perhaps the townpeople were concerned to see that a rough form of poetic justice was enforced. A paper mill caused it, they believed, a paper mill should cure it. It was finally pulled down in 1916. We have two very useful inventories of the mill, almost a century apart. In 1816 the details indicate a two vat mill. In 1900, when the mill was for sale, the auction particulars speak of room for four vats. There were two water wheels, an overshot one with the reputed horse power of 22, a useful power source, as well as a smaller one. A pleasantly rural note is struck by the information that the double drying loft had a thatched roof. It was a big mill, then, with a fine mill house, fishing rights on the stream, and some five acres of land. It had no fortune as regards a paper manufacturer buying to continue the trade and was finally knocked down to the Wycombe Town Council for £2300—the estimated value of the land.

No less than three mills come into my survey around the year 1759. Marsh Green, the highest on the back stream, Overshots, the third and last on that short tributary, and Kings. Marsh Green fairly certainly started from scratch around that time and the first recorded maker there was Hugh Stratton. The other two are different. Kings, in 1759, was certainly paper, the master being Robert Davis, but Kings was most probably first known as New Mill (a common practice) and we have some strong evidence for this. As early as 1725 Richard Beck insured a paper mill "in the Parish of High Wycombe" and by a process of elimination it should be the mill later called Kings. Beck, in 1733, also insured "his mills" and this time the name is definitely New Mills. A Gilbert Beck appears in 1764 but he is definitely associated with Claptons and that is in the Parish of Wooburn. Overshots is another problem mill. The name would scarcely be given to any mill but one having an overshot wheel, and I think that only the back stream would have a sufficient fall to operate such a wheel, though this cannot be proved. Assuming that it was on the back stream then it was for long associated with a corn mill. Its name, Overshots, also appears to be just another name for a mill on the same site called Tredway, and Tredway, or Treadaway Hill, is adjacent—but which took its name from the other? Tredway or Treadaway, was sometimes used for a curious combination of wheels where there was a very good fall indeed. The main wheel would be overshot, and a second, undershot, or even breast, could be run in the tail race without backwatering the main wheel. Such a pair of wheels would "tread away" from each other, one revolving one way, the other in the opposite direction. The one certain fact from our point of view is that it was occupied by a paper maker, one of the Spicers, in 1759. There is more work yet to be done on the mill called Tredway!

Last on my eighteenth century list of mills comes Rye. As a corn mill it was most probably one of the Domesday mills. At some time it had a fulling mill added to it but the earliest firm mention of paper comes in a lease of 1798 which deals with "all those two water mills under one roof, formerly one mill, one of which two mills was there-to-fore used as a fulling mill ... and the said two mills then was [sic] and for some years last past, had been used as and for a paper mill". Some idea of the difficulties involved in tracing individual mills is given by simply listing the names with which this mill is identified in actual documents associated with it. Mr Bradshaw's mill, Sales' Mill, Bowler's Mill, Rye Mill, New Mill (inevitably) and this does not include casual reference to it by the name of the score or more men who occupied it, or part of it, at various times.

Towards the end of the century there occurs one of those windfalls which help to counteract the despondency engendered by such multi-naming. Napoleon was threatening an invasion of the country and the High Sherriff of Bucks issued an order to every parish constable that he should make a nominal roll of every man in his parish between ages of fifteen and sixty. This amazing document, the Posse Comitatus, was very efficiently compiled, and, joy of joys, it includes with every name, its owner's occupation. The five parishes which concern us are West Wycombe, Wycombe Parish, Wycombe Borough, Wooburn and Hedsor. The list was made in 1798 at which time the area was, in the main, agricultural. True, in the borough a trade in chairmaking had begun, and employed 33 such men—but look at the list of papermakers:

Papermakers in the Wye Valley Parishes: Names of men between the ages of 15 and 60 taken from the Posse Comitatus, the County Roll, made by order of the High Sherriff of Bucks in 1798 when England was expecting an invasion from France

Parish of West Wycombe   *Total 250   Paper Makers 6*
Ambrose Newell, William Hawkins, William Darvill, William Cubbidge, Michael Fryer, John Piercy.

Borough of Chepping Wycombe   *Total 395   Papermakers 17*
Richard Wall, John Loader, William Grey, Humphrey Somerville, ?Unreadable name?, John Somerville, Samuel Somerville, Richard Atkins, William King, Thomas Atkins, William Barrett, Michael

Walter, Samuel Somerville, Thomas King, Thomas Plumridge, Thomas Line, John Crook.

Parish of Chepping Wycombe   *Total 327   Papermakers 75*
Ralph Spicer, Matthew Stanworth, Samuel Randall, William Frier, George Lane, Senr., George Lane, Jnr., Haley Lane, William Hawes, John Hobbs, Joseph Dell, Richard Smith, Joseph Bryant, Francis Bryant, John Heather, George Dean, William Bryant, Robert Briant, Richard Clark, Joseph Rutland, John Rutland, Senr., John Rutland, Jnr., Charles Smith, John Lane, John Atkins, William Pymm, John Budd, John Dean, Joseph Hearn, William Collins, Richard Massey, William Briant, William Plastow, William Shrimpton, Doctor Francis, Robert Stratford, John Wilson, William Shrimpton, John Smith, Abraham Wingrove, Charles Dean, John Keen, Henry Gaddesden, John Hulls, Thomas Jones, Ralph Spicer, William Rippington, Harry Henry, John Wildman, Thomas Gould, Jacob Hale, Thomas Gunnell, Francis Bowery, Richard Medwin, Josiah Saunders, Thomas Parr, Robert East, John Goodwin, John Goodwin Jnr., Abraham Darby, Richard Nash, Thomas Hatch, James Briant, William Very, James Barnes, Joseph Child, George Hargrave, John Bates, Joseph Weedon, Thomas Saunders, Thomas King, Robert Jigger, William Buckwell, Thomas Saunders, Thomas Briant, John Lane, Senior.

Parish of Wooburn   *Total 307   Papermakers 62*
William Thompson, Henry Church, Solomon Deane, Richard Rose, Charles Wethered, Richard Hayns, William Fellows, John Bristowe, William Paslow, Thomas Crutch, Thomas Harding, James Harding, Francis Randall, George Howard, Henry Jones, Thomas Clark, William Hughes, Sen., William Hughes, Jun., Joseph Hancock, William East, John Allnutt, James Wheeler, John Bowdery, Joseph Wright, Henry Pegg, William Pegg, James Clark, Thomas Weller, William Wapshott, James Clarke, Henry Hearn, James Biddle, James Pegg, Ralph Griffin, William Eddington, Joseph Plater, William Briggs, Jun., William Cook, Joseph Hearn, John Howard, William Allen, Sen., William Allen, Jun., Joseph Wingrove, Richard Brown, William Wise, William Grove, Richard West, William Robinson, John Wheeler, Stephen Hooker, James Lane, James Rance, John Wingrove, John Lawrance, William Howard, Richard Deane, James Wheeler, James Howard, Thomas Keen, Thomas Wingrove, John Heather, Daniel Pearce.

Parish of Hedsor and Lillifee   *Total 36   Papermakers 6*
William Lunnon, Joseph Gurney, Ralph Rose, Jonathan Gurney, William Gurney, Richard Lunnon.

Spellings are given as given in the manuscript. Occasionally the identical Christian names and surnames appear and this is quite

144

natural, many families had the same surnames, though possibly quite unrelated, and very few Christian names were in common use. There might well have been four or five men with identical names in the same village. The list does not include the ancilliary trades such as mould maker, and, in addition, it is very probable that many men who are listed simply as labourers also worked in the mills. It is unfortunate that we have no record of the under 15's or over 60's, many in the two age groups would have been papermakers.

It was not only in the Wye Valley that paper production was booming and becoming a money making trade. The Government recognised this fact and accordingly laid an excise duty on all home produced, as well as imported, paper. In the early years of the nineteenth century considerable irregularities in the appraising of duty and collecting the revenue gave the Customs and Excise department much trouble. Eventually, in the years 1815 and 1816, a grand survey of all the paper mills was carried out, each mill located and identified and then given a "mill number", a number still proudly placed on the letter heading of surviving mills. The results of the survey can be seen in the library of the Customs and Excise department in London, at King's Beam House. From this record it is possible to construct a map of the paper mills in our valley and from other sources I can add some fourteen corn mills, ten attached or associated with paper mills, four entirely separate, Bowdery's or Temple, Bridge and Pann in the borough, and Bassetsbury in the parish. This last mill almost became a paper mill but though an enabling lease was made, the change never took place. In view of this tremendous concentration of mills on the nine-mile-plus-small-tributary stream it would be fascinating to know just what each mill's output was. Fascinating, but impossible, though an idea can be obtained from the records kept at one mill, Lower, or Bourne End Mill, the last on the stream, standing where Andrews' Boat Yard now stands. The mill was a double one, paper and pasteboard, but the record I am going to use seems to apply only to the vat paper mill. The occupier was a woman, Mrs Wildman, and among the records she preserved was one detailing all the excise payments she made in the year 1815. The amount was £3 670 13s 6d. The librarian of the Customs and Excise department has informed me that in 1815 the duty payable was three (old) pence per pound weight, so the payments represent the very considerable output of something over 120 tons of paper a year and as to value, in modern terms (1976) the duty paid alone would represent something like £80 000—the value of the paper would be well over the quarter million pound mark as the annual turnover from a vat mill. We can make some sort of comparison with other mills in the area by referring to rateable value at the time. The figures for the eight nearest to her were, in pounds, 18, 15, 14, 15, 15, 27, 14, 31, and her figure, for her whole enter-

145

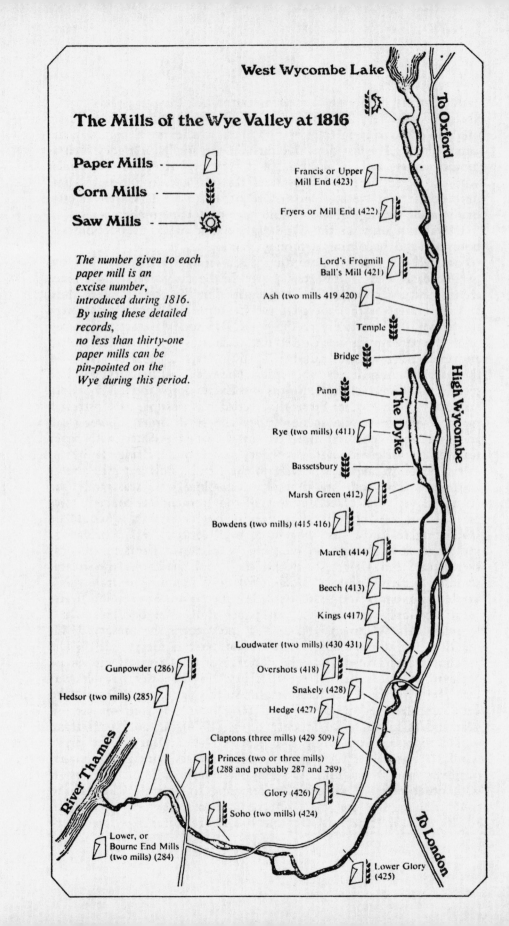

The Mills of the Wye Valley at 1816

West Wycombe Lake

Paper Mills ⸺

Corn Mills ⸺

Saw Mills ⸺

*The number given to each
paper mill is an
excise number,
introduced during 1816.
By using these detailed
records,
no less than thirty-one
paper mills can be
pin-pointed on the
Wye during this period.*

To Oxford

Francis or Upper
Mill End (423)

Fryers or Mill End (422)

Lord's Frogmill
Ball's Mill (421)

Ash (two mills 419 420)

Temple

Bridge

Pann

High Wycombe

The Dyke

Rye (two mills) (411)

Bassetsbury

Marsh Green (412)

Bowdens (two mills) (415 416)

March (414)

Beech (413)

Kings (417)

Loudwater (two mills) (430 431)

Gunpowder (286)

Overshots (418)

Hedsor (two mills) (285)

Snakely (428)

Hedge (427)

Claptons (three mills) (429 509)

River Thames

Princes (two or three mills)
(288 and probably 287 and 289)

Glory (426)

Soho (two mills) (424)

To London

Lower, or
Bourne End Mills
(two mills) (284)

Lower Glory
(425)

prise, paper and board, was 15, so it is likely that her business was about average.

The list of mills shown on this map represents the peak as to numbers, the reason being a new development in the technique of paper making. This was the invention of the Fourdrinier machine which made paper in a continuous reel instead of one sheet at a time, an invention which led to great unemployment in the trade. By 1830 several of the bigger mills had installed machinery and the number of men out of work soared. In normal times this would have meant that such men would have found jobs reasonably easily in the normal main occupation of the area, agriculture, though they would have had to face a considerable drop in income, from being the highest paid craftsmen down to something like one half of their former earnings. The trouble was that even this second best was denied to them, for this was the period of mechanisation of many farm techniques. Steam had come to the farm, the ploughman and his team were yielding to it, the threshers' flails were yielding to it, and it was forcing more and more agricultural labourers out of their jobs and on to scanty parish relief or horrible, semi-slavery, systems that were almost worse. In a village not far from our river a farm labourer, with wife and five children, was receiving, for his work plus parish relief, a total of seven shillings a week. Even that poor reward was in danger, for the funds available for relief were very limited and were rapidly running out. In the year 1830 families from that and surrounding villages were uprooted and transported to the Manchester–Liverpool areas to work in the great cotton mills. They travelled from Wendover in canal boats with their few possessions, up one side of England and then across on the Trent and Mersey canal to their new homes. A ghastly journey, but once there, most of them found work straight away, hard work and long hours, but paid at rates which seemed to them to be fantastic. One man sent word back to his friends, from seven shillings a week for all purposes, he, his wife and his three eldest children were now earning twenty-eight shillings a week, plus a cottage. All the barge horses in Bucks, he said, would never drag him back to that county. But to return to our people, and their descent from well above average pay and conditions to abject poverty. Leaders arose and meetings were held with mill owners, but no compromise was reached. Machine breaking was rife among farm workers and eventually the paper men decided to join in, and after more abortive meetings, at one of which a typical rabble rouser, nothing to do with the trade, made inflammatory exhortations to them, the decision was finally made, the machines must go. They assembled at five o'clock on Monday morning, November 29th, 1830, gathering at Flackwell Heath where one of their leaders lived and marched off through Loudwater and Wycombe to the highest mill on the stream to be mechanised, Ash, just

147

inside the parish boundary. They carried, quite openly, sledge hammers, crowbars and the like and made no secret of their intentions, which were to smash the machines, no more and no less. Violence would be avoided as would be any other form of damage, after all, they wanted the mills to remain as going concerns, but as vat and not machine mills, and the less offence they gave to their old employers, the better chance they had of getting their jobs back. Well aware of this the local authority had taken certain steps, including raising a force of some fifty special constables, many of whom seem, at any rate at the beginning of the affair, to have had a lot of sympathy for the machine breakers. Not all were well disposed though and at this very first mill, Ash, the men received a terrible test of their pacific intentions. A special constable, not a paper man but, reputably, a butcher, got up on the main beam above the mill gates and as the men surged through to get at the machine, he poured four gallons of the sulphuric acid used in rag preparation over their heads. The burns and agony can be imagined and it says much for their determination that though they caught him, they contented themselves with ducking him in the mill stream where those who had caught the worst of the acid had rushed to wash themselves. They duly smashed up the machinery at Ash and marched through the town to the next on their list, Marsh Green Mill. On their way through the town they were joined by great numbers of hangers on, ostensibly sympathisers, but in many cases merely opportunists who indulged in looting from the shops which had not taken the precaution of boarding up their windows. At Marsh Green the master, and we shall hear more of him, was a young man named Zachary Allnutt. He begged them to spare his machine, but they wrecked it without any further incident; except that a local Justice of the Peace, the Rev. Vincent Price, arrived and read out that part of the Riot Act which calls on all people unlawfully assembled to depart peaceably to their houses. On past the hand mills and so to just about the most important mill in the district, Marsh. The master, John Hay, had already partly dismantled his machine and he came to the gates and tried to reason with the men. He promised that the machine would not be worked again until a compromise had been worked out. He pointed out that by wrecking his machine they would certainly hurt his purse, but would hurt even worse the labour force of fifty-three men, women and children employed at the mill. They heard him out, for he seems to have been a good employer, but still they breached the doors and smashed his machine. Opposition in this case came from the workers in the mill and one of them did a lot of damage with a red hot poker, while another thrust a red hot iron rod through the keyhole of the lock and put out the eye of a man who was trying to force it open. At this point the men made a small detour. Apparently they had agreed among themselves to make one

148

small addition to their declared programme, for nearby was the main farm of a wealthy local land owner who had been very much in the fore in declaring that if any mob came anywhere near his place they would regret it. The small detour was simply to smash one of his farm machines, presumably just to "learn 'im". From the farm, the mob, for so they were now being called, adjourned to a local inn where they regaled themselves with beer and food, and since by now they numbered something like five hundred it must have been big business for the landlord who most probably had more than an idea of their coming and stocked up accordingly. After this break for refreshments they went on to Loudwater Mill where Mr Plaistowe met them and, like Mr Hay, tried to reason with them—he too had partly dismantled his machine and promised not to restart it until negotiations had been held and a suitable compromise agreed. Again, as in the case at Marsh, the men heard him out but went on with the wrecking but, by now, in the face of stiffening opposition. The High Sherriff of Bucks, Colonel Vyse, had come on the scene accompanied by a number of the local gentry, some on horse, some a foot, and he tried to use his "troops" to arrest some of the men. Stones began to fly and the Colonel was soon bleeding from face wounds, while one of his mounted men, armed with a sword, tried a sort of one man cutting out expedition to arrest the ringleaders. He was repulsed and in making his escape, he knocked down two of the many women who had followed the paper men all day. He was pulled from his horse and roughly handled but was finally allowed to remount and make his escape.

Snakeley Mill was next on the list and here the situation was different. Even the mechanised mills were not finding business too satisfactory and this mill had been idle for some time, following the bankruptcy of its occupant. The owner of the mill met the men and explained the situation to them, the machine was not working and could not work until a new tenant had been found, and he promised that even then discussions would be held with the workers before it was restarted. Once again, the reasoning was in vain and the smashing started. By now the forces of law and order had been much augmented—there were the original specials, Colonel Vyse and his "local gentry", a few soldiers from Windsor Barracks, and now came re-inforcements in a form which I should hesitate to introduce in a work of fiction, but in a factual account, fact it is. Over the local hill came riding the gentlemen members of the Royal Stag Hounds. Probably the writer of the original story was aware that it sounded unlikely for he gives a wealth of detail, even to describing the tame stag which was regularly brought out to be hunted and, honour satisfied, was returned to his comfortable quarters to wait his next outing. What happened was that the members promptly abandoned the chase and offered their services to Colonel Vyse as a cavalry

149

detachment, and, with his forces so augmented, a serious onslaught on the machine breakers was made and many of them rounded up and finally taken to Aylesbury Gaol to await trial. The "riot" was over, and possibly it was just as well for all concerned, for the papers of the period had a very circumstantial account of the preparations at the next mill on the list, Claptons, where the master had a sizeable cannon charged with nails and scrap iron trained on the mill gates, and expressed his complete determination to fire it if any attempt was made on his machinery.

A Special Assize was held in Aylesbury on 10 January 1831. Few could offer any defence though one made a particular plea which throws an interesting light on paper trade union practice at that time. This man, rounded up and then taken to prison, was named James Stone and his defence was that he took no part in the proceedings at all, except as an innocent bystander. True he was a paper maker, but not of the district—he was "on tramp" from Dartford to Leicester where a good job awaited him and, in keeping with the custom of his union, he was making his way by walking from inn to inn. Was not Loudwater out of his way? he was asked. Yes, but he had to use inns in paper making districts, inns with which the Society of Paper Makers had made special arrangements so that he would receive free overnight accommodation and, on his departure, a shilling, sixpence to drink and sixpence "for his pocket" to maintain him on his progress. His story was confirmed by Samuel Griffin, landlord of the inn concerned, and he was acquitted. Finally, about twenty of the paper men were found guilty and had "sentence of death" recorded against them. This meant that their cases would be reviewed and the sentence commuted to a term of transportation to the penal colonies, and this duly happened. Some men returned, others stayed on after the expiry of their terms—it was not difficult for a skilled man to do this and find employment and even wealth in the new lands. Two men, however, the accepted ringleaders, were sentenced to be hanged and that meant just what it said. John Sawney or Sarney, aged 54 and Thomas Blizzard, aged 30, came perilously near to finishing on the gallows but at last they, too, were reprieved and their sentences changed to transportation. In an age of mass illiteracy the narrative, often doggerel, ballad was much used to arouse interest and sympathy in such cases and a long poem was printed, and widely distributed. It is worth reproducing:

The sorrowful lamentations of Thomas Blizzard, and John Sarney,
Who were Sentenced to Die, at the late Commission for the
County of Bucks held at Aylesbury, on the 10th of January, 1831,
they being the leaders of the Rioters and Machine Breakers in and
near High Wycombe, Bucks.

You must the feeling heart deplore,
This sad and awful time,
When want misleads the Labouring Poor,
To misery and to crime;
And now upon the fatal drop,
To meet the public eye,
Two poor men in a healthful state,
Must a sad example die.

Thomas Blizzard is one of these men,
His age is thirty years,
He has a tender loving wife,
And three small children dear;
John Sarney is the other man,
His age is fifty-four,
He has six children and a wife,
His case for to deplore.

To see their loving wives and friends,
Come to these wretched men,
Such a horrid sight, I hope that we,
May never, never see again;
I hope this will a warning be,
To all and every one,
And never throw themselves away,
By visiting unlawful bands.

In Aylesbury dark Condemned Cell,
These wretched men do lay,
Awaiting for the mournful knell,
To summons them both away;
May God in mercy have their souls,
By penitence made pure,
And yet with comfort cheer the hearts
Of the Industrious Poor.

Hark! 'tis the dreary midnight bell,
That breaks the gloom profound,
It seems to toll our funeral knell,
How dismal is the sound;

151

A few short hours and we must stand
Exposed to shame and scorn;
Ah, sad and luckless was the day,
When these poor men were born.

That awful hour will shortly come,
The time is drawing near,
When we must meet our fateful doom;
And on the drop appear,
And let religion be our guide,
In God put all your trust,
That after this you may reside,
In the regions of the just.

O what our friends they now must feel,
To think upon our doom,
That we are sentenced for to fill,
A sad untimely tomb.
They wring their hands in grief,
And send to heaven a prayer,
That he would kindly give relief,
And ease them of their care.

So all young men a warning take,
By your untimely end,
And may your conscience now awake,
Your evil ways amend.
Before the judge the sentence passed
My kindred near stood by,
'twod melt a heart of stone to hear,
How bitter they did cry.

Ah little did our parents think,
Who nurs'd on their knees,
That we should meet our awful doom,
Upon the gallows tree.
But now our youthful years are fled,
And they are pass'd and gone,
And O what bitter tears we shed,
To be thus snatch'd away.

We hope no person will reflect,
On those we leave behind,
Our family's quite innocent
Of this our wicked crime.
We hope you will a warning take
All you who come to see,
These most wretched men,
Hanging on the tree.

152

So the Wycombe Paper Riots ended—but the long-term effects were extensive. The mills where the machines had been smashed were in a bad way, and if just one such case is chosen, the overall picture will emerge. Marsh Green will answer the purpose. The mill is at a standstill, the customers cannot wait too long, although they sympathise with Mr Allnutt, unless he can get into production again fairly quickly, well, they will have to start buying elsewhere—and perhaps never return to him. But when would he be able to start again? Take the matter of finance first. A special rate was levied to provide a fund to compensate the makers, and pay for the necessary repairs, but this rate was very unpopular, especially in parishes such as West Wycombe where no damage had been done and, in consequence, it took a long time to collect it. Once collected it was handed over to the County Treasurer, and though there is no suggestion of actual malpractice on his part, it proved extremely difficult to extract the money from him. There is a mass of correspondence which starts in the usual formal, courteous way, but which, as the months and even years go by, becomes more and more acrimonious and ends in threats of action before the High Court. There are letters from individuals, including Mr Allnutt, who pleads for even part settlement. His mill is idle, his workers have dispersed, his goodwill is gone, even his personal credit is tainted and his wife dares no longer go into the shops where unpaid bills produce a very poor reception for her. He, like others, finally got some satisfaction but for him it was too late, he had been forced into bankruptcy, and the mill never made paper again. Even those who could ride out the financial crisis had their serious troubles, for there was really only one firm that could undertake repairs to such special machines, that of Bryan Donkin, and he was extremely busy fitting new machines in mills in more fortunate areas. Gradually the machines *were* repaired and soon another problem arose. Many of the vat mills had been associated with corn mills and when the occasional shortage of rags forced up the price, they simply closed down until the trouble was over, relying on the corn side to keep them going. With a big expensive machine continuous production was necessary to achieve financial stability and the inflated prices *had* to be met, a proceeding which meant that such increases would be likely to continue and the closing of the small mills would change from temporary to permanent. Bowden's and Lord's are two mills where the paper side was given up and, for the rest of the active life of such mills, corn milling was the sole occupation. This was the real beginning of the trend from many and small to few and big which has produced the pattern which we see in the valley today.

Even after the coming of the paper machine the motive power was for many years the force of the stream. How important this force was can be judged from legal proceedings concerning Bourne

End, or Lower, Mills, by this time occupied by another lady, Mrs Angell. Her water wheels, two of them, were so situated that their tail races discharged almost directly into the Thames, an arrangement which was quite satisfactory except on the occasions when flood conditions caused the river to rise and "back up" the water level around the bottom of the wheels. Mrs Angell recognised that one cannot alter nature but now man took a hand. In 1829 the Thames ran unchecked from Marlow to Boulters Lock at Maidenhead. This caused great difficulties for barges both in drought times, when shallows were very troublesome, and in flood time when the stream ran fiercely. The Commissioners of the River Thames decided to put in a lock at Cookham, not far below Mrs Angell's mill, to obviate these conditions. It did so, but it also *permanently* raised the level of the main river and prevented the wheels developing their full horse-power. Mrs Angell was a very determined lady and she promptly took legal advice, and, as so often happens when litigation is in the offing, an enormous amount of information emerges including in this case, a detailed description of the mill and an inventory of the equipment.

When steam power came into the valley, we were again fortunate in that one of its protagonists, Thomas Burch Ford, who took over Snakeley Mill, left many records concerning his calculations which finally led him to adopt the new power. He also left a great deal of material which gives a good insight into the working conditions, wages and the like. His "Instructions to Stokers" is a case in point—

INSTRUCTIONS TO STOKERS—TO BE READ BY THEM EVERY DAY

Stokers are requested seriously to consider the great responsibility resting upon them, and that upon the proper execution of their Duties, the safety of the Mill and the Workpeople therein as also that of their own lives depends:

The following Rules are to be observed and to be read over every day:—

1. Stokers as much as possible to keep themselves to their own Department.
2. To attend to their duties faithfully and never to let their attention to be directed or engaged upon other things. To have their eyes constantly on the gauges and keep the Steam regular and the Water Supply the same.
3. Never to depend upon anyone else or what they may say, but to do everything themselves, and to see for themselves that everything is right in reference to the Boiler and everything under their charge.

154

4. To have their meals in the Stokehold and not elsewhere.
5. Never to leave their own work to do other work for other people. Never to leave their work in order to gossip with others—or to go outside at mealtimes to witness other men at Cricket or any other game.
6. To get proper rest when at home so as to be fresh and fit for work when commencing work, and so as to leave no temptation for dozing or forgetfullness.
7. To report anything amiss as regards the Boiler or anything else under their charge immediately it is discovered.
8. To make himself thoroughly acquainted with his duties and to understand rightly every communication and every Cock, etc., and not to remain in ignorance of a single matter.
9. *Every quarter of an hour to ask himself the question "Is everything right and safe" and to answer it by seeing for himself that it is so.*
10. To have his whole mind on his work the whole of the time he is here, and to be thinking of nothing else.
11. Remember everything and never be able to say in reference to any duty to be performed "I forgot it" or "I was thinking of something else" and "I didn't mean to do it" and so forth.
12. At the end of your time-on to be able to say on every occasion "I have done my duty—and everything is alright".

These rules were written by Thomas Burch Ford for the stokers working on his new steam engine at Snakely Mill.

It would be interesting to have the comments of modern trade union officials—though they would probably be unprintable. At the lower end of the valley, and around the same period, another name was emerging which was to become a household word, Jacksons. The first mill to be taken over was Gunpowder but later Princes was added, the sole survivor of the group of three mills which had stood on or near the site. Even this mill had had a very chequered career and when it became part of the Jackson enterprise it had been making half stuff for Soho but now it had a new lease of life as a hand mill for best quality work and so continued until it was demolished around 1929. Two more mills went into the Jackson group, the two at Hedsor which had been run as hand made board mills. In a copy of the Jackson house magazine, the Mill Stream, it is said that these mills were purchased primarily to provide a good through route, for raw materials one way and finished goods the other, between the mills and the River Thames. To digress for a moment, this sort of problem was probably the reason for a movement which was set on foot in 1790 to construct a canal alongside the River Wye from the Thames to Wycombe or else to turn the Wye itself into a "navigation" with the necessary locks and weirs. The scheme failed to get

155

the necessary support, probably due to the fact that, short of providing a weir and a lock at every mill site, some people were going to lose their source of power. A much smaller scheme was considered later on to make the Wye navigable as far as Jacksons Mill but was dropped because of the problems posed by existing road bridges. To return to Jacksons. In the 1950s they began to produce a house magazine and a file of this is very valuable to the valley historian. Like most such publications there is much purely ephemeral material but there is also a series of articles alas, all too short, which outlines the history of the enterprise and includes extremely interesting photographs, maps and similar things.

Steam power and modern machinery hastened the progress of the trend from many to few and from small to large with an increase in the use of smaller mills for half stuff production. Fords, for example, took over Overshots and most of Claptons, Soho took Princes, Marsh took Kings and Loudwater, though in this case the two mills were run in association with the parent mill, but each continuing its own special types of production with the obvious advantages of bulk buying and also interchange of staff, this latter of very great importance when either extra staff were needed at any one or other of the mills or when some calamity, such as the breakdown of equipment, temporarily crippled a mill and would, had the mill been independent, most probably have meant dismissal of the work force and quite possibly the end of that particular enterprise. There were exceptions, Hedge, still working, always seems to have continued independently and so does Glory. Strange that these two should always have had so much in common; an early start, independence and long and continuing life. The nineteenth century was not an easy period for paper makers and many of the valley mills had to ride out severe financial difficulties and even bankruptcies. Some fell by the wayside. Notably Bourne End, or Lower Mills which by the end of the century had developed into a truly major concern, even having its own gasworks, but then, when one might have thought it had everything going for it, a good site, water transport, or, if preferred, rail with a station near at hand, it foundered and within a few years had gone completely, leaving just a scrap of evidence in Andrew's Boat Yard, and the name "Mill House" as memorials. Claptons has been mentioned earlier. Even before it was a paper mill it was important. In 1748 an advertisement appeared offering for sale the estate called Claptons in the Parish of Uborn. The estate included "three mills, worked by water supplied by the largest head of water on the river or within forty miles of the place (advertiser's licence) one of which mills used for making iron and steelwire, another for fitting iron hoops, plates, etc. and the third for tilting (smithing) of iron and melting of copper and brass". The estate also included a paper and a corn mill called Glory Mill. It would be interesting to know if brass wire for paper moulds was also produced. Later on hand paper mills were started and then a machine, one of the earliest in the valley, was added. Still later, the mills divided again, the machine ceased work, one part became a half stuff mill, the other a canvas manufactory, then a factory producing hollow-ware, pots, pans, kettles, etc., then a furniture factory and finally an engineering works, the last named persisting until the last of a series of fires made the place virtually unusable for trade purposes in 1921. Some of the smaller mills returned to corn milling first and then, still further down the scale, to grinding waste wood from the chair factories into wood flour for the linoleum mills at Staines. This last occupation was usually short, the intense heat generated by wood grinding usually resulting in a disastrous fire which merely left a desirable site for some trade utterly different.

Today (1976) there are but four mills making, though Jackson's still manipulates board and Ford's has only just closed. It is most important that not only the past history of the trade should be recorded, as has been done here, but that history should be considered as an ongoing process—it is sometimes easier to find out what happened a century or two ago than to detail the changes within the past few decades. The house magazine can help here, but one mill has gone usefully further, Marsh. Marsh had an excellent labour relations record and, in consequence, has a pensioners' list of many men and women with forty or more years service. A selection of these pensioners was visited and invited to take part in an exercise designed to record (literally, by means of tape recording) everything they could remember, good or bad, about life in the mill and, especially, memories of changes of machines, processes and the like, not forgetting working and social conditions. The aim was to be comprehensive rather than selective, that came later when the tapes were edited. The results were very interesting—and sometimes quite surprising. It is a truism to say that rows and troubles are what cause things to be remembered—and in this case at times the Company's good record proved a handicap. Some of those questioned had been quite content to go to work year after year, confident that, provided they worked well, they had nothing to worry about, and consequently they hadn't bothered about changes or anything else. They went to work, did their work whenever and however they were told to do it, drew their wages and that was that. Others were much more forthcoming, people born with enquiring minds perhaps, and they produced the material which makes this experiment well worth while. It *was* an experiment and possibly it may lead others to follow suit for it is not an expensive business. The results will be of ever increasing value. Even now it is difficult to remember when listening to them that these are the voices of living people, providing an intimate description of life in a major mill, a social document as well,

157

highlighting the sweeping changes which have taken place so recently. The memories were gathered just in time, for when that generation is gone the information available will be at secondhand.

So this brief account ends. There is no list of acknowledgements. It is sufficient and very satisfactory for the writer to be able to report that on no occasion has a request for help or information been met even with impatience, much less rebuff, and all that remains is to offer sincere thanks to everyone concerned.

Herbert Green
(1855-1940)

THOMAS, STEPHENS & GREEN

Personalities of the partners

John Barcham Green was born in 1823. In 1839 he came to Hayle Mill, owing to the failure of his uncle, John Green, and the purchase of the business from John Green's estate by his brother Samuel Green. So, at the age of sixteen, John Barcham Green entered into work at Hayle Mill and continued to work under his uncle, John Green, who was left there as Manager until Samuel Green died in 1852. Then John Barcham Green became proprietor of the business under his father's will and John Green, the uncle, retired.

The business proceeded under J.B. Green until 1860, when the business of Thomas, Stephens & Green was formed. The second partner in this business was Mr J.C. Stephens, a lawyer in Maidstone. He, being a well-to-do man and well known to Mr J.B. Green, provided some of the capital and, having several sons, he stipulated that his youngest son, Clement, should represent him at the mill when the business was formed.

The first partner and of course the most important member of the firm was William Thomas who was born at Shoreham in Kent. He was engaged as journeyman papermaker under Mr George Wilmot or his father, the well known hand-made papermaker.

Young William Thomas, desiring to improve himself, went to Tovil to join the firm of Simpson & Hargreaves, or Simpsons, as it was then, as Foreman. Mr Thomas was considerably older than Mr J.B. Green but they conceived a great respect for each other which ripened into something like friendship, and Mr Thomas remained at Tovil Mill (which was the first mill making paper out of straw in England) until he had a favourable offer from Townsend, Hook of Snodland, to whose mill he went as foreman.

After a few years with Mr Hook, William Thomas came to J.B. Green and put before him a proposition that there was a mill in the market down in Buckinghamshire, Soho Mills, which could be acquired cheaply, which was well suited to the manufacture of paper from straw and that he, William Thomas, was competent to conduct it with his experience of making paper from straw—if he could find the capital.★

★ *(Note by J.B. Sedgwick*. I was told, I think by Mr Roland Green, that Mr W. Thomas, when with Simpson & Hargreaves, assisted in the development of a new

159

Family tree of the Barcham Green papermaking family of Hayle Mill, Maidstone, and Soho Mill, Wooburn Green

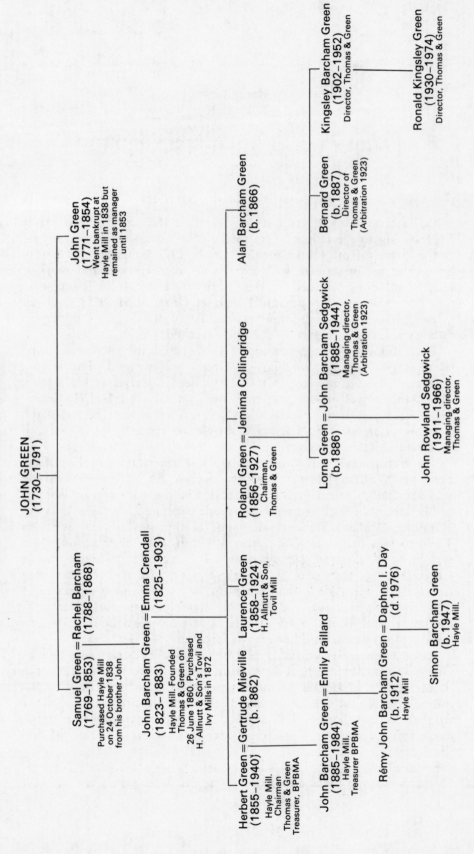

JOHN GREEN
(1730–1791)

Samuel Green = Rachel Barcham
(1769–1853)   (1788–1868)

Purchased Hayle Mill
on 24 October 1838
from his brother John

John Green
(1771–1854)
Went bankrupt at
Hayle Mill in 1838 but
remained as manager
until 1853

John Barcham Green = Emma Crendall
(1823–1883)   (1825–1903)

Hayle Mill. Founded
Thomas & Green on
26 June 1860. Purchased
H. Allnutt & Son's Tovil and
Ivy Mills in 1872

Herbert Green = Gertrude Mieville
(1855–1940)   (b. 1862)

Hayle Mill.
Chairman
Thomas & Green
Treasurer, BPBMA

Laurence Green
(1858–1924)
H. Allnutt & Son,
Tovil Mill

Roland Green = Jemima Collingridge
(1856–1927)
Chairman,
Thomas & Green

Alan Barcham Green
(b. 1866)

John Barcham Green = Emily Paillard
(1885–1984)
Hayle Mill.
Treasurer BPBMA

Rémy John Barcham Green = Daphne I. Day
(b. 1912)   (d. 1976)
Hayle Mill

Simon Barcham Green
(b. 1947)
Hayle Mill.

Lorna Green = John Barcham Sedgwick
(b.1886)   (1885–1944)
                 Managing director,
                 Thomas & Green
                 (Arbitration 1923)

John Rowland Sedgwick
(1911–1966)
Managing director,
Thomas & Green

Bernard Green
(b. 1887)
Director of
Thomas & Green
(Arbitration 1923)

Kingsley Barcham Green
(1902–1952)
Director, Thomas & Green

Ronald Kingsley Green
(1930–1974)
Director, Thomas & Green

Mr J.B. Green, although at the time making a comfortable income out of his small business, was not in a position to put up much capital, but he favoured the project owing to his knowledge of Mr Thomas's energy and general character and he approached his lawyer friend, Mr Stephens as to whether he might possibly be prepared to find some of the capital required. This was finally done, Mr Thomas himself finding little or none of the money, Mr J.B. Green finding £4100 and Mr Stephens a similar amount.

The mill was then purchased and on 25 June 1860 possession was taken and the business was started.

Mr Thomas lived in the Mill House in the yard (now offices) his eldest son, John, lived in the village and his youngest son, Edwin, also lived close by and they practically composed the office staff.

It is probable that at first the business was a hard struggle but personally I know nothing of that as I was only a small boy at the time, but from records in my father's Private Ledger I can see that right from the start of the business profits were being made and divided.

A most important happening in the early history of the Mill was the very serious illness of Mr Thomas, probably about 1863. He was affected with some heart trouble of an obscure nature which the local doctors could not make out and my father called in a consulting physician well known in Maidstone, Dr Stephen Monckton, who declared that Mr Thomas was suffering from a very rare heart trouble which would in all probability prove fatal in perhaps six months. He said that it was absolutely essential that Mr Thomas should be removed from the active worries of the business, that he should not live in the Mill House, which was noisy, and that he should on no account go upstairs, take any violent exercise or be subject to any worries or excitement.

This was a most serious thing to this young business because there was no doubt that Mr Thomas was the moving spirit and the life and soul of the concern. However, it was necessary to act if his life was to be spared even for a time. Therefore he moved to High Wycombe, where a house was taken in the Easton Street, and all the regulations laid down by Dr Stephen Monckton were impressed upon him most seriously.

Mr John Thomas, then married, came to live in the Mill House, and the business went on as before, except that Mr William Thomas was only to attend when he felt equal to it. Mr Thomas, however, was not the sort of man to be hemmed in by medical restrictions

process for boiling straw and in consideration of his services to the Patentee, he was allowed to use the process himself free of royalties and that his rights in connection with this process was one of the reasons which induced Mr J.B. Green to favourably consider the purchase of Soho Mills.)

and it does not appear that his energy and vitality were affected by this obscure heart trouble and he went about very much as before. He certainly had his bedroom upstairs and his method of reaching the mill was by driving himself in a high dog-cart. This went on for at least two or three years.

In the course of 1865 my father, Mr J.B. Green, had a very serious illness, rheumatic fever, so much so that his life was despaired of. When he was convalescing from this illness, his doctor (I imagine Dr Stephen Monckton) strongly recommended that under no circumstances should he continue to live down in the valley at Hayle Mill, and as the winter was coming on, it was arranged that the whole family should move down to Dover for the winter, where a house was taken in Waterloo Crescent and from there my father travelled to Maidstone by train twice a week in order to attend to his business as well as he could.

Early in the following year, Mr Thomas came down to see my father at Dover and suggested that I, Herbert Green, the eldest son, then a boy of ten years old, should go and spend a long visit with him in High Wycombe, which I did. At this point I came into direct contact with the Thomas family, of course. Hitherto I had been too young to know anything about them. I stayed with them for a very considerable time and from my own knowledge I can say that Mr Thomas was living the life of an ordinary, healthy, vigorous, middle-aged man. I frequently drove in with him by the high dog-cart and even then as a child I often wondered why a man who was supposed to be suffering from a serious illness should go about in that way. He was rather hot tempered and when the horse did not do just as he liked he used to get very excited.

When I went to Soho Mill the office was one single large room and the staff consisted of Mr John Thomas, Edwin Thomas, his brother, and Mr Clement Stephens, representing his father, Mr J.C. Stephens. I cannot remember anything about the business in those days as I was far too young and my only participation in the business was breaking coal in the coal shed.

After a month or two with Mr Thomas, my father suggested that it was too much to expect me to stay on as a guest continuously and he proposed that I should go to school in High Wycombe, which I did, to a small private school, where I remained for several months. This was my first visit to Soho Mills and I am afraid cannot say much that would be interesting from a business point of view.

I then returned home and was sent to a school in Brighton and I do not recollect whether or no I visited the Thomas family again until two years later when I went with my two brothers to Crauford College at Maidenhead. While there I and both my brothers frequently visited the Thomas's. At that time Mr Thomas had moved to another house on the other side of Easton Street with a nice garden which stretched back to the stream which runs through High Wycombe below the Wycombe Abbey Park, and my visits to the mill were very much on the same lines as on the previous visit.

This is practically all that I can tell of the early history of the business.

In 1871 I finally left school and at Mr Thomas's suggestion my father sent me down to Soho Mills to be "licked into shape" before entering my father's office.

Of course, as I spent nearly a year there I did get to know something of the conduct of the business.

As I stated previously, the office staff consisted of John Thomas, Edwin Thomas (who was then married) and Clement Stephens, who incidentally did not take any active part as he was not considered by Mr Thomas Snr. to be of much use. The only addition to the staff was a clerk whose name was Fred Francis, and I worked very much with him. One of my duties was to make a complete copy of the Sales day by day and post it to my father. I have very little doubt that this was done to find something for me to do but it was a big job and quite a good one.

In those days the office was very much the same as it had been when I was a lad of ten but, of course, the activities of the business had increased very much.

My recollection is that they made News very largely and one of the orders was for making the paper for the Bucks Free Press, for which they got $4\frac{1}{4}d$ per lb and it was very poor stuff, very far from what we should call "White".

They had Evaporators at the back where they sent the liquor from boiling the straw and evaporated the liquor and calcined it, as they were only doing a few years ago.

The Carpenter's shop and the Fitters' Shop were at the corner of the Salle, the Fitters' Shop downstairs and the Carpenters' Shop upstairs. I spent a good deal of time in the Carpenter's Shop when I was not practising Finishing in the Salle.

There was at that time a railway siding, I should think quite recently added and I can remember that there was a weighbridge under the shade of a very tall tree and I used to help weigh in the trucks. Also the straw was bought from farms in the neighbourhood and brought in by wagons and one of my jobs was to weigh every truss as it was taken out of the wagon and bring an account to the office. Each truss ought to weigh 36 lbs and there were very many trusses in a load. It was my duty to check them.

Mr Thomas, with his usual energy, used to go about the country buying straw and I can remember very well accompanying him on one occasion to Henley where he met numerous farmers and took me to dine at the Farmers' Ordinary Inn.

The question arises in my mind as to when Princes Mill was added

163

to the business. For a long time all the paper was made of straw but when Esparto became the regular material for papermaking, the Esparto was prepared at Princes Mill and the half-stuff was carted to Soho. There is no doubt about it, Princes Mill was in full swing when I was living with Mr Thomas, because he lived at the "Elms" just outside Princes Mill and I can very well remember the iron gear was very noisy and most noticeable at night time. The curious thing was that the liquor was prepared at Soho Mills and was pumped to Princes Mill for boiling the straw, afterwards I think, being pumped back again to Soho to recover the Soda. (On this last point I am not certain—possibly at that period they did not try to recover the Soda.) I cannot give the date when Princes Mill was taken but it was some time between 1866 and 1873.

I spent nine months at Soho being "licked into shape" and then, as my father was purchasing the business of H. Allnutt & Son at Tovil, he wanted me home and I left at the end of October 1872.

The straw boilers, of which there were two, were cylindrical boilers and steam was admitted through the shaft on which they revolved, the chopped straw being fed into the boilers until they were full, caustic liquor was run in and the top screwed on, steam admitted and the boiler revolved.

One of the things which interested me very much in connection with this straw boiling was that it involved an automatic device blowing off the steam with a most tremendous noise and I always tried to avoid being present when the steam was blown off.

From this time my connection with the business, until the formation of the Company, was not very close.

My brother, Roland Green, left school about a year after I did, so that he must have been sixteen or seventeen years old and he was sent down to Soho Mills. I have the impression that he lived at first with the Thomas's, with old Mr Thomas, his wife and daughter, but later on he certainly lived in the little house attached to Princes Mill because I can remember going there to stay with him. It was arranged when he went to Soho that he was eventually to take over my father's share in the business and to learn all about it from top to bottom.

In 1874 Mr William Thomas died.

Roland Green, working with John and Edwin Thomas, carried on the business.

In 1883 my father died (on September 2nd) and by his will Roland Green took over his share. At the time my father had arranged to build a house, which was actually in course of construction at the time of his death.

The business then became "J. & E. Thomas & Green", consisting of John Thomas, Edwin Thomas and Roland Green.

WILLIAM THOMAS
Founder of Thomas & Green in 1860
Died 1874

JOHN BARCHAM GREEN
1823–1882
Founder of Thomas & Green
1860

Sir JOHN THOMAS
1834–1920
Chairman Thomas & Green Ltd

ROLAND GREEN
1856–1927
Chairman Thomas & Green Ltd.

Group of workers in the Fitter's shop at Thomas & Green in 1912

Group of workers at Thomas & Green in 1912

Two views of Thomas & Green Soho Mill in 1912

No. 2 Paper Machine 65 inches wide at Thomas & Green 1912

No. 1 Machine House with 65-inch Machine at Thomas & Green 1912

In 1884 Roland Green married and moved into the new house "Fairhome", which had been built for him.

Very soon after this there arose very strained relations between Edwin and John Thomas. John Thomas was the elder by at least ten years and Edwin had had the chief management of the accounts and sales department but he had a very strong wish to be more associated with the manufacturing side, in fact he thought he was a born manufacturer, but his brother John did not agree and therefore the problem arose that if the two brothers could not agree, one of them must go, and my brother Roland Green had to face the problem as to which of the two brothers he would support because it was a case of two to one. Roland Green felt that Edwin of the two was probably the man of greater ability but not so trustworthy as John and, finally, when it came to the point, he decided to support John, and therefore Edwin was bought out. All this, of course, required a lot of negotiations and the records of Godden, Holme & Ward would tell us more about it than I can tell. Anyway, the Partnership having been dissolved, it was decided that the business should be turned into a private Limited Company, and here I think my record must end.*

★ (*Note by J.B.Sedgwick*. Mr Roland Green told me that this friction between the two brothers had gone on for years. Mr William Thomas, the father, thought they might get on better together if they lived next door to each other and he built Brook House for Mr John Thomas and the "Chestnuts" for Mr Edwin Thomas, and to help them to get on well there was no fence between the two properties!!

Mr Roland Green also told me that towards the end things got very strained, so much so that two signatures were required for cheques. This led to complications and on at least one occasion Mr Roland Green was pursued to the river on his way to Henley Regatta, to sign the wages cheque.)

J.B. Sedgwick
(*1885–1944*)

PERSONAL RECOLLECTIONS OF THE BUSINESS FROM 1901 TO 1904

During the period I was apprenticed at the mill, its reputation for being an up-to-date mill was probably at its height and there was a constant stream of papermakers visiting it, among others, Mr Cornett of Ford Works (a very great personal friend of Mr Roland Green), Mr Jardine of Esk Mill and Mr Peter Dixon of Oughtibridge.

While I was there, however, not very much expenditure was incurred on new plant and from this date the state of the mill began to decline.

Items which occur to me were the Adeline Steam Engine and the Fullner Rotary Filter. Superheated steam was applied to the boilers for the first time and, as a consequence, there was a fire in the Atalanta House, owing to the oil absorbed in the wooden floor catching alight. I think a new Web Stock Room (the one next the Calander House) was built during this period. Also two new beaters were added in the Clay Stores. These were not very successful as the rise in to the roll was made too great therefore circulation was bad and they were scrapped in the reconstruction after the war.

This was, however, the time when the real development began in Stock Papers. The bank and bond series at about $3\frac{1}{2}d$ was started with five or six colours only. The Art Covers at about $3\frac{1}{2}d$ which were almost the first British Series to be produced, and the Azure Laid at about $2\frac{7}{8}d$. Tinted Writings, Pamphlets and 424 Printings sold at $3d$ per lb. Cream Laids at $2\frac{1}{8}d$ (to make).

The *Combination Pattern Book* was produced, I should think the first of its kind, expensive and rather crude but an effective advertisement, as no one else had done anything else like it. Also a show card advertising special sizes was got out. In general I should say they were making the first attempts among British Papermakers at publicity.

At that time all stock papers were made on No. 1 machine and No. 2 machine made Cream Laids, Posters and other White Make orders. I only recall one occasion on which colours were made on No. 2 machine and that was when the Imperial Tobacco Co. was formed and we made the application form insets in two colours (I think Rose and Buff 288). This had to be delivered in a great hurry and both machines were put on it, within three or four hours of receipt of the order. In addition the whole of the available stock was used and I think there were some six or seven makings in the deliveries for each colour, which speaks well for the colour matching.

In those days we made a large tonnage of Poster Papers for R. Herring, Cream Laids especially for Edwards, Dunlop and Dickinsons and according to my memory the *Telegraph* paper trade was much bigger than it is today. The Cream Laids were never good and generally dirty and after my time were gradually eliminated in favour of more profitable makes.

The mill was, of course, lit by gas and we made our own. It was then the usual practice on the paper machines to light it at the calanders with a spark from one's fingers by standing on some very dry paper and allowing one's hand to be close to the calandered web passing along the machine above one.

Amid great excitement electric light was put in the offices but had not been extended to the mill. Incidentally it frequently went out for some reason or other.

The buildings were generally much as they were in 1918 except that the Welfare Room was not yet built.

The mill was started at midnight on Sunday and, of course, twelve hour shifts were worked, shutting as at present at about 6 p.m. on Saturdays.

There was an old speaking tube from the office to the Salle which, not unnaturally, caused a fair amount of friction due to practical jokes.

The practice of handling all orders was very cumbersome and laborious and the General Office in particular rarely finished before 6.30 p.m. Stocktaking was a most lengthy business, in which the Directors took part, especially Mr Roland Green, and there was very little competition to be in his stocktaking gang.

The Esparto Boilers were emptied by hand and it was not a very pleasant task to be in forking out the hot grass on to a travelling band.

I remember getting into great trouble once when on the Esparto Boilers. The Foreman (W. Glisbey) was searching for me to do some unpleasant job when I got word of it. I nipped out of the top of the boilers, slid down the rope hanging from the little hand crane then used to haul up Esparto bands, and nearly landed on Mr Green's head, as he happened to be passing underneath. I got well and truly ticked off, as he was annoyed at nearly getting a knock on the head and at the danger.

One night we had the paper on fire on No. 2, burning as it was made. This was due to the fact that the calanders had been still for some time and oil had got into the joints. On starting up, turpentine was thrown into the joints to wash out the oil and the friction caused this to vaporise and take fire from the gas jets. Not unnaturally the paper was dirty for two or three days and the subsequent enquiry was not pleasant for those concerned.

PERSONALITIES

Mr Roland Green. He was of course the dominant personality. He started sharp at 9 a.m. and worked until 5.30 or later and he saw that everyone else did his bit too. He always left the impression in my mind that he knew he could do any man's job better than the man himself and in most cases he could. Nothing but the best was good enough, and often even that was not. Intensely just, if a bit hard, he had everyone's respect, but to be on the carpet for a mistake was not pleasant. He had a habit of saying "What is the good of you if you make a mistake like that?" which was rather unanswerable!!

On Saturday mornings at about 10.30 he used to go off on his bicycle to visit any of the workpeople who were ill and see that they had all they wanted and he really did look after them, but he got back in time to have the weekly strafe over deep colours that were always made on Saturday mornings. I do not remember if the Foreman, W. Glisbey, was really a good man on colours, probably not, but John Puddifoot, the best beaterman, certainly was. As long as you were not in it, it was as good as a play to watch those two, R.G. and J.P., when they disagreed as to what was necessary to get the colour right, but it was a bit tiring if you were in it as it meant a lot of running up and down the beaterhouse stairs. Blackley Blue and Nigrosine were the two favourite colours and mixing them, especially if Ochre were used as well, was too horrible for words, owing to the smell—personally it really made me ill. The beauty of the whole thing was that it was an even chance whether Mr Green or John Puddifoot was right and neither would give way, except that in the end, of course, R.G. had the casting vote.

Every letter leaving the mill had to be initialled by a director, generally Mr Roland Green. This was before the days of typewriters.

All the letters were opened in solemn conclave at 9 o'clock each morning by the Directors and all letters received were entered in a log (in my time by one of the Directors) and as each letter was replied to it was ticked off with the date of the reply, and woe betide anyone who neglected to answer a letter by return.

Personally, I consider Mr Green's only real fault was that he could not delegate work and, as a consequence, his subordinates in general were third rate machines who could not and were not allowed to think for themselves.

Mr John Thomas. To me he was practically only a name. He rarely came into the mill, about once a week I should say, and then he took a stroll round, peering over the top of his glasses. He put in a certain amount of time at the office and spent a good deal of time in London, but I fancy at that time he was more interested in his political and other activities. He was always well turned out in a sober sort of way, in contrast to Mr Roland Green. While I was at the mill, the present railing along Brook Bank was put up and it is related that Mr Reeves, the farmer, congratulated Mr Thomas on having it erected before his annual dinner party—Mr Thomas was a staunch teetotaller!!

Mr W.A. Kershaw. Mr Kershaw gave me the impression of being the smartest turned out. He was mainly interested in the engineering side of the mill and seemed terrified when, in Mr Green's absence, he was in charge of the mill and especially the Make. You see there was only one way of arranging the Make, and that was Mr Green's own way and no one else knew it, and if a change had to be introduced in a hurry it was 100 to 1 that neither Mr Kershaw nor anyone else would do it in the right way to meet Mr Green's approval on his return.

Mr Kershaw was a reserved and shy man who had had great troubles and was extremely difficult to get to know. Personally, it was not until later years, during the last six or nine months of his life, that we really understood one another and then one realised how charming he was under the surface. I spent many delightful hours with him at tea at his club and on a business trip to Norwich—and what a job I had to persuade him to travel first class.

R. Loosemore (Chief Clerk). He was an autocrat in the office who waged perpetual war with the Order Office staff (W.B. Clifford in charge). Judged by present-day standards he would be considered a second-rate man but he ruled the office with a rod of iron and the tales he could tell of his experiences took some believing. Having been brought up in the railway, what he did not know about railway matters was not knowledge, at all events in his own opinion but as a matter of fact he was very sound on this subject. Under him, however, the balancing of the books was a matter which lasted months sometimes.

W.B. Clifford (Order Dept). He was a man who knew our papers and trade inside and out, but he had a conscientious objection to starting the actual work of the day until about 2.30 p.m. such as sampling and letter writing. As a result everything was always late, which was a bit trying to everyone's temper, especially if Mr Green did not approve of a letter at 5.15 p.m. when he had to countersign it.

I do not think I ever saw Clifford in a complete suit but by ringing the changes in trousers, waistcoat and jacket he was rarely, if ever, dressed alike.

P. Cooke. He was put in charge of the orders during my apprenticeship in place of a Mr Macfarlane, who is now a paper agent. Macfarlane was a good man but to my mind Cooke was the first really good man taken into the business. He came from Edwards

169

Dunlop and died as a prisoner of war in Germany. Latterly, before the war, he was given a much freer run and did very good work in modernising the practice as regards handling of orders etc. The present Card System was introduced by him after a visit to me at Bristol, where I had started it—where I got the idea from I have forgotten.

H. Glisbey, the mill foreman. He was a character, a good driving force but unfortunately not too steady and a wangler who was ultimately found out and discharged. There is no doubt that for many years he worked very hard for the firm but to my mind Mr Roland Green was not so blind to his faults as many people imagined, but kept him on for his good qualities, overlooking his bad ones as long as possible. Even in my time it was common knowledge that if a bad lot of paper was made it was sometimes re-made in a night subsequently and not rebooked.

He was the first person in the district whom I knew to have a motor bicycle. You put a sixpence in a sort of slot to make the electrical contact to allow it to run. He let me have a trip on it.

N. Harris, Chief Engineer. Harris suffered from angina pectoris and as a consequence was more than a little difficult especially when, as was frequently the case, he was in pain. He was a good man in his way but there were far too many breakdowns in the mill and he never did a repair thoroughly, which frequently led to further breakdowns. A keen amateur photographer, some of his photographs were I think reproduced in the *Combination Pattern Book*, for instance one of Wooburn Church.

Sam Wheeler, foreman of the Cutting House. He was an outstanding character. He had lost an arm and had a hook which he wielded with great vigour to keep order in the Cutting House, and I might say it hurt when it caught anyone on the head. His trouble was that he cut what he liked and as a result the day came when Mr Green discovered that there were some thousands of reams cut of Opal Green and Pale Violet 288 (the two worst sellers) in stock and so Wheeler was pensioned off. Had he used his brain half as much as he did his hook, he would have gone on much longer.

John Puddifoot, the Beaterman, was one of the finest and most likeable men in the mill and it is not too much to say that Thomas & Green's reputation for colour matching rests between him and Mr Roland Green. I worked under John Puddifoot for a long time and he and his son, George (our present mill foreman) taught me all I know about colour and beating. Later John Puddifoot was made under-foreman and subsequently retired on a pension. His loss was very much felt until his son George Puddifoot, who in the meantime had been at Peebles of Rishton, re-joined us and was subsequently promoted to mill foreman, which position he fills extremely satisfactorily today.

Joe Hare was a fine machineman of the old fashioned sort. He knew his job absolutely and ran No. 2. I should say he and John Puddifoot were the only two who really got under Mr Roland Green's guard and more or less stood up to him and to a certain extent joked with him.

Reuben Ludgate, machineman on No. 1 till about a year ago. A first rate machineman, intensely keen on his work, so much so that if things went wrong he almost made himself ill. He had a very cheery disposition and with only about two teeth in his head, he had a smile for everyone and a volume of amiable abuse. He was a great contrast to—

J. Wheeler, also a machineman on No. 1, probably actually the best machineman of all, but he was dour to the last degree and most difficult to get on with—but he certainly could make paper. I understand sometimes he would hardly talk to his mates for weeks on end.

Hobbs, who ran the Rotary Ovens—a most likeable little man, then very old with a goatee beard, who did a very trying job well and served the Company faithfully for many years. A favourite with Mr Roland Green, if he had any.

Tommy Wheeler, a fitter. A very capable and first class man who worked for us until two or three years ago, when he had to give up owing to cataract. He was one of those men who had been with the firm for so long that he was a reference book of every Chief Engineer as to the whereabouts of pipes etc. long forgotten. His mantle has fallen on—

Fred Bincham, who still works with us and is also a first class fitter whom everyone likes and has a joke for. I have pulled his leg for many years and hope to continue to do so for a long time to come.

Reprint from
THE BRITISH PRINTER
JULY 1905

PAPER MANUFACTURE OF TODAY
Thomas & Green, Ltd

As opposed to the usual run of manufacturing premises, the paper mill is, as a rule, situated not merely quite away from the larger centres of population, but possesses country surroundings calculated to arouse the wild envy of those not so fortunately placed in respect to open space, green fields, fresh air, and unlimited light. The Soho Mills, at Wooburn, Bucks, where Thomas & Green, Ltd, produce the papers they have earned such a reputation for, form no exception to this rule in respect to situation. In the heart of agricultural Buckinghamshire—a land of undulating pasture, many-acred farmsteads, and hawthorn-bordered lanes—the mills adjoin a tiny village nestling in a bend of the road leading to that Mecca of all business, the metropolis.

The first intimation of the presence of the paper mills is the rapidly flowing stream of dull water following the course of the road for some distance, and next the view of reservoirs and filter beds on the upper side of the grouped buildings. The hum of the machinery is by no means out of harmony with the surroundings, and one enters the premises with the feeling that the firm in question possesses that essential for paper manufacture, an ample supply of water, and that operations are conducted on a large scale.

Entry down the yard shews a series of detached irregular buildings ranging all the way from a single-storey office to the four-floored mills. The steel rails down the yard shew that it is itself practically a railway siding, a most convenient arrangement, and it is seen later on that a very considerable area is covered by the buildings themselves and the various equipments for supplying water, steam, heat, light, and so on.

Calling at the busy counting-house, and explaining that some little reference to the home of "288 mill," "Papers cut to any size," and one or two other little specialties might interest readers, Mr Roland Greene readily took us in tow for a look round.

A most profitable journey resulted, albeit the "look round" took the form of a closely detailed examination into the workings and methods of a truly up-to-date manufactory.

We have no intention, however, of inflicting a course of technicalities referring to the industry upon our readers, but rather an outline of the process of paper-making as carried on to-day, in the form of a brief reference to the work of the mill in general, dwelling upon certain directions more particularly interesting to printers.

Art cover papers seemed to be much in evidence, and, remembering the foreign competition in this class of paper, the activity thus displayed and the excellent results achieved pleased us at the very outset. But cover papers form a mere fraction of the mills' output, tinted and coloured writings, printings, machine-finished and super-calendered, azure laid account book, esparto papers, laid and wove writings, all being represented in the somewhat unusual range of supply the Soho factory is occupied with. There are two mills, denoted in the trade by the cryptic numbers "288" and "424."

Instead of entering into detail as regards the closely corrected departments, it will be more to our purpose to briefly describe the regular order of the processes involved, and thus afford some notion of how paper is made.

ESPARTO

Crossing to a high shed detached from other buildings, a whiff as of dry grass introduces us to the great stores of esparto. Besides esparto grass, chemical wood pulp, rags and kindred materials are used, according to the grade of paper, and stocks of these are seen later on.

The esparto grass plant grows wild on the sandy wastes along the north coast of Africa and in the south of Spain. The latter is the finest and smallest grass, and makes the best paper, but its price is much higher than the African, and it is therefore used only for the finest papers. The African grass is collected by Arabs, who load it in huge nets on the backs of camels, and in this manner it is brought to the coast, where the shippers sort the grass into grades and press pack it into bales in order to take up less room in the ship's hold. Boats varying from 500 to 1,500 tons bring it over to London. The supply for Thomas & Green is unloaded into barges and floated up the Thames to the G.W.R. Co.'s wharf, from whence a special train each day runs to Thomas & Green's siding at their works until the ship is cleared. On arrival at the mills, the grass is unloaded and stored in large sheds until needed.

As will be inferred, very considerable quantities of this grass are consumed—4,000–4,500 tons annually—besides from 800–1,000 tons of chemical wood pulp, rags, etc.

DUSTING

When required, the iron hoops around the bales are cut and the grass forked into a willow or duster revolving at a high speed. By this means, any particles of the Arabian desert still clinging to the grass—

and there is usually a large amount of dust—are shaken out, sucked away by the action of a fan and deposited in a settling chamber. The clean grass falls on to an elevator which carries it right out of the storage buildings, across the road, up to the top of the next building, and thence into one or other of the esparto boilers.

BOILERS

These boilers are stationary, and hold three tons of grass each. When full, the manholes are closed, and a standard strong solution of caustic soda run in, steam turned on and this boiling process continued for four or five hours. The liquor is made to spray over the top of the grass, soak down through it, and round again—all in constant circulation. This boiling dissolves the siliceous and resinous gummy matters in the esparto and carries them away in solution. When the boiling is completed, the liquor is run away to the evaporators, and the grass washed with several washings of hot water circulated over it as before, with the intention of extracting any remaining chemical liquors. The grass is then emptied into a conveyor, which carries it into the disintegrating machines. When it comes out of these boilers, it is, as one might expect, quite soft, having lost all the elements which in the raw material cemented the skeleton of the plant together. That skeleton, or "cellulose"—to use its correct title—alone remains, and this is what the paper-maker requires as the base of his paper.

It will be seen that a very considerable amount of cost and handling, besides an involved mechanical-chemical process, need to be undergone before the material reaches even the very first stage in the necessary preparation.

BREAKING

The disintegrating machine—the "Cornett" breaker—dashes these fibres about in water and roughly separates them into pulp without any cutting or grinding action of the cellulose. After more washing in clean water, and the extraction of dirty water through a very fine wire cloth, the pulp passes over a series of sand traps, to extract by settlement any remaining particles of sand, into the strainers; these catch any particles of improperly boiled grass, roots, seeds, etc., that have not been reduced by the boiling, and which would inevitably give trouble later on, such as in the form of specks in the paper, if allowed to pass.

BLEACHING

More washing ensues, and the pulp is then pumped into the potching machines or bleaching engines, in which it is kept circulating, a standard solution of chloride of lime being run in, bleaching the fibres from a greenish-brown colour to a white. About 350 tons of bleaching powder are used every year for this purpose.

PRESS PÂTE

From here it is run into steeping-chests and kept agitated until pumped up to the next machine, the press pâte. In this machine it flows continuously on to an endless coarse wire cloth, fine enough to retain the fibres on the surface and allow the surplus water to run through. The wire carries it over a vacuum box, which sucks out more water, and through a pair of "couch" rolls, which give it a further squeeze and deliver it off the wire in a rough blanket form, convenient for storing till required at the beaters.

It is in this department that we first came across the pamphlet cover paper, and curiously enough it was a pile of blue jeans which drew attention. The admixture of the blue cloth into the ordinary pulp—half rag, the rest esparto and wood—furnishes the mottled surface paper, and in the same way other colours are added to the white. The mixture is made mechanically by the pulp being run into huge automatically-stirred tanks, and thence pumped on to wooden chutes to be sent to the press pâte.

The array of colour dye tubs formed quite a contrast to the elsewhere prevalent white and grey tones of the pulp, paper and appliances. Deep reds, blues and strong yellows seemed much in evidence.

TESTING

At this stage we found that the opportunity was taken to test all stuff thus made, white and coloured alike, and the examination brought to light some of the many difficulties met with in preparing paper pulp. These we need not particularise; but *even* the paper-maker has troubles of his own.

In this department we witnessed a method of testing. This is nothing less than the old hand-made process. An oblong tray with fine wire mesh base and raised sides is dipped into the prepared pulp, taking up a light layer. A dexterous shaking motion is applied, with the effect of smoothing the surface; water oozes through the sievelike base, and the embryo sheet is smartly turned out on to a piece of felt slightly larger in size. This is then placed between other felts, and the pile subjected to pressure in an ordinary hand screw press. Whilst the method answers perfectly as a test at this stage, it is also a reminder of the great disparity in the rate of output between the real hand-mades and machine-mades.

Hard by we see the operation of mixing, or, as it is known technically,

BEATING

In these machines the different ingredients are mixed in their proper proportion and beaten to make the paper required. Each machine has a roll fitted with a great number of extremely hard bronze knives. It revolves at a high speed, and can be raised or lowered by hand until the knives come into contact with a number of stationary knives in a box underneath, on the expert manipulation of which so much depends, the fibres being drawn out, cut and pulped to desired requirements. Here also the size is put in to prevent the sheet being nothing more than blotting paper, and the matching and colouring to shade is effected. When ready, the valve is drawn in the bottom of the engine, more water let in, and the pulp flows down through pipes to the storage chests for the paper machine, where it is again kept in motion.

THE PAPER MACHINE

So far we have seen the pulp prepared ready for the actual turning into the more solid form we know as paper. Moving on to the machine-rooms, we find two of the long and complicated machines, Nos. 288 and 424 respectively—each a veritable machine-room in itself—upon which paper is made.

From the storage chests the pulp is pumped to a service chest having an overflow so that it keeps the same steady flow to the machine through a cock near the bottom. The regulation of this cock and the speed of the machine give the machineman control of the thickness or weight of the sheet he needs. It passes through a very fine set of strainers, to keep back any little strings in the stuff, and flows on to a very fine mesh endless wire cloth, travelling forward on small rolls which tend to draw the water out of the pulp as it is carried along. There are also vacuum boxes further on which suck out more water, and it is here the dandy roll is run on the top of the pulp.

WATER-MARKING

There is a roll made of wire on a frame and covered by either woven wire cloth, which makes a wove paper, or straight wires laid flat along the roll and sewn to the strengthening discs to hold it, which makes the "laid paper" marks in a laid paper, and on these coverings the watermark is sewn if one is needed, impressing a rather thinner place in the pulp, which can be seen when the sheet is held to the light.

DRYING

The pulp in the form of a sheet then passes through a set of "couch" rollers, covered with woollen felt, which squeeze out more water and consolidate the sheet so that it is able to travel almost by itself to the press rolls with felt just to help it. It passes through two sets of these, and is then carried round a great number of iron cylinders heated with steam and covered with endless felts, all revolving at the same speed, which dry the paper passing over them.

MACHINE CALENDERING AND REELING

It is then passed through several stacks of hard chilled-iron rolls, so hard that a file will not mark them, and revolving one above the other with a tremendous pressure on them, which imparts the finish required, and the sheet is then rolled on a wooden or iron roller until it becomes a large reel of paper, many miles long. Each machine is driven by two steam engines.

CUTTING AND SLITTING

The reels are put on trolleys and taken to the cutting or slitting machines, where the paper is cut into sheets or rolled into narrow reels as wanted.

There are various classes of machines—duplex cutters and single cutters—and with the many attendants necessitated these make up quite a busy scene.

SUPER CALENDERING

Before being cut it is passed through super calendering machines, consisting of lofty tiers of smooth-surfaced hydraulic pressed cotton bowls and chilled-iron rolls between, if a super-calendered surface is required. In these machines the paper passes over the top roll down between each nip of the huge rolls, each of which weighs several tons, having an enormous pressure on the top, and the surface is rolled by the pressure.

FINISHING

From here the paper passes to the finishing house, where it is counted out into reams, folded, and loaded into the railway trucks, which come right into the building.

In the foreman's office alongside we find that tests for matching colours are made by the aid of magnesium light, as the purest for ensuring true colour tones. The Mullen Testing Appliance, for testing the breaking strength of paper, was also noticeable.

REEL STOCK

Messrs. Thomas & Green make a speciality of keeping a tremendous stock of paper on the reel, room after room of it, so that they can promptly supply any size the printer wants in any of their stock lines bearing the 288 mill numbers and in a few of the 424 papers as advertised.

In these days of "send per return" enormous stocks must be maintained, and the firm under notice has entered upon this phase of business most thoroughly. The web stockrooms, four in number, are fitted with lofty substantial-looking racks—they need to be strongly built to hold row after row of the heavy reels of paper—and by means of a travelling crane the reels are readily moved to and fro.

This naturally led to the subject of cutting to any size, specialised by Thomas & Green for some time. We found that they will practically cut any size from the roll, and, even further, now meet the requirements of the printer by breaking reams if desired.

Besides a very considerable ream stock, the firm always keep in stock about 275 tons in the web, consisting of, for instance, some 180 tons in 19 colours of 288 Tinted Writings, 47 tons in 15 colours of 288 Art Covers, 8 tons in 11 colours of 424 Covers, and from 2 to 10 tons each of Silurian Laid Writings, Azure Laid Account Book Papers, Cream Wove Superfine Writings, Cream Laid Superfine Writings, Cream Wove Banks, Yellow Wove Banks, and Tinted.

PAPER STORES

The stores for regular stock are well arranged and warmed throughout in winter, whilst the arrangements for the despatch of the paper are such as to facilitate the promptest delivery that can be managed. Besides the London trucks, every day at least one special covered wagon runs out of the siding to Reading for West of England traffic and to Basingstoke for all the South Coast towns; another runs to Oxford, Birmingham and Wolverhampton, carrying the Midland and North of England, Scottish and Irish goods direct, other special trucks being made up as required by the orders in hand.

NOTE CUTTING

Other paper is cut, folded and trimmed into notepaper by ingenious special machines which ensure absolute squareness. Girls packet it into 5-quire or 1-lb packets, ready for the wholesale customer.

MAIN STEAM ENGINES

There are three main engines, the "Adeline," "Atalanta," and "Lorna," the former a fine compound tandem condensing engine, with Corliss valves, by J. & E. Wood, of Bolton, and has automatic cut-off from the governor, shutting down automatically by throwing out the catches, which admit the steam, in case of accident. This ensures control in case of breakage of any part, and obviates danger of racing away and breaking everything else, as engines may do when something goes wrong. The flywheel, 16-feet in diameter, carries ropes for transmitting the power to the mill and to a 100-h.p. dynamo which produces the electric light and drives about eight electric motors about the works. Of the other two engines, one is belt driven and the other direct on to the shaft.

An enormous amount of steam is required during the process of paper manufacture, and this explains the large plant here busily occupied. In the earlier stages of preparation the material is "cooked" by steam, and after screening it is passed into beaters, where steam is again employed. Steam also is drawn upon to assist the flow of pulp as it enters upon the machine proper, and is used to maintain drying cylinders at a proper degree of heat. And these, of course, quite apart from driving, heating, boiling and other purposes.

STEAM BOILERS

The battery of steam boilers is a good one, and consumes some 200 tons of coal every week. The steam is all heated, or "superheated" as it is called, up to a temperature of some 500 to 600° Fah., after it comes from these boilers, so as to prevent condensation in the pipes. The water used in the boilers is all softened before use, and there are four feed-water economisers. The chimney draught, i.e., the draught created by the chimney, although 160-ft high, being insufficient, there is a large fan, 10-ft in diameter, at the base, driven by a high-speed enclosed engine with four cylinders, capable of 50-h.p., which sucks the draught through the flues and draws the fires.

An extensive plant, housed in specially erected buildings, is found to be occupied entirely with soda recovery. Soda is a chief agent in the preparation of materials forming the constituents of paper, and an enormous amount is in use at one stage or other in paper mills. Thus it comes about that modern chemical research has been drawn upon to enable this constant and high source of expense to be minimised. The method adopted is that of using the soda in regard to its active principle over and over again, and thus we found a department apparently less to do with making paper than anything else in the world, and certainly more akin to the average manufacturing chemist's fearful and wonderful plant as it strikes the on-looker.

179

Hence the soda-charged liquid undergoes filtering, concentrating and "cooking" in a long row of furnaces, which recover the unspent soda, and being further prepared by means of a long, involved chemical-mechanical method, certainly neither picturesque nor clean, but, as a hard matter of fact, resulting in a saving of 40% on the soda bill under other conditions.

EVAPORATORS

The liquors used for boiling are pumped over to tanks in the alkali works, and from there are pumped through a quadruple effect Yaryan-Chapman Evaporating Machine. This machine evaporates the liquors in the first chamber; with steam in the shell and the liquor in a great number of horizontal pipes half-full, the steam given off passes over to form the heating agent in the second chamber or "effect," as it is called, and so on through the four effects. A vacuum pump keeps a good vacuum over the liquor in the latter effects, so that as the temperature falls below the atmospheric boiling point it still keeps boiling and getting rid of the water, and so continuing to concentrate, because liquids boil at lower temperatures in a vacuum than they do in the open air. In this way every pound of coal evaporates four or five times as much water as it would by simply boiling in an open vessel with direct fire.

OVENS

The liquor then passes to long flat shallow ovens with a fire at the end, which passes over it and evaporates the last remaining water, and when this is effected the resinous matters in the liquor catch fire and themselves burn. In this flaming state it is raked out into barrows and shot in heaps to burn itself out; the heat generated melts the soda, which runs out in the form of a molten lava, cools and sets hard as a rock in a solid mass. These masses are broken up when cold with steel wedges and sledge hammer, redissolved into soda liquors, and by a chemical process converted to caustic soda solutions, strained and pumped over to boil more esparto, and so on ad infinitum, less the loss of soda each boil.

MECHANICS' SHOP

The repairs of the machinery necessitate a large mechanics' shop fitted with lathes, boring machines, shaping machines, screwing machines, planing machines, hacksaw machines, two forges, steam hammer, fitting benches, circular saws, drawing offices, carpenters' and pattern makers' shop, and brass foundry—all in the hands of an efficient staff.

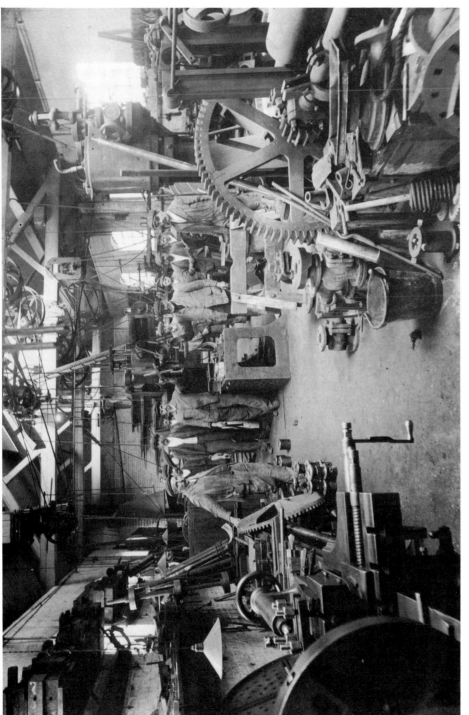

Engineers shop at Thomas & Green in 1912

Half Stuff House with Esparto Pulp Brakers and Washers at Thomas & Green in 1912

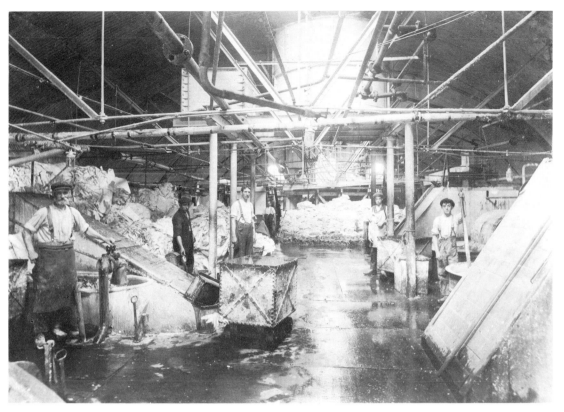

Beater Room at Thomas & Green in 1912

Boiler House at Thomas & Green in 1912

Calendering and Slitting room at Thomas & Green in 1912

Cutting House at Thomas & Green in 1912

Finishing Dept at Thomas & Green in 1912

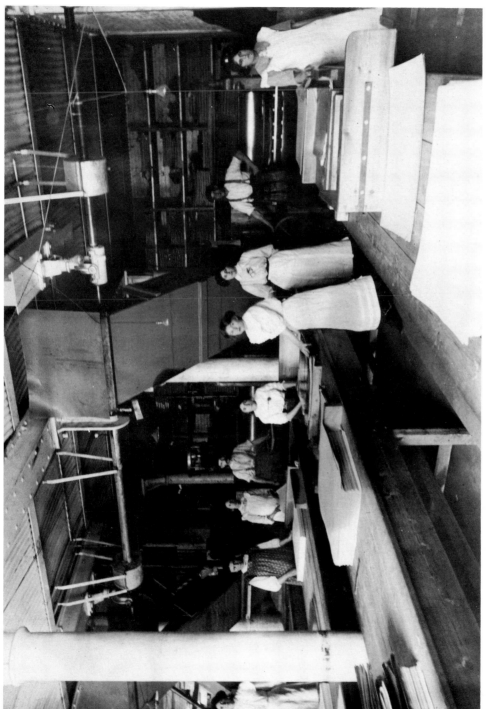

Plate Glazing and Linen-facing Dept at Thomas & Green in 1912

Salle at Thomas & Green in 1912

Thomas & Green's own Esparto Company "SATA" loading bales of Grass in North Africa in the 1920s

LIGHTING

These shops are driven by two electric motors and gas engine, with steam engine in reserve. The firm have for years made their lighting gas, and have a plant of ten retorts and gasholder; but this, however, is fast being superseded by the electric light.

SIDINGS

The railway sidings run all over the works, the unloading of the chemicals and heavy goods being done direct from the railway trucks by a very ingenious friction crane.

FIRE BRIGADE

Thomas & Green have to work, as in all paper mills, day and night, and they have a fire brigade in each shift, which has regular drills. There is a manual fire engine on wheels and a stationary steam fire pump, with hydrants underground all round the mill and in the main buildings, always ready with steam on.

WAREHOUSE

Following into the general warehouse, this is seen to be fitted with miles of racks and storage accommodation for cut paper, whilst the guillotines and folder point to other demands often required at the hands of the paper-maker. The commodious packing-room—and packing is a very serious business at a paper mill—is next visited, and we are "through." The firm have a London office at 196 Upper Thames Street, E.C., three floors fitted with electric lift, where a considerable stock of paper is also kept.

THE FIRM

Whilst chatting over samples of paper on the return to the office, we learn incidentally that the business was started in 1860 by Mr Thomas, sen., conjointly with Mr John Barcham Green and Mr Stephens, of Maidstone, under the style of Thomas, Stephens & Green. In 1875 Mr Thomas died, and in 1881 the partnership deed expired, Mr Stephens retired, the business being carried on by the founder's two sons, Mr John Thomas and Mr Edwin Thomas, and Mr Roland Green, who took his father's place. About 1889 Mr Edwin Thomas retired, but the firm continued as Thomas & Green until it was incorporated as a limited company in March, 1890. Our illustrations include portraits of Mr John Thomas and Mr Roland Green, the managing directors.

ADVERTISING

Amongst paper-makers, Thomas & Green, Ltd, have become well known through the skilful and persistent advertisement of a good article. We have carefully examined a batch of advt. matter representing circulars, booklets, and so on, prepared for the prospective customer, and these are well worth mention alike as business-bringers and as indicative of the class of material made and sold.

A combination colour pattern book is $7 \times 5\frac{1}{2}$ in, oblong, stiff boards, and presents a series of variously-coloured papers. One page of each bears half-tone subject in two printings, six to the page, all different colour sets, and thus, quite apart from the catalogue value, an exceedingly useful lesson in colour combination is provided. Equipped with this book the selection of suitable colours for working on tinted writing and coloured pamphlet covers is made very easy.

Pamphlet cover pattern books are numerous. They vary in size from the 11×9 to the 6×4 folder. The larger shews 15 colours in stepwise succession, the size allowing of the specimens being handled and examined. Another, $9 \times 5\frac{1}{2}$ in, is silk cord tied, with cover design in white, insides shewing half-tone cuts and type lines on plate-rolled cover paper in a range of 11 tints.

Even more noticeable is the 13×10 in monthly tear-off calendar, shewing as many samples of colours—an excellent combination advt. and specimen cover.

Odd sheets, such as the insets for B.P., shew figure design in colours, forming an attractive announcement.

Then come sample sheets without end, for cream wove, yellow wove, writings, plate-rolled and ledger, and so on in great variety.

The equivalent weight card, and the many references to "Kept in the web" and "Any size cut" are, of course, very noticeable.

We are said to be nothing if not practical, and thus naturally turn up the latest price lists. The figures shew that prices are right and terms eminently reasonable.

IN SHORT

We find the firm in every way progressive, alike in business policy, advertising and kindred methods of reaching the trade, whilst most admirably equipped in truly modern fashion in respect to premises and plant; as the result of this, turning out a thoroughly reliable set of goods at a fair price. That they have deserved their success is as evident as the bright prospect assuredly before a firm of such enterprise.

A couple of sample sheets of paper placed before us suggest some interesting comparisons. The one was made in 1860, at $6d$ per lb, the other made in 1905, at $2\frac{1}{4}d$. The latter, at little over one-third the price, is immeasurably the superior of the older paper in quality, colour, hardness and finish. All this points on the one hand to a constantly increasing standard of production, and on the other to a noteworthy decrease in price. It is a practical illustration of the hard and continual fight paper-makers have had during the past half-century to make ends meet on a steadily falling market.

Of course, the consumer benefits vastly by this condition of affairs, for the cheap books and periodical literature to-day would be impossible with paper of such quality and price as that made in 1860 at 6d.

In this connection it is further interesting to learn that in 1873 the mill was making 30 tons per week, the whole of the beating being done by two 50-h.p. engines, and the price was about $4\frac{3}{4}d$ per lb. The whole stock of paper at that date was probably considerably under 50 tons; it is now well over 550 tons in all. The power absorbed by the beating alone, with all the improvements made, is to-day about 450-h.p. These figures in themselves form a record of change and progress, and further point to the continual growth of a veritably "live" manufacturing concern.

DARD HUNTER

It is worthy of note that in 1909 Thomas & Green processed a shipment of bamboo through its esparto boilers. It was, in fact, the first time bamboo had been used as a raw material for paper making and the only trace now remaining is a booklet by R. W. Sindall describing the process, on paper made from bamboo at Thomas & Green, Soho Mill recorded by Dard Hunter in *Paper Making—The History and Technique of an Ancient Craft*, as follows:

1875
During this year there appeared a pamphlet entitled *Bamboo, as a Papermaking Material*, by Thomas Routledge. This booklet of 40 pages is printed on paper made from bamboo, probably the first use of this material in the Occident for papermaking. In 1876 at Arnhem a book under the title *Bamboe em Ampas als Grondstoffen voor Papierbereiding* was also printed on paper manufactured from bamboo. Routledge states that the rapidity of the growth of bamboo is unequalled and says in his pamphlet "... at Gehzireh, the gardens of the Khedive of Egypt in Cairo it has grown nine inches in a single night and at Syon House, the Duke of Northumberland's, stems of Bambusa gigantea have attained a height of 60 feet in twelve weeks; at Chatsworth, the Duke of Devonshire's, the variety of Bambusa vulgaris reached a height of 40 feet in forty days". In 1908 the government of Burma sent eight or nine tons of selected bamboo to England, where it was made into paper by Thomas and Green, Soho Mills, Wooburn Green, Bucks. In 1908, R. W. Sindall issued his treatise, Bamboo for Papermaking, a booklet of 60 pages on paper made from bamboo by Thomas and Green Limited.

Reprint from

SOHO NEWS

Works Publication of Thomas & Green Ltd. Vol. 1 No 3
1919

EDITORIAL

We are again sincerely grateful to the friends who have rallied round us and shown their interest in the "Soho News" by their liberal and interesting contributions.

We should however like to see more departmental news. The value and quality of the product of our Mill so very much depends on each stage of the process being carried out properly and in conjunction with the next, that an interchange of views and criticisms would be of great interest to the workers as a whole.

We should also be glad to receive letters or criticisms upon the articles which appear in our news. Events move so rapidly and social ideas and conditions alter to quickly that we are afraid no good purpose would be served by commenting upon them. We would however, remind our readers that whatever is said or done, cannot be unsaid or undone, it behoves us in the momentous times in which we are living to think, and think seriously and carefully before taking any particular line of action. So many desire to reach a solution of social or national difficulties by rushing into a policy upon which under more thoughtful consideration they would not have entered. The social outlook of this country is changing and changing quickly and some of the changes so hastily conceived will require considerable re-adjustment. We are not going to have the millennium in this country under the present agitation for higher wages and less output. Let us get the high wages if we can, but let's have high production with it, so that we don't have to pay 40/- for a pair of boots and £5 to £7 for a suit of clothes. We make no apology for borrowing the following article from the journal of a trade run by masters and men under a Whitley Council:—

CAPITALISM

If it can be proved that the Capitalist is the enemy of Labour, let us destroy Capitalism. If it can be shown that High Production means misery for the worker, let us forbid High Production. No one will pretend that there are not grave evils and gross injustices in our present

185

capitalist system, or that production is possible without labour and pain. Only before destroying these things let us make sure that we are not repeating the old error and throwing away, under the delusive charm of peace and security, the very arms through which alone we enjoy these things. We know that in Capitalistic America Labour prospers. We know that in China and India, and the countries with no capitalist system, Labour is infinitely miserable. We know more. We know that the way out of that misery pointed to his countrymen by so fervent an Indian patriot as Aga Khan, is precisely the Capitalism which Labour here is urged to destroy. We see that Russia has destroyed it, and we know with what result. We know that the War has been won by High Production, and we know that by no other means could it have been won. If these things are evil, it is clear at least that there is much good in them. If they bring with them labour and sorrow, it is certain that by their means worse labour and worse sorrow have in the past been escaped. Nay, it is indeed clear, that just those things which our revolutionaries seek to destroy are the things without which no society has ever been able to exist, save in the horrors already described.

It will interest readers to know that on June 26th, 1860, Capitalism raised its head in this peaceful Thames Valley. On this day 59 years ago Thomas, Stevens and Green started Soho Mills. We leave it to our readers to say whether the paper produced and the employment given has not been of benefit to the inhabitants of Wooburn and district.

Stop Press.—Since going to Press the unfortunate "contretemps" by a Trade Union has happened. Comment on the appositeness of our paragraph is needless.

Owing to want of space, a most interesting article on Music by Mr F.C. Brasher is held over till our next issue

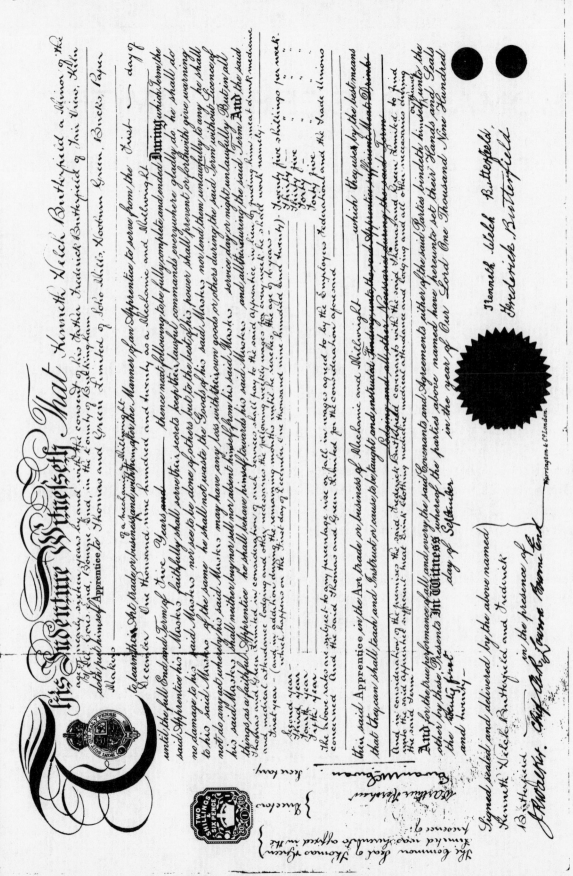

This Indenture Witnesseth That Kenneth Welch Butterfield a Minor of the age of sixteen years or thereabouts and with the consent & [testified] of his Father Frederick Butterfield of Fair View, Kiln of the New Road, Bourne End, in the County of Buckingham doth put himself Apprentice to Thomas and Green Limited of Soho Mills, Wooburn Green, Bucks, Paper Makers

To learn his Art trade or business and with them after the Manner of an Apprentice to serve from the first — day of December One Thousand nine hundred and twenty as a Mechanic and Wheelwright ____ thence next following to be fully completed and ended During which term the said Apprentice his Masters faithfully shall serve this secrets keep his lawful commands everywhere gladly do he shall do no damage to his said Masters nor see it to be done of others but to the best of his power shall prevent or forthwith give warning to his said Masters of the same he shall not waste the Goods of his said Masters nor lend them unlawfully to any he shall not do any act whereby his said Masters may have any loss with their own goods or others during the said Term without licence of his said Masters shall neither buy nor sell nor absent himself from his said Masters service day or night unlawfully But in all things as a faithful Apprentice he shall behave himself towards his said Masters and all theirs during the said Term And the said Thomas and Green Limited in consideration of such services shall pay to the said Apprentice in lieu of finding him meat drink medicine and medical attendance lodging and other necessaries the following weekly wages every week (and in addition during the remaining months until he reaches the age of 21 years First year— — — which happens on the first day of December one thousand nine hundred and twenty)—

First year — — — — — — Twenty five shillings per week
Second year — — — — — — Thirty ,, ,, ,,
Third year — — — — — — Thirty five ,, ,, ,,
Fourth year — — — — — — Forty ,, ,, ,,
Fifth year — — — — — — Forty five ,, ,, ,,

the above sums are subject to any percentage rise or fall in wages agreed to by the Employers Federation and the Trade Unions concerned And the said Thomas and Green Limited for the consideration aforesaid

these said Apprentice in the Art trade or business of Mechanic and Wheelwright ____ which they use by the best means that they can shall teach and instruct or cause to be taught and instructed Finding unto the said Apprentice [Meat Drink] And in consideration of the premises the said Frederick Butterfield covenants with the said Thomas and Green Limited to find unto the said Kenneth Welch Butterfield sufficient meat Drink clothing medicine medical attendance and lodging and all other necessaries during the said Term

And for the true performance of all and every the said Covenants and Agreements either of the said Parties bindeth himself unto the other by these Presents In Witness whereof the parties above named have hereunto set their Hands and Seals the twenty first day of September in the year of Our Lord One Thousand Nine Hundred and twenty—

Signed sealed and delivered by the above named
Kenneth Welch Butterfield and Frederick
Butterfield in the presence of

Kenneth Welch Butterfield.
Frederick Butterfield

Bourne Green

{ Received

Witness
ASW[...]... Chief Clerk, Fairview, Bourne End

Warrington & Co London.

THOMAS & GREEN, LIMITED.

IN THE MATTER of an Enquiry pursuant to the Resolution of the Board of Directors, dated the 20th November, 1923.

REPORT OF UMPIRE.

1.   The following are the circumstances which gave rise to this enquiry.

2.   During the latter part of the year 1923, differences arose between Mr. Bernard Green and Mr. John B. Sedgwick, two of the Directors of Thomas & Green, Limited, as to the manner in which they were carrying out their respective duties.   Mr. Sedgwick also held the position of General Manager, and Mr. Bernard Green that of Mill Manager to the Company.   These differences culminated in Mr. Bernard Green obtaining the signatures of a certain number of the Shareholders of the Company to a requisition calling upon the Directors to convene an Extraordinary General Meeting of the Company with a view to the appointment of a Committee of Shareholders to consider certain matters.   Although the name of Mr. Sedgwick was not mentioned in the requisition, it was common ground that the subject of that enquiry was to be the manner in which Mr. Sedgwick had carried out his duties as General Manager.

3.   The Directors thinking that such an enquiry would not be in the best interests of the Company, persuaded Mr. Bernard Green not to present the requisition and prevailed on both these gentlemen to agree to an independent arbitration into the matters in dispute between them, and on the 20th November, 1923, the following Resolution was passed by the Directors:—

> "That all the matters mentioned in the requisition for the Extraordinary General Meeting, and any further matters which Mr. Sedgwick may bring forward be referred for consideration and enquiry to Mr. Wilfred Godden and Sir Stanley Johnson (and if they should fail to agree, then to a third person to be nominated by them) with a request that they will advise the Board as to whether it would be in the interests of the Company, by reason of any of the matters referred to in the requisition or by Mr. Sedgwick and which may be ascertained by the consideration of and enquiry into the same, that Mr. Sedgwick and Mr. Bernard Green either or both

should retire from the positions they hold under the Company. The expenses of all parties to be borne by the Company up to £500 in all."

4.   Mr. Wilfred Godden and Sir Stanley Johnson having difficulty in agreeing upon an umpire, asked the President of the Law Society to nominate an umpire on their behalf, and on the 11th March, 1924, the President nominated me, ARTHUR LIONEL BRUCE THESIGER, of 12, King's Bench Walk, Temple, Barrister-at-Law, to act in that capacity, and I accepted the burden of the said reference.   Mr. Bernard Green, Mr. John B. Sedgwick and the other Directors of Thomas & Green, Limited, further signed undertakings to accept and act upon the award either of Mr. Wilfred Godden and Sir Stanley Johnson, the arbitrators, or of their umpire.

5.   By consent of all parties, and to save the expense of a fresh hearing in the event of the arbitrators failing to agree, it was agreed that I should sit with them and that the matters should be heard by the arbitrators and myself at the same time.   Accordingly, we sat and heard the evidence and arguments on 24th, 26th, 27th, and 28th March, 28th and 29th April, 1st, 6th, 8th, 9th, 15th, 16th and 20th May, 1924.   The interval between 28th March and 29th April was due to the unfortunate illness of Sir Stanley Johnson.   Mr. Latey, Solicitor, appeared on behalf of Mr. Bernard Green, and Mr. Piesse, Solicitor, on behalf of Mr. Sedgwick.

6.   On the 21st May, 1924, the arbitrators notified me that they were unable to agree upon an award, and that I was therefore at liberty to enter on the reference in lieu of them and to determine the matters referred.

7.   Before the first hearing of the enquiry, documents setting out particulars of the matters complained of by Mr. Bernard Green against Mr. Sedgwick and by Mr. Sedgwick against Mr. Bernard Green were supplied to me.   Mr. Bernard Green's complaints against Mr. Sedgwick did not altogether agree with the matters raised in the requisition, some matters referred to in the requisition being omitted from the Particulars of Complaints, while the latter contained matters which were not covered by any paragraph in the requisition.   No objection to this was taken on behalf of Mr. Sedgwick, and, as it was agreed by all concerned that it was most desirable that any matter which either of these gentlemen wished to raise should be considered by the arbitrators and myself with a view to finally disposing of the differences between them and to advising the Board with a full knowledge of all the facts, we allowed evidence to be given of all the matters referred to in Mr. Bernard Green's complaint, and even of one or two other matters which were not mentioned either in the requisition or the Complaint.

8.   It was agreed that the two complaints should be dealt with separately, and that, as the proceedings were initiated by Mr. Bernard Green, his complaint against Mr. Sedgwick should be dealt with first.   For reasons which are explained below, very nearly the whole of the enquiry was taken up with investigating the case made by Mr. Bernard Green against Mr. Sedgwick.

9.   Mr. Bernard Green's Particulars contained 17 heads of complaint against Mr. Sedgwick, though some of these complaints to a certain extent overlapped or might be regarded as alternative ways of alleging the same complaint.   In addition, as already stated, some two or three other matters of which Mr. Bernard Green complained were also investigated by us.   I have read over my notes of the evidence and arguments adduced before us and the copies of the various letters and other documents put in evidence and have considered each matter very carefully.   Having done so, I have come to the conclusion that none of the matters complained of have been established against Mr. Sedgwick, and I so find.   I have therefore to report to the Board of Thomas & Green, Limited, that it would not be in the interests of the Company by reason of any of the matters enquired into before the arbitrators and myself that Mr. Sedgwick should retire from the positions he holds under the Company.

10.   I should like to make it clear that in coming to this conclusion, I have not considered any of the subjects complained of by confining myself to the exact wording of the complaint, nor have I decided any matter on a technical point of strict pleading.   I have endeavoured to take a broad view of the subject and to consider from that aspect whether Mr. Sedgwick is fitted to act as General Manager of the Company.   Nobody who was only a human being could be expected to carry out his multifarious and important duties without making an occasional mistake, and there are some few matters, not in my view of the greatest importance, in which it is possible to criticise his actions, especially in the view of subsequent knowledge. But it is easy to be wise after the event, and I am quite satisfied that in Mr. Sedgwick the Directors have got a General Manager of absolute integrity, boundless energy, and, speaking generally, of sound judgment.

11.   Mr. Sedgwick's complaint against Mr. Bernard Green gave eight instances which, it was alleged, went to show that the latter was not suitable to manage the Company's Paper Mill without supervision, and that he had not the ability and general business qualities necessary to act as Managing Director.   At the close of the case made by Mr. Bernard Green against Mr. Sedgwick, Mr. Piesse stated that he would offer no evidence on any one of these eight instances, but

would rely on the evidence given in the case against Mr. Sedgwick to show that Mr. Bernard Green should not remain a Director of the Company.   He also relied on the evidence already given to prove the 2nd paragraph of his complaint which read as follows :—

> " The following is an instance which Mr. Sedgwick alleges goes to show that Mr. B. Green is not submitting to the authority of the Board of Directors either directly or through the General Manager and is not loyally serving the Company in its best interests :—
>
> None of the complaints or charges which Mr. B. Green now makes against Mr. Sedgwick were ever brought before the Board of Directors of the Company, but, on the contrary, Mr. B. Green, during the months of October and November last, discussed these matters with Shareholders without giving Mr. Sedgwick an opportunity of defending himself, and caused to be prepared a requisition directed to the Directors of the Company to convene an Extraordinary General Meeting of the Company for the purpose of considering, and if thought fit, of passing a Resolution to the effect that a committee be composed of five Members of the Company to enquire into and report and make recommendations to the Members of the Company upon the matters now in question."

I find as a fact that Mr. Bernard Green did not bring any of the complaints or charges against Mr. Sedgwick before the Board of Directors, that he did discuss these matters with certain Shareholders without giving Mr. Sedgwick an opportunity of defending himself, and that he did cause the requisition referred to to be prepared.

12.   It was alleged by Mr. Piesse that Mr. Bernard Green's actions were part of a conspiracy into which he had entered with certain other Shareholders, inspired by jealousy of Mr. Sedgwick's position and a desire to take his place.   I am quite satisfied that Mr. Bernard Green was not actuated by such motives or by any ulterior motive.   I am satisfied that he was genuinely convinced that Mr. Sedgwick was not carrying on his duties as General Manager in the best interests of the Company, and that his continued occupation of that post would jeopardise the Company.   At the same time, as already indicated, I am of opinion that there was little if any, justification for these suspicions, and that, if there were, it was Mr. Bernard Green's duty, in the first instance at least, to bring the matters before his fellow Directors.   His explanation for not taking that course is that Mr. Sedgwick had obtained such a dominating influence over them that they would be incapable of judging the matters raised fairly and impartially.   All the Directors were present during practically the whole of the enquiry, and I have seen and heard them all in the witness box ; I am satisfied that there is no ground for this opinion.

Mr. Sedgwick is undoubtedly a man of strong personality, and his co-directors, with the exception of Mr. Bernard Green, have a high opinion of him, but I am convinced that they are all men of sound judgment, though no doubt in somewhat varying degrees quite capable of forming their own views, and of opposing any proposal put forward by Mr. Sedgwick with which they do not agree. Mr. Roland Green and Mr. Herbert Green, in particular, are men of many years' experience in the paper trade, well able to form independent judgments based on that long experience, and not in the least likely to be dominated by a man much younger than themselves.

13. In my view, the dispute between Mr. Bernard Green and Mr. Sedgwick had their origin in the fundamental differences in their respective characters. Mr. Sedgwick is quick, impulsive, and even at times impetuous, in act and speech. Mr. Bernard Green's mind moves much more slowly, and he would not be likely to come to a conclusion on any subject without taking a much longer time for consideration than Mr. Sedgwick would require. Mr. Sedgwick's rapidity aroused the suspicions of Mr. Bernard Green, who found himself unable to follow the workings of his mind sufficiently quickly ; Mr. Bernard Green's suspicions and slowness to grasp his reasons and motives irritated Mr. Sedgwick. The result was, I think, that Mr. Sedgwick at times treated Mr. Bernard Green with some brusqueness, and did not always give him as full explanations as he was, as a Director of the Company, entitled to. Mr. Bernard Green, on the other hand, worked himself (possibly as a result of discussing the matter with other Shareholders) into a state in which he could not believe that anything that Mr. Sedgwick did was right. An instance of this was shown in the fact that the requisition suggested an investigation into the position and functions of the Sales Manager. At the enquiry this point was dropped, Mr. Bernard Green frankly admitting that he thought he had been too much influenced by the fact that the Sales Manager had been brought into the Company on the suggestion of Mr. Sedgwick.

14. Accepting, as I do, the honesty of Mr. Bernard Green's motives, and realizing the seriousness of his position should he have to relinquish the appointments he holds with the Company, I might hesitate to advise the Board that such a step was necessary. But Mr. Bernard Green admitted in the course of the enquiry that if his complaints against Mr. Sedgwick were not established, he must resign his position, and I am afraid it is clear that it would be almost impossible for him and Mr. Sedgwick to work together amicably or satisfactorily in the future. He has brought charges against Mr. Sedgwick which he has failed to substantiate,

and he has failed to bring those charges, as he should have done, before the Board in the first instance.   Had he done so, it is possible that an enquiry, which must have considerably disorganised the working of the Company for some time past, and has involved it in expense, might have been avoided.   I must therefore report to the Board of Thomas & Green, Limited, that it would be in the interests of the Company, by reason of the matters enquired into before the arbitrators and myself, that Mr. Bernard Green should retire from the positions he holds under the Company.   As I am quite satisfied as to his integrity, I trust that this advice will not prevent his finding suitable and satisfactory employment elsewhere.

15.   In conclusion, I should like to express my thanks to both the arbitrators for the assistance and support they gave me throughout the enquiry, and to Mr. Latey and Mr. Piesse for the able and temperate way in which they put their respective cases before us.   Their example was followed by Mr. Bernard Green and Mr. Sedgwick, both of whom gave their evidence with admirable self-restraint and freedom from exaggeration.   I hope that Thomas & Green, Limited, will in the future be free from any further troubles, and will maintain the prosperity and high reputation which have been theirs for so many years.

Dated this 28th day of May, 1924.

ARTHUR L. B. THESIGER.

Witness :

GEORGE FOULSHAM.

ENLARGEMENT OF SOHO MILLS 1936

(Reprinted from *Bucks Free Press*, May 1936.)

Big extensions, involving the rebuilding of two machine houses and the lengthening of a third, will shortly be completed at Soho Mills, Wooburn, by Messrs Thomas and Green Ltd.

Among the largest and the oldest established paper manufacturers in Buckinghamshire, Messrs Thomas and Green are now recognised as the leading colour paper producers in the country, and increasing demand for their products in recent years has made extensions of the mill imperative.

The work of reconstruction has been carried out during the last two years without any serious disturbance of the general working of the mill and, apart from the steel contracting, all the work has been done by members of the mill staff themselves.

Wholehearted and generous co-operation by the staff of nearly 300 people—nearly all of whom are local men and women born and bred in the paper trade that has, for a century or more, been the staple industry of the district—is to be recognised by the directors on Saturday, May 9th, when everyone has been invited to a celebration party to mark the completion of the extensions.

Since the war, Soho Mills' weekly production of paper has increased from 60 tons to an average now of 100 tons.

All the new extensions have been planned with a view to still further additions in the future to meet the possibility of increasing trade.

The Main Changes

Principal changes have been made in the three machine houses. Two of them, No. 1 and No. 2 machine houses, have been entirely rebuilt and lengthened to 210 feet. The third machine house has been lengthened by about 40 feet. In No. 2 machine house there is at present no machine.

All of the buildings have been equipped with 5 ton hand-operated cranes and 1 ton electric travelling cranes.

Soho Mills may now boast every modern contrivance of the paper-making industry. Super-calenders and slitters in the machine houses have been renewed and the drives of all modernised.

A new web stock room, about 70 feet by 48 feet, has been built and equipped with one-ton electric hoists. The room replaces two or three old web stock rooms, but there is also another, 70 feet by 50 feet, which has been modernised and equipped with electric hoists.

A new cutting house, 95 feet by 48 feet wide, has been built, and all cutters are now equipped with electric hoists for reels.

In readiness for a conditioning machine, at present under construction, a conditioning house, 78 feet by 35 feet, has also been erected.

Every labour-saving device has been ingeniously exploited in the mills, and by the erection of a new salle, about 150 feet long, with an area of about 7,000 square feet, the mill's produce is transported with least possible delay and difficulty.

A covered loading bay holds five railway trucks and a verandah to load three lorries has also been added.

During the rebuilding, the level of the floors has been raised in such a way that now the floor of the salle is level with the floor of the railway trucks and lorries—an improvement that still further facilitates rapid and effective loading.

Another new wing, to accommodate an embossing department, about 100 feet by 90 feet, had previously been constructed.

The completion of the extensions will mark another stage in the steady progress made by Thomas and Green Ltd., who, established in 1860, formed into a company in 1890.

Specialists in colour paper-making, they have also done a good deal in recent years in the way of fancy embossed papers, and new scope in the industry is constantly being sought.

Perhaps the most striking feature at Soho Mills is the happy and harmonious co-operation among the 300 employees and the goodwill that has existed for many years between staff and employers.

The respect and, indeed, affection with which the directors are held by those in Soho Mills' happy family of workers was manifested way back in 1919 when employees presented to the employers an illuminated address as a token of the great esteem with which they held them, and in recognition of the kind interest they had shown in their welfare.

The address now holds prominent place in the managing directors' room.

Generations of families pass through Soho Mills. There are three generations there now, and more than twenty men have achieved the proud record of working for Messrs Thomas and Green for forty years or more.

When they achieve that, they receive a gold watch and a couple of easy chairs, and their photos find a place among the select circle of veterans in the mill's social room.

Mr H. Norris, who works on the guillotine, has the distinction of longest service among the mill employees. He was eleven years old when he started with Messrs Thomas and Green, and he will be 69 on May 28th. He has a close rival in Mr George Plumridge.

Mr J.B. Sedgwick and Mr J.S. Peacock are joint managing directors of Messrs Thomas and Green.

THE SOHO, WOOBURN GREEN, PAPER MILLS RECONSTRUCTION SCHEME COMPLETED 1936

(Reprinted from *Paper Market & Printing Technique*, Annual Number 1938.)

During the past few years there has been in progress at the Soho Paper Mills of Messrs Thomas & Green a carefully planned programme of expansion and renovation which has brought this old-established mill completely up to date. The whole scheme is now practically finished and has been carried through with characteristic thoroughness. There has been no sensational and hurried destructions and reconstructions but a sound solid realisation of a well conceived plan typical of a mill which has for generations maintained an enviable reputation for the manufacture of high-grade coloured papers. Neither has there been any attempt at experimenting: "an expensive hobby, best left to others," say the management.

The work has been carried through without any serious disturbance of the general working of the mill and the greater part of it has been done by their own staff and workers. Soho is a two machine mill, one 87 in wide by James Bertram and one 64 in wide by J. Milne. Both machine houses have been entirely rebuilt and converted into a single building designed to have ample room for a third machine. This house is 70 feet longer than previously. In fact all the buildings have been reconstructed not only to provide for the immediate requirements of the mill, but also to allow for a considerable increased future output. The output has been increased from 60 tons to 100 tons a week; the alterations made to one of the machines enable imitation art papers to be manufactured.

One of the most interesting items is the new web stockroom about 70 feet by 48 feet designed on unique lines and equipped with electric cranes. All the buildings have in fact been equipped with 5 ton hand-operated and one ton electric cranes.

A most up-to-date conditioning plant has been installed in a house 78 feet by 35 feet. Super-calenders have been reconstructed with electric drives and in the new cutting house each cutter is operated by its own electric lifting gear. This building is 95 feet by 48 feet. The salle is completely new and is about two and a half times the area of the old one, and at a higher level so that five railway trucks can be loaded under cover at floor level without any lifting. In addition, provision has been made for three lorries to be loaded under cover, and the export baling press has been moved into the

Two views of Thomas & Green Soho Mill after the re-building in 1936

Dinner and Dance held at Thomas & Green Mill on 9 May 1936 to celebrate completion of re-building of the Mill. At the piano is SYDNEY JEROME, front row include Directors from *l. to r.*: J. B. SEDGWICK, A.J. CLARKE, Mrs LORNA SEDGWICK, KINGSLEY B. GREEN. Further back on left JOHN TYLER (with bow tie) and J. R. SEDGWICK

No. 3 Paper Machine 84 inches wide at Thomas & Green in 1936

Conditioning Machine at Thomas & Green in 1936

Salle at Thomas & Green in 1936

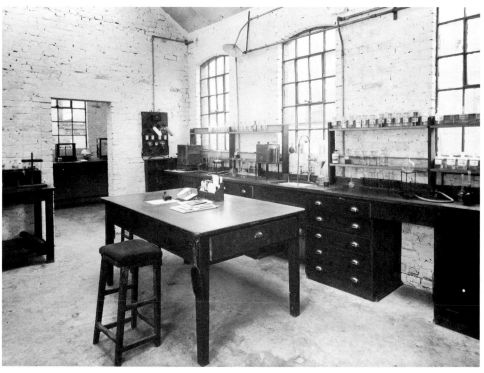

Laboratory at Thomas & Green in 1936

Sales & Sample office at Thomas & Green 1936

General office at Thomas & Green in 1936

Director's office at Thomas & Green in 1936

Thomas & Green Ltd. Centenary Dinner at Stationers' Hall on 6 November 1970

Thomas & Green Soho Mill in 1970

salle, so avoiding an immense amount of unnecessary labour. A few years ago the management started manufacturing embossed paper and a new wing has been built to accommodate the most up-to-date embossing plant.

The rest of the plant is of the ordinary type to be found in a modern esparto mill. The power plant includes a 1,500 hp Parson Turbine & Stirling boilers with Babcock & Wilcock under feeds. A very efficient soda recovery plant, six 3-ton grass boilers and 28 beaters are amongst the rest of the equipment. A mill such as this, making such a numerous range of colours, must keep large stocks. About 800–900 tons are kept, including 400 tons of web stock.

As mentioned before, Messrs Thomas & Green are famed chiefly for their coloured banks and bonds, tinted writings and cover papers, which enjoy quite a remarkable reputation for (to coin a word) their unvariableness. There was an instance some years ago of a certain paper merchant who, when unearthing some old documents, came across a Thomas & Green pattern book of forty odd years ago. Comparing the shades with those of the present samples he found them identical! Anyone who knows anything about colour matching will readily grant that as a consistency of which to be proud.

The records of the company go back to 1860, when the firm was founded by Mr J. Barcham Green and Mr William Thomas, but it was then an established mill, so paper has been made at Soho for perhaps a hundred years or more. Mr William Thomas, by the way, was originally foreman at the Tovil mills at Maidstone. Mr Green had three sons, for all of whom he provided paper mills; one son, Mr Herbert Green, went to Hayle mill, Maidstone, another, Mr Roland Green, went to Soho mill, and the other, Mr Laurence Green, to Allnutts, also at Maidstone.

The present managing directors are Mr J. B. Sedgwick and Mr J. S. Peacock.

Mr Sedgwick, who is a grandson of the original Mr Barcham Green, has been personally responsible for all the reconstruction work and is essentially a practical engineer and paper-maker. Mr Peacock controls the sales organisation. The London office and warehouse is at 196, Upper Thames Street, London, EC4.

G.T. Mandl

FROM 1940 TO THE PRESENT DAY

Following the dispute between Bernard Green and John Barcham Sedgwick (details of which are printed in full in the Arbitration Report on page 188), John Barcham Sedgwick was in control of the mill with J.S. Peacock as Joint Managing Director for Sales.

After Mr Sedgwick's death in 1944 his brother-in-law, Kingsley Barcham Green (1902–1952), was briefly in charge of the mill together with A.J. Gibbs, who rose from being Company Secretary to Joint Managing Director from 1949 until his death in 1957.

Having provided Chairmen and Managing Directors without interruption from its foundation in 1860 until 1951, and with the death of A.J. Gibbs in 1957 the era of the Green family came finally to an end. What had been at first predominantly a family business under their own very competent management, began to transform itself during the 1950s into the structure of an unquoted public company with declining influence and shareholding by the founder families. The board were, therefore, looking for the first time outside the family for a new Managing Director. The position was widely advertised and the board, which at that time consisted largely of non-Executive directors drawn with only one exception from outside the paper industry, made the unhappy choice of George Gordon, who was appointed Managing Director from his position as Engineer with Smith Anderson in Scotland. Under his management the company experienced a decline in labour and customer relations, as well as credibility.

Following the retirement of the Northern representative, F.W. Bishop, in 1956, G.T. Mandl's Manchester office operated in partnership with C.D. McFarlin as Northern representative for Thomas & Green and H. Allnutt & Son. Under this arrangement G.T. Mandl first became involved in the reorganisation of Allnutt's and unsuccessful negotiations for its sale took place with the board of Thomas & Green during 1957 and 1958. He became a shareholder in 1958 and held approximately 3% of the share capital. Following his acquisition of the majority shareholding in Fourstones Paper Mill Co. Ltd in July 1962, the agency of his company for Thomas & Green was terminated by G. Gordon.

Although, after a loss for 1958, marginal profits were still being made up to 1961, subsequent profits in 1962 and 1963 were not genuine and the company was clearly set on a disaster course. On

198

the initiative of A.G.W. Freeman, the board met without the presence of the Managing Director on 24 March 1964 and decided to dismiss Mr Gordon with immediate effect and appoint G.T. Mandl to the board. The Sales Director, J.R. Sedgwick, was appointed Managing Director.

The following proposals made by G.T. Mandl upon his appointment were approved by the board of Thomas & Green Ltd. The overall sales and marketing activities of Thomas & Green Ltd., H. Allnutt & Son Ltd. and Fourstones Paper Mill Co. Ltd were to be pooled through G.T. Mandl's sales organisation covering the whole of the UK. Engineering services of the three mills were to be co-ordinated in order to establish the greatest possible saving in costs.

The audit to 31 March 1964 showed the true extent of the company's state of affairs with a loss in excess of £36,000. It became evident that, without substantial capital investment and restructuring of both Soho and Lower Tovil mills, losses would continue and a further loss of almost £33 000 was incurred during the financial year of 1965.

In order to strengthen the connection between Thomas & Green and Fourstones Mills, the two companies subscribed 5% of each other's share capital which resulted, together with 20 000 shares subscribed by G.T. Mandl in the following year, in Mr Mandl's control of more than 25% of the share capital and the carrying out of a very substantial capital investment programme during 1967, whilst the company incurred a loss of almost £94 000. This year was also one of a very severe depression for the industry, with many mill closures taking place up and down the country.

An attempt was made to acquire the share capital of Y. Trotter & Son Ltd in Berwickshire with the intention of concentrating manufacture of paper at Soho Mills and maintaining the buildings and plant of the virtually bankrupt Scottish company as a finishing and warehousing operation for the group. The offers, involving an exchange of shares, were not accepted by a sufficient majority of the Trotter shareholders and the company subsequently went bankrupt with a substantial deficiency to its creditors. Details of the offer are reprinted on page 249.

The Thomas & Green investment programme was financed in part with the sale in 1967 of 10 acres of building land at Soho Mills for the sum of £100 000, on which a housing estate has been built. It consisted mainly of a new oil-fired boiler substituting the uneconomical coal boilers and turbine, the installation of a fibre recovery plant which reduced the fibre loss from 17% to 4% and at the same time enabled the installation of an effluent system to comply with the new legislation.

In February 1968 paper manufacture at Allnutt's was closed down after almost 300 years and the programme was transferred partly to

Thomas & Green and partly to Fourstones against payment of a royalty. The surplus properties at both Soho and Lower Tovil were let for industrial and warehousing purposes, thus providing an alternative source of income. 1968 showed a great reduction in the loss of Thomas & Green to below £10 000 and in 1969 the company was once again able to show the first profit of almost £30 000 before the closing-down losses of Allnutt's.

J.R. Sedgwick's term as Managing Director ended suddenly with his unexpected death in August 1966. The board decided not to appoint a new Managing Director and the company was managed by an Executive Committee of the board under the chairmanship of G.T. Mandl, who was at the same time made Deputy Chairman in place of MacA. Bexon.

The new board, including three Executive Directors under the continued chairmanship of R.P. Clarke, continued to manage the company with positive results. Great strides forward had also been made in marketing, introducing a wide range of speciality products in the field of filter papers, as well as the acquisition of some of the trade following the closure of the Craig and Harold Jackson Mills.

The recession of 1972 necessitated further structural changes within the group. It became evident that the production of the low-volume, high-priced specialities carried on originally on three 163 cm Fourdrinier machines, which were about 100 years old and capable of speeds of around 50 metres per minute, located at Maidstone, Wooburn Green and Fourstones, could not continue in the long term. Even after the closure of Allnutt's the concentration of this trade on the remaining two old machines did not bring the necessary improvement, as the hitherto profitable trade of the relatively modern 214 cm machine at Thomas & Green became unprofitable under severe competition in the Writings and Printings market.

It was therefore decided to rebuild this machine for the production of creped papers and absorbent specialities, whilst maintaining its ability to produce a smaller quantity of the more profitable end of the predominantly coloured Cover, Writings and Printings range.

This necessitated the transfer of the entire Fourdrinier programme from Fourstones to Thomas & Green and the closing down of the remaining two old machines. This major transfer of trade from two independent companies, whose only link was the by then majority shareholding of G.T. Mandl, necessitated a merger which was carried out with the consent of almost 100% of shareholders in both companies on 31 March 1972. Fourstones Mill, which held over 51% of the shares in Thomas & Green, made an offer to exchange the rest of the Ordinary and the entire Preference Capital for loan stock. It then changed its name to Thomas & Green Holdings Ltd and transferred the operation of its paper mill to a new wholly owned subsidiary under the name of Fourstones Paper Mill Co. Ltd.

R.P. Clarke, the chairman of Thomas & Green, agreed to join the board of Holdings, whilst the operating boards of the two subsidiary companies consisted entirely of Executive Directors.

The highly successful results subsequent to the merger more than justified the action that had been taken and the group achieved a total capital expenditure in excess of £5 million of largely self-generated funds in the 16 years from 1967 to 1983.

During 1968 informal discussions had also taken place with the board of Towgood and Beckwith Ltd, Helpston, Peterborough, with a view to merging the two companies and strengthening their structure. These discussions did not, however, come to fruition and Towgoods subsequently became a member of the Brittain's group of companies.

Following the bankruptcy of the Brittain's Group in December 1979, Thomas & Green purchased Arborfield Mill in Helpston from the receivers, Cork Gully & Co.

Whilst the 1968 negotiations would have involved an exchange of shares between Thomas & Green and Towgood & Beckwith and the maintenance of paper making at both locations, the closure of Arborfield Mill by the receiver enabled Thomas & Green to acquire its converting operations and trade without being involved in the loss making paper manufacturing activities at a time of over-production and severe recession.

Arborfield Mill was started in 1856 for the purpose of utilising couch grass as a raw material for paper making. A patent had been taken out at the time and the company traded under the name of The Lincolnshire Patent Twitch Paper and Millboard Company Ltd, and received the Excise no. 296. The project failed.

In 1861 the mill was purchased by Alfred Towgood for the sum of £2600 after it had been in disuse for some time. The object of the purchase was to replace the mill at Arborfield, near Reading in Berkshire, which had been destroyed by fire during the previous year, hence the name "Arborfield". The object of both mills was to produce wrapping papers for the other Towgood mills at St Neots (Huntingdonshire) and Sawston (Cambridgeshire.)

The Helpston mill operated under the name Towgood Brothers until Robert Louis Towgood and Arthur Beckwith entered into partnership soon after the turn of the century. Beckwith owned a mill in Crickhowell (South Wales). The two men were both members of the Fishmongers Company in the City of London where, in all probability, they met. After some initial teething problems the mill was able to produce friction glazed qualities, laminated manillas, cover papers, and ammunition papers for rocket, flare and shotgun usage. The mill operated profitably until the second World War under the management of the papermaker, Vincent Jackson.

The Towgood family originally entered the paper industry by

mistake. They were successful bankers who numbered amongst their customers the brothers Henry and Sealy Fourdrinier, who were wealthy wholesale stationers and well known through their financial backing of Robert's patent, which subsequently became known as the Fourdrinier machine. Fourdrinier's ultimate bankruptcy resulted in property and plant coming into the hands of the Towgood bank and it is quite possible that the Towgoods were the first people to actually make money out of Fourdrinier machine-made paper.

A very considerable expansion occurred when the management was taken over by Malcolm R. Towgood after the Second World War when in addition to the existing 72 inch Fourdrinier machine a second, 100 inch machine, was purchased second-hand from Henry Cooke in Westmorland and the programme was extended into the manufacture of imitation book cloth, hospital sterilisation paper, vacuum dust bag, laundry tag and other speciality papers. A substantial converting department involving embossing, impregnating, laminating, coiling, perforating, varnishing and printing had been installed, and the company soon became market leader for paper-based case binding materials under the trade marks "Glintene" and "Glindura".

In 1971 the entire share capital of Towgood and Beckwith Ltd was acquired by Brittain's Ltd who changed the name of the company from Towgood & Beckwith Ltd to Brittains Arborfield Ltd and created a hospital division under the name of Brittains Hospital Supplies Ltd, for the marketing of sterilisation papers. After the closure of the mill in December 1979 the M.G. machine was exported to Zambia whilst the Fourdrinier machine was scrapped.

During 1983 Thomas & Green Ltd moved all of its converting operations, stock of branded lines, administrative and sales offices from Buckinghamshire to Peterborough, where the company now operates under the name of Thomas & Green Ltd, Arborfield Mill.

Due to falling demand on the home market, the production of coloured papers, both branded covers and book cloth, as well as making orders, became uneconomical, which led to the re-structuring of Soho Mill. In February 1984 the manufacture of coloured papers was discontinued and the trade transferred to James Cropper Plc, in which Thomas & Green Holdings had acquired a minor equity interest.

The production of filter paper continued until July 1984 when production ceased with the loss of only 25 jobs and the manufacture of filter paper for the group was concentrated on the Netstal Mill in Switzerland, where a substantial modernisation programme was carried out. This difficult re-structuring was carried out under the outstanding management of Mr George Meadows, who had joined Thomas & Green after a life-long service with the Wiggins Teape group. He made the Antique laid paper on which this book is printed as one of the last orders before Soho Mill closed in July 1984.

THOMAS & GREEN CELEBRATES ITS CENTENARY

DISTINGUISHED GATHERING AT STATIONERS' HALL

(Reprinted from *The World's Paper Trade Review*, 3 December 1970.)

Thomas & Green Ltd, as briefly reported in our news columns on 19 November, celebrated its Centenary with a dinner at the Stationers' Hall in London on 16 November. Mr G.T. Mandl, deputy chairman of the company, presided, and the guests were representative of a wide cross section of the paper and board industry.

Among those present were visitors from overseas, the president of the Stationers' Social Society, Mr R. A. Oswick; the president of the Paper Agents' Association, Mr J. I. Harris; the president of the Birmingham & District Wholesale Paper Merchants' Social Society, Mr P. Blow; the general secretary of the National Association of Paper Merchants, Mr S. R. W. Bailey; the secretary of the British Paper & Board Makers' Association, Mr H. K. W. Hodges; and the secretary, Southern section, of the Employers' Federation of Papermakers and Boardmakers, Mr W. J. Bartlett.

Among the directors of the company present was Mr R. A. Purssell who read a number of messages of greeting and congratulations from friends of the company who were unable to be present.

In his toast to the guests, Mr Mandl said that they should really be celebrating their 110th anniversary, as it was on 25 June 1860 that the partnership of Thomas, Stephens & Green, which was at that time the name of the company, was formed. The management in 1960 decided not to hold an official celebration of the Centenary and the difficult period through which the company was at that time passing certainly did not warrant any celebration.

The partnership formed in 1860 was by no means the beginning of paper making at Soho Mills. Records of the subsidiary, H. Allnutt & Son Ltd, at Lower Tovil, Maidstone, go back to 1686 when Peter Musgrove was first entered as paper maker at Lower Tovil in the Maidstone rate book. The roots of their business all went back to Maidstone which was at that time and, to a large extent, still was, one of the main paper making centres in Britain.

The first mention of Soho Mills went back to 1705 when the widow Hayden was entered as occupier in the parish rate book at Wooburn. The mill was then a corn mill and it was not until 1759 that first evidence of paper making was recorded.

John Fellows, maltster, miller and paper maker of Beaconsfield, had insured his stock of rags and paper in a paper mill adjoining the corn mill in Wooburn with the Sun Fire Insurance Company on 13 October 1759—"We are indebted to much valuable research of the early activities at Soho Mills to Mr John Mayes, Librarian of High Wycombe, and the late Dr. Shorter, of the University of Exeter," said Mr Mandl.

The Fellows family were in occupation of Soho Mills for over 50 years before it changed hands and was owned by the Harrison and Wright families. By 1842 the mill was recorded as empty and was owned for the last 10 years before its sale to the present company by Charles Venables, Junior, a well-known paper maker in the district.

In 1860, first Soho and later the adjoining Princes Mill at Cores End were sold to Thomas, Stephens & Green. The earliest records of Princes Mill, whose excise number 288 they still used, together with Soho's number 424, also went back a very long time and the earliest entry in the rate book shows William Church as occupier in May 1705. He was followed by the Russell, East and Howard families before the mill passed into the hands of Thomas Lunnon in 1819 and Charles Venables, together with Soho Mills, in 1842, before being sold to the present company in 1860.

Princes Mill was used mainly as a half-stuff mill for straw pulp and a pipeline was said to have existed between the two mills for the disposal of waste liquor and the recovery of chemicals.

Princes Mill was subsequently let to Jacksons in 1895 and finally sold to them in 1899. Nothing remained of Princes Mill today apart from the excise number 288.

Following the installation of paper machines in place of vats in the area, many paper makers were thrown out of work. They decided to take the law into their own hands and organised a march to destroy the machines. On 29 November 1830 they started with the highest mill on the stream, near West Wycombe, and destroyed every single one all the way down as far as Snakely (now T. B. Ford), beyond Loudwater, before being stopped and rounded up by police in sufficient numbers, reinforced by the Royal Staghounds, who gave up the day's sport to join the forces of law and order. Soho Mills were spared due to their location on the lower reaches of the River Wye.

A self-inflicted destruction of an even larger number of paper machines took place some 130 years later when more than 35 mills in Britain closed down under the strain of economic, rather than riotous, violence. As in 1830 their mill was only just spared, and they were grateful to Providence for both occasions.

William Thomas was a well-known and experienced paper maker in Kent who had particularly developed the process of manufacturing paper from straw, long before esparto was thought of as a substitute for the ever-growing shortage of rags. He developed the straw-pulping process at the Upper Tovil Mills of Simpson & Hargreaves (now Reeds) in Maidstone which was used mainly for the manufacture of newsprint from straw. The lane leading to the mill is still called Straw Hill.

After a few years with Townsend Hook as foreman, Mr Thomas decided to have a mill of his own and when Soho Mill came on the market, he approached John Barcham Green, of Hayle Mill, in Maidstone, in order to form a partnership and raise the necessary funds. Mr Green then brought his friend, J. C. Stephens, a solicitor, in to the partnership and thus Thomas, Stephens and Green was formed.

Soho Mill was initially run by William Thomas on his own, and he was later joined by his two sons and the son of Mr Stephens representing his father's share. The main product was newsprint made from straw and the business prospered.

Following the death of William Thomas, in 1874, John Barcham Green moved to Soho Mills, where he remained until his death in 1883.

The two founders were followed in the management of the company by their two well-known sons, Roland Green and Sir John Thomas, who were leading personalities on the paper making scene of the late 1800s. Sir John was very well known locally and became a Member of Parliament and a Liveryman of the Stationers' Company.

The mills were originally leased by the partnership and the freehold of both Soho and Princes was acquired in 1892. In 1894 straw was substituted by esparto and Soho became a fine paper mill specialising in colours and produced one of the very first pattern books in Britain.

Mr Mandl continued that some interesting names had appeared in the company's records from time to time: thus it was recorded that the selling commission of the country agents, Spicer Brothers, was reduced to $7\frac{1}{2}$% on 8 December 1891; that John Dickinson were appointed Colonial agents for the sale of coloured papers on 16 May 1898 and that, in 1899, the company established its own network of provincial representatives, having terminated the agency with Spicers.

The partnership of Thomas, Stephens & Green, which subsequently became Thomas & Green following the purchase of the Stephens' share by the two partners, was converted into a limited liability company in 1890, under which form it continued to the present day. The Green family provided the chairmen and managing directors (with the exception of Mr Kershaw and Mr Peacock) without interruption until after the Second World War, when John Barcham Sedgwick, chairman and managing director, died, very soon followed by Kingsley Barcham Green. The company became a public company with over 250 shareholders.

Although the family connection with Lower Tovil Mill, Maidstone, goes back to 1872, when it was purchased, together with Ivy Mill, from Alfred Allnutt by J. B. Green, its formal incorporation as a subsidiary company did not take place until 1925 following the death of his son, Laurence Green, in Maidstone.

Thus both Ivy and Lower Tovil Mills were owned by the Green family, as well as Hayle Mill, which was still in their possession to this day. Lower Tovil specialised in deep colours and, following a fire, much of the paper was made at Soho Mills. This enhanced the growing reputation of the company as a speciality colour mill.

The high standard of Soho Mill was commented on in the well-known book *The Paper Trade*, by A. Dykes Spicer in 1907 (page 195), and the mill was frequently referred to as the Rolls-Royce of paper making between the wars.

A new 84 inch machine was ordered in 1920 and went into production in 1923. The increased demand for this machine was based on the immediate post-war boom, but when the machine was delivered, the market was, as very often happened, in the depth of depression. The London County Bank refused to finance the project and the account was transferred to the National Provincial Bank, where it had been ever since. "They have seen us through a number of worse storms than the new machine project of 1923 in the intervening period, and we are very happy to see a representative from this Bank with us this evening," Mr Mandl continued.

The new No. 3 machine was a very modern unit for its day and had subsequently been modernised with the installation of a new drive, a suction roll and couch. In 1957 a new wet end was put in followed by a size press. In recent years they had been able to bring it completely up to date with relatively modest investment in preparation capacity and moisture control systems.

A major breakthrough occurred in January 1932 when the two managing directors visited Germany and ordered their first embossing machine and rollers. This was followed by a second embossing machine in November 1932 and, by February 1933, it was decided to build the embossing department as it was known today. The combination of many different colours stocked at the mill with various embossings provided a very important new outlet for the production—initially in cover substances, but ultimately followed by the company's range of friction embossed pastings. These were developed by embossing various colours of Superfine Bonds and thus Thomas & Green entered the fancy paper trade.

The development and marketing of this product was carried out in conjunction with Ihlee & Sankey, who subsequently became main stockists. "We owe a great debt of gratitude to Mr A. G. W. Freeman, partner and head of the fancy paper department of Ihlee & Sankey, who subsequently joined the board of our company in 1952 and who is also directly responsible for my connection with Thomas & Green. Mr Freeman remained on the board for 16 years until his retirement due to ill-health in 1968 and I am sure you will all join me in sending him our greetings from this Centenary Dinner, which I am certain he would have attended had his state of health permitted.

"The depression of the early 1960s caught our company unprepared, both technically and financially, for the storm to come," Mr Mandl continued. "Due to the enormous slow-moving stock of many different colours and substances, the liquid resources were immobilised while hundreds of pounds per day drained away in the effluent due to the total absence of any fibre recovery plant. There was considerable over-staffing in the finishing department and by 1963 the mill produced barely 55 tons a week with an establishment of well over 200. The steam boilers and power plant, which had been constructed for the Esparto Pulp and Paper Mill, were in a hopeless imbalance following the closure of the grass-boiling plant and generated both steam and electricity at more than double the normal cost.

"Margins were fast dwindling under the pressure of over-production and whilst previous profitability helped to absorb all these enormous on-costs, this no longer became possible and increasing heavy losses were being incurred. The foresight of our founding fathers, who had bought large areas of land around the mill, saved us in this situation and we were able not only to recover most of the losses from the sale of only one fifth of the land, but also to raise sufficient funds for the essential investments to bring the mill up to date in terms of steam generation, pulp preparation and introduction of control systems.

Today the mill employed a total of some 130 people and produced 80-90 tons a week.

"As one would expect on an occasion such as this, we have been looking a great deal into the past. In order to continue in existence under present-day competitive conditions, we must look to the future and assess our position in the industry—if not over the next 100 years, at least over the next 10.

"I have often been asked the question how a mill with our type of equipment can withstand the competition from integrated units with 200 inch machines running at over 2,000 feet a minute. I actually believe that the installation of these units in fact benefit a mill such as ours; their production is invariably geared to bulk output, with which we ceased to compete many years ago, and as long as our free society directs individual demand and individual tastes, the growth of our speciality makes of short runs in colours or whites, woodfrees and espartos, plain and embossed, is secured for the future.

"It is evident that a service of this nature, backed by very substantial stocks, will demand an increasing premium over bulk-produced commercial papers. Due to the general depression in our industry, this differential has not been anything like as high as it should be, but we are confident that we shall soon be able to obtain similar prices for our speciality products on our home market as we are currently obtaining in our exports to Europe, including—of all places—Sweden. We are also very fortunate in having very loyal and conscientious workpeople. This is a rarity nowadays, particularly in an area with the greatest shortage of labour in this country.

"We are now, slowly but surely, regaining our image and it is our policy to remain a small speciality producer, basing our costing on profitability rather than volume.

"We must be one of the very small number of mills in this country producing less in terms of tonnage now than we did before the war. Our basic marketing concept is that demand cannot be stimulated by price and if only more people in our industry were to follow this rule, how much better off we would all be.

"We are now in the process of turning the third year of modest profits and feel the time has come to spend a little more of our Bank's money in celebrating, if somewhat belatedly, the 100th anniversary of our foundation and to welcome all of you who have come to join us here tonight."

When looking through the old Thomas & Green records, he had found that there was actually a time when not only Spicers and John Dickinson, but also Price & Pierce, were their agents.

Thomas & Green owned, for many years, one of the principal Tunisian esparto grass shippers, SATA, for whose shipments, apart from the parent company, Price & Pierce acted as agents.

"I now have much pleasure in asking my friend, Ray Oswick, who needs no introduction to any of you, to say a few words on behalf of the paper makers. He adds distinction to our gathering by being president of the Stationers' Social Society—that friendly organisation, which embraces our entire trade.

"Our second speaker, representing our merchant customers, is Mr F. T. Jackson, whose connection with our company goes back so many years that I hesitate to mention the figure, but may it suffice to tell you that he was dealing with Thomas & Green when I was two years old. He is very well known in circles of paper historians, and should really be a member of the British Paper & Board Makers' Association, as he operates the smallest privately owned hand-made paper mill at his home. No statistics of output are available! I have the pleasure of sharing his affection for fine hand-made and mould-made paper which, I am sorry to say, is increasingly restricted to the realm of a hobby rather than commerce."

Mr Oswick, responding for the British Paper & Board Makers' Association, said that in the extremely interesting historical record

Mr Mandl had outlined, he always found it remarkable how the same family names seemed to crop up with great regularity in pretty well all paper mill records.

"I find myself," Mr Oswick continued, "in the position of being a supplier through one of the companies in our group, a competitor as a paper maker, a colleague in many trade association activities, and a supporter of Mr Mandl's forcibly expressed views on the use of the centimetre and many other matters upon which I regret that neither of us has met with any marked degree of success.

"As I first met him at an annual general meeting of the company for which I have the pleasure of working, for all I know I work for him too!"

"It was in these days very encouraging indeed to see one of the smaller and non-integrated mills achieving the success which Thomas & Green had done under George Mandl's leadership.

"I would like to add my good wishes personally, on behalf on my own company and of all paper mills here represented, for success during the next 110 years, and I say that with all goodwill, though in these days one sometimes wonders if one is not going out on a limb to say anything about the next 110 days, let alone years."

Mr Jackson, for the paper merchants, said that 110 years ago, during the reign of Queen Victoria, the year 1860 was undoubtedly most eventful. Thomas & Green was founded; Sir Richard Cobden introduced some free trade arrangement with France; Garibaldi and his 1,000 Redcoats were involved in a frolic at Naples; Sir James Barrie, author of Peter Pan, was born; and it was the year of the outbreak of the American Civil War.

"I think, however, you will all agree that the founding of Thomas & Green was the most important event of that year, 1860!

"A Centenary dinner is a time for reminiscing, and I well remember nearly 50 years ago, walking out of the front door of Herring, Dewick & Cripps, in Cannon Street, down to Upper Thames Street to W. S. Muir, Woollacott, East Lancs, and Robert Fletcher to turn up Queen Street Place to Mr Knopp, of Oldham—round the corner where Mr Raison ran a sample office for Lepard & Smith—then on the right before Queenhithe to the office of Thomas & Green where Mr Harrison and Mr Starling politely put the stock book on the brass rail and attended to one's inquiry.

"On to J. A. Kidd, St Cuthberts, Venables & Crompton in Queenhithe—past Allan Strong, Rennie in Bread Street Hill to Joynson for rare samples of Parchment and Superfine—Towgood, Richard Herring, Strong Hanbury, Davidson, Gidney Rourke, Olive & Partington, Bartons, Barrow, Archer & Lowe, Tullis, and Livingstone Page.

"One popped up to Reed & Smith to buy 5 cwt of a special size, weight and colour at $3\frac{5}{8}d$ per lb, which was better than Thomas & Green at $4\frac{1}{4}d$ (whose minimum quantity was 8 cwt delivery city limits)—and generally overmade. It was, however, an infinitely superior cover.

"On behalf of us all here this evening, I would like to thank you and the directors and the company of Thomas & Green, for a very excellent dinner and your generous hospitality in this fine Stationers' Hall. We wish every prosperity, progress and good fortune to this independent English paper mill. We assure you that you are held in the highest possible esteem, and a regard, almost amounting to affection, in our paper trade."

H. ALLNUTT & SON

The account of the Thomas and Green history would not be complete without a record of its subsidiary Henry Allnutt & Son Ltd in Maidstone. Paper manufacture was started at Lower Tovil Mills by Peter Musgrove in 1686. His successors were Wm. Gill in 1722, Thomas Pine in 1728, Simon Pine in 1750 and John Pine in 1781. The mill remained in the hands of the Pine family until 1816. The earliest known reference under the name Allnutt is that John Allnutt became apprentice to Wm. East Paper Maker at Cores End Paper Mill in Buckinghamshire (very close to Soho Paper Mills of Thomas & Green Ltd) in 1791.

John Allnutt became a partner in Lower Tovil Mill and a watermark, Smith Pine & Allnutt, is recorded in Heawoods Watermarks No 2767.

After 1816 Lower Tovil and Ivy Mills were in the hands of Smith and Allnutt and a watermark with this name and the date of 1828 is in existence. Smith was born in 1778 and died in 1855 having retired from business in 1835. He was succeeded by Henry Allnutt who was in possession of Lower Tovil Mill in 1884. His son Alfred Allnutt sold both mills to John Barcham Green in 1872 on his retirement, and he died in 1883. John Barcham Green continued to manufacture coloured papers at both Tovil and Ivy mills. Great Ivy Mill also had a vat and made a small quantity of hand-made paper.

John Barcham Green's third son, Laurence, had been from the very first destined to take over this business eventually and he had been sent there straight from school to learn the business and fit himself for it. He remained there as manager under his father until his death in 1883. It then became Laurence Green's business but he had a partner, his uncle, Mr W. Laurence, who had found part of the capital, but he remained a sleeping partner, taking no active part whatever.

There was a disastrous fire at Lower Tovil Mill which almost entirely destroyed it, at any rate the damage was so serious that papermaking ceased completely for many months. At that time it appeared possible to get Thomas & Green to make some of these coloured papers. The foreman from Lower Tovil came to Soho Mills and helped in matching the colours.

After Allnutt's Mill was rebuilt Thomas & Green were in a position to take orders for coloured papers, and this was their beginning of making coloureds.

In 1924 Thomas & Green Ltd took over Lower Tovil Mill, Ivy

Mill having been closed down before the First World War. The partnership of H. Allnutt & Son was turned into a limited company and became a wholly owned subsidiary of Thomas & Green Ltd. It continued to operate the 62-inch Fourdrinier machine installed in 1890 and was one of the very few mills which never operated the three shift system, running the mill on day shifts only from 6 a.m. to 6 p.m.

During the Second World War security papers were produced for the War Office including watermarked papers for German passports and ration books used by Allied Military personnel parachuted into Europe. It operated on a single shift basis only, producing specialities such as Seidlitz Blue, Tea Sampling, Gold Braid and other unusual and rapidly declining kinds of paper, with filter paper being the main product by the time it was closed down in 1969. The filter paper production was transferred to Fourstones Mill and subsequently concentrated at Thomas & Green.

Lower Tovil Mill, with its original waterwheel site dating back to the 1680's, is still in the possession of Thomas & Green Holdings Ltd and used as an industrial trading estate with a number of tenants carrying on various small industries in the mill buildings.

The following historical notes have been provided by Dr A.H. Shorter:

KENT *Mill No. 24. Lower Tovil Mill*
1686.   The name of Peter Musgrove appears in the *Maidstone R.B.* He was assessed in respect of property in Tovil (which was in the parish of Maidstone). Neither his trade nor the property is specified, but the assessment appears to refer to a site which might well have been a mill in 1686, and very possibly Lower Tovil Mill. PETER MUSGROVE, paper maker, is named in the Apprentice Papers, Smythe Mss, 1, Maidstone Museum, with reference to the same year.
1701.   Peter Musgrove, paper maker, took an apprentice, Thomas Gilford. Apprentices' List, Smythe Mss, 1, Maidstone Museum. In December, 1701, the assessment in the *Maidstone R.B.* was on the widow of Peter Musgrove....
1702.   The relevant assessment (on £20, later increased to £25) was again on PETER MUSGROVE, *Maidstone R.B.* This must have been the son, who had been apprenticed to his father, of the same name, paper maker, in 1692. Apprentices' List, Smythe Mss, 1.
1721.   The amount of £25 was entered against the name of Peter Musgrove for the last time in the *Maidstone R.B.* He appears to have transferred to Upper Tovil Mill (No. 25, below), about that time....
1722.   From 1722 to 1727 WILLIAM GILL appears to have had a direct interest in this property. He was presumably the paper maker who was working Turkey Mill at this time (see Kent, Mill No. 21,

above). In 1722 the relevant entry in the *Maidstone R.B.* (section under Tovil) reads "Musgrove, now William Gill". In 1723 the entries read "John Robbins† late Musgrove" and "Mr John Robbins". The last of similar entries occurs in 1725. Robbins's trade is not known. In 1726 the relevant entries in the *Maidstone R.B.* are "John Robbins now Gill", and later "Mr Gill".

1727. The name of Mr Gill appears for the last time in connection with this property. *Ibid.* . . .

1728. As with Otham Mill (Kent, No. 23, above), it is not always possible to decide from the available evidence which member of the Pine family was the occupier or master paper maker here (or at Ivy Mill, No. 26, below). In 1728 two paper makers named THOMAS PINE took an apprentice, Joseph Hollis. Apprentices' List, Smythe Mss, 1, Maidstone Museum. This probably refers to Thomas Pine of Lower Tovil and Thomas Pine of Ivy Mill. An entry "Mr Pine late Gill" appears against the amount of £25 in the *Maidstone R.B.* (1728). In 1730 the entry reads "Mr Thomas Pine late Gill". In 1731 a paper mill at Maidstone was destroyed by the blowing up of a powder mill. *G.M.*, 1 (July, 1731), 309. The powder mills were at Tovil (*K.P.C.N.L.*, 21st July, 1731) and were the lowest mills on the stream. J. Smith (publisher), *Topography of Maidstone and its Environs* (1839), 86. The paper mill concerned was therefore almost certainly the one at Lower Tovil. It appears to have been rebuilt almost immediately. Entries of Thomas Pine, assessed at £25, continue in the *Maidstone R.B.* Beginning in 1741, a series of relevant assessments were on Thomas Pine senior, and in 1745–6 on Thomas Pine junior. *Ibid*.

1746. In 1745 Thomas Pine junior, paper maker, insured a mill-house, drying house etc. in Tovil. *S.F.I.P.* 103461 (30th Sep., 1745). It is possible that he continued to be assessed for this mill after 1746, but no *Maidstone R.B.* covering the period 1747–62 is available. . . .

1750. SIMON PINE, paper maker, took apprentices, Thomas Stroud and Richard Holloway. Apprentices' List, Smythe Mss, 1, Maidstone Museum. Although the name of Thomas Pine still appears in the *Maidstone R.B.* in 1763, it appears probable that he was by that time assessed on Ivy Mill (for £40) (Kent, Mill No. 26, below), and that Simon Pine, who in 1763 was assessed £30, was by that time at Lower Tovil.

1780. Similar assessments on Simon Pine continue up to 1780. *Maidstone R.B.* . . .

1781. JOHN PINE, paper maker, took an apprentice, Thomas James. Apprentices' List, Smythe Mss., 1, Maidstone Museum. In that year the name of John Pine is entered against the amount of £50, apparently replacing that of Simon Pine, previously entered against £30. *Maidstone R.B.* In August 1782 the relevant entry reads Thomas Pine, but in 1783 the name of John Pine again appears against £50. From 1795 the entry reads John Pine & Co. *Ibid*. The mill was in their hands after 1800. In 1802 there was an accident at John Pine's paper mill at Tovil. Kentish Chronicle (28th May, 1802). John Pine was at Lower Tovil Mill in 1805–7. *Holden's Triennial D.* (1805–7), 2, 207. A master paper maker or proprietor of that name was at that mill in 1816 also. *E.G.L.* (8th Oct., 1816)....

Lower Tovil Mill is still working in 1956, under the firm of HENRY ALLNUTT & SON, LTD., Lower Tovil Mills.

NOTES ON PARTNERSHIP OF
J. & E. THOMAS & GREEN
1882 to 1890

(Obtained from old Balance Sheets)

In 1882 each of the following had invested £5,750 in the business, on which they drew 5%—

John Thomas
Edwin Thomas
Roland Green

making £17,250.

In addition Roland Green had invested £6,000 on which he was not paid interest.

March 31st, 1882
Stocks were made up as follows:

	£
Raw Materials	3,954
Repairs	1,688
Paper Stocks	6,089
	11,731

Of Paper Stock £4,356 was their own regular stocks.
£1,733 was Customers' Stocks.
During the year a new Calender was bought for £1,274, and various other small items amounting to about £760. Profit was £7,410, of which they drew £5,700.

March 31st, 1883
Partners' Capital as above had been increased to £6,250 each plus £6,000 in the case of Roland Green.
Paper Stocks were up to £8,011.
Profit £8,023, of which they drew £2,674 each.
Capital Expenditure was not great.

March 31st, 1884
Capital as before.

Expenditure
£821   Steam Engine House (Atalanta)
£115   Mixing House

£142 Evaporator House
£87 Various other houses
£474 New Oven and two pans
£175 Siding Extension
£366 Gas Holder and Tank
£150 Cotton bowls for Calender
£600 approximately spent on other items.

Total Profit £13,717 of which each drew £822, and each added £3,750 to Capital.

March 31st, 1885
Capital of each Partner £10,000 (R. Green extra £6,000)
Paper Stocks £8,996.

Expenditure
£244 Galvanised Iron Paper Stock Room.
£511 Atalanta House
£448 Mixing House
£109 Steam Boiler House
£123 For other Buildings
£98 New Oven
£2,463 Atalanta Engine
£819 New Steam Boiler etc.
£1,448 Mixing House Plant
£500 Alteration to Machine
£125 Various other items
£248 Esparto Willow and Steam Engine
£175 Gas Main to Partners' Houses.

Total Profit £5,116 of which each drew £705.

March 1886
Capital of each Partner £12,000 (R. Green £6,000 extra)
Paper Stocks £9,823
Profit £8,040
Profit drawn £1,680 each.
Capital Expenditure—no large items.

March 1887
Capital of each Partner £12,000 (R. Green £6,000 extra)
Paper Stocks £12,256
Profit £3,203
Profit drawn £1,110 each.
Capital Expenditure—Steam Boiler £465.
                    No other large item.

March 1888
Capital of each Partner £12,000 (R. Green £6,000 extra)
Paper Stocks £7,377
Profit £3,464
Profit drawn £555 each.
Capital Expenditure— Esparto Boiler at Princes £378.
Steam Engine £166.

March 1889
Capital of each Partner £12,000 (R. Green £4,000 extra)
Paper Stocks £10,813
Profit £3,545
Profit drawn £582 each.
Capital Expenditure—Economiser at Princes £136.

September 1889
Capital as above.
Paper Stocks £9,780
Profit for 6 months £2,845
Capital Expenditure—Yaryan £1,783.

March 31st, 1890
E. Thomas now retired and Capital is held as follows:-
J. Thomas £22,500
R. Green £22,500
Loan from R.
Green £4,000.
Paper Stocks £8,510
Profit for the six
months £3,504
Profit divided for the year between the two remaining Part-
ners £3,174.
Capital Expenditure mainly No. 7 Boiler £495

Edwin Thomas appears to have been paid out for £12,000, £6,000
being contributed each by J. Thomas and Roland Green.

EXTRACTS FROM THE DIRECTORS' MINUTE
BOOK AND FROM THE MINUTES OF THE
ANNUAL MEETINGS OF

THOMAS & GREEN LIMITED
1890–1956

The Company was incorporated in 1890 and the first meeting was held at the offices of Godden, Holme & Ward, Solicitors, of 34 Old Jewry, London, on April 15th 1890.

Authorised capital	£
Ordinary Shares	20,000
6% Preference	19,000
	39,000
5% Debentures	10,000

The following were the original Directors—

> John Thomas
> Roland Green
> Herbert Green
> James Thomas
> Laurence Green

Secretary	Roland Green.
Auditor	Arthur B. Russell.
Solicitors	Godden, Holme & Ward.
Bankers	London County Bank, High Wycombe (name since changed to Westminster Bank).
Registered Office	Soho Mills.

The Original Ordinary Shareholders were—

> John Thomas
> Mrs Ada Thomas
> Roland Green
> Mrs Jemima Green
> James Thomas
> Miss Eliza Thomas
> Herbert Green
> Laurence Green.

Ordinary and Preference Shares were in £100 units.

Aug. 15th, 1890	Yearly tenancy of Princes Mill to be continued. Steps taken to purchase freehold of Soho.
Mar. 6th, 1891	Fourth effect (Chapman) ordered for the Evaporator. (Note JBS. Presumably this Evaporator was at Soho.)
Jan. 12th, 1891	Forced draft successfully applied to three boilers and ordered for remainder.
Sep. 14th, 1891	Short time reported.
Dec. 9th, 1891	New steam boilers and economiser on order. Also Lorna Engine ordered. Selling Commission to mill country agents (Spicer Bros.) reduced to $7\frac{1}{2}$%.
Feb. 2nd, 1892	Purchase of freehold of Soho Mill to be completed on February 8th, 1892. (Actually completed on Mar. 14th, 1892.) Authorised capital increased to £59,000 by the creation of 100 new Ordinary Shares of £100 each (£10,000) and 100 new Preference Shares of £100 each, (£10,000).
Feb. 11th, 1892	Apparently both the freehold of Princes and Soho Mills was bought—Vendors, Pascoe du Pre Grenfell and others. Debentures renewed and amount issued increased to the maximum of £15,000.
June 13th, 1892	Extract from Minutes—"In addition, the Directors recommend that (the sum of £2032.2.7. having been spent in new plant and paid for out of undivided profits over and above the sum of £1679.10.4. written off for depreciation in the two years during which the Company has carried on business). Debentures or shares or cash for £2000 be paid to the Ordinary shareholders as the Directors may think fit (this to be done by way of bonus and not as dividend) leaving a balance to be carried forward of £469.10.6. This was subsequently confirmed at the General Meeting on June 13th 1892.
Aug. 10th, 1892	Reported that the Ordinary Shareholders had been paid the bonus decided upon at the Annual General Meeting, the Managing Directors taking £900 in Ordinary Shares and the balance £70 each in cash. (Note. JBS. What happened to the other Ordinary Shareholders I do not know.)
Oct. 29th, 1892	Valuation effected by Mr A. Masson of Masson, Scott & Co.) exceeds Balance Sheet Value at March 31st, 1892 by £3987.0.2. Decided to re-

duce goodwill by £1000 and balance to be carried to Special Reserve against the loss in removal or disposal of Princes Mill property.

Dec. 21st, 1892	Owing to bad trade the minimum weight of paper made each week above which tonnage was paid was increased from 30 to 35 tons per week. (Note. This is wage rate cutting.) A further steam boiler has been put in and is at work.
May 6th, 1893	First minute of an apprentice being Indentured, G.W. Hill, as Engineer and Millwright.
May 17th, 1893	Mill has been on short time owing to bad trade. Slackened energy reported among the workpeople, possibly as a result of the tonnage cut (Dec. 21st, 1892). Leishman, foreman since 1885 is retiring and a new man has been engaged.
June 22nd, 1893	First sale of part of land of Princes Mill property to F. Pheeby (employee) for £27.10.0.
Dec. 4th, 1893	The Managing Directors having visited Ford Works with a view to maturing their plans for the use of Grass and the construction of Half Stuff Mill and decided to adopt Mr Cornett's plan for using Esparto Grass, including the Cornett Breaker (finally scrapped about 1924. JBS.) Building of new Half Stuff Mill had been started and plans for the remainder were being prepared. Estimated cost £5000 to be met by issue of £3,500 Pref. and £1,500 Debs. Macey's (London Manager) Agreement extended for further three years.
May 10th, 1894	Reported that the continued high cost of straw had proved the wisdom of the decision to use Esparto Grass. Hoped to start the plant in early Autumn. Mill has been on short time. Hutchinson (Chief Engineer) left in Nov. 1893 to better himself. (Inventor of Hutchinson Strainer, went to E. Lloyd—JBS.)
Aug. 8th, 1894	Apprenticeship of P.J. Ashdown. (Note. His father owned the mill at Loudwater now owned by National Paper Co.)
Apl. 11th, 1895	Princes Mill let to F. Jackson (rent not stated).★
May 30th, 1895	Installation of new stack of Super-calenders decided on, also Tangye's producer-gas plant and engine to drive both sets. (Note. This was a very bad purchase. I personally spent many hours inside the cylinder of this engine. It gave endless trouble. JBS.)

★ Foundation of Jacksons Board Mill, Bourne End.

Decided to build new Mechanics' Shop—old one to be used as extension of Cutting House and for slitting, reeling and packing. (A.B. Green was connected with the erection of this building. JBS.)

Production	1894–5	2,397 or about 46 tons per week.
	1893–4	2,286 or about 44 tons per week.
Sales	1894–5	£63,251
	1893–4	£57,287
Profit	1894–5	£3,914
	1893–4	£3,508

June 24th, 1895	A new economiser has been ordered.
Sep. 18th, 1895	Two promissory notes given jointly and severally by the Managing Directors to the Bank for £500 each to secure a loan for £1,000 owing to heavy stocks of raw materials etc.
Jan. 1st, 1896	Water softener had just been started.
Jan. 2nd, 1896	Capital to be increased from £59,000 to £70,000 by issue of further 110 Preference Shares of £100 each £11,000.
Dec. 16th, 1896	Macey (London Manager), has a new agreement and his salary increased again to £150 per annum with commission on sales as before.
May 21st, 1897	Foreman (Robinson) discharged. W. Glisbey appointed. Engineer (Dawson) left to go to Croxley, and W. Harris appointed. Noted that the men wanted to go to Ramsgate for their Annual Outing and paid for the day as it was Jubilee Day.
July 1st, 1897	In recognition of good work W. Glisbey allowed to buy 1 Ordinary Share of £100 at par.
Nov. 29th, 1897	Large extra depreciation (total £1345.13.5. for six months) due to removal of Old Straw Boiler, tanks, wood pulp engines, drainers and Kollergang.
May 16th, 1898	J. Dickinson & Co. appointed Colonial Agents for sale of Coloured Papers. Esparto bought over 1899 at £2.14.4. per ton (presumably C.I.F.) which will help to neutralise extra cost of wood pulp and coal.
May 31st, 1898	No. 1 Machine wire widened and lengthened. Additional cylinders and another stack of chilled rolls. S.J. Taylor appointed Birmingham agent.

	W.A. Kershaw appointed Manager for three years.
Jan. 25th, 1899	W.A. Kershaw commenced his duties Jan. 16th, 1899. Sale of Princes Mill to Jacksons Millboard and Paper Co. completed.
Mar. 29th, 1899	Cost of Mr Kershaw's salary to be borne by Mr J. Thomas and Mr R. Green.
May 25th, 1899	Bleach £4.12.6. per ton, but coal rising seriously.
June 29th, 1899	C.A. Buzzard appointed Bristol agent.
Dec. 11th, 1899	Serious flue explosion in September. No one hurt.
	Old boilers in front of office removed. A new 30 × 8 boiler is added to new range.
	Old No. 4 Boiler refixed in new range, making seven boilers in all.
Dec. 11th, 1899	Notice given to terminate Spicer Bros. Agency.
Feb. 8th, 1900	F.J. Fuller taken on as Fitters' apprentice at a premium of £10. (Why this premium? JBS.)
June 11th, 1900	Chimney Boiler House and Steam Boilers in front of office have now been removed.
	New web stock room being built (Probably the one next to Calander House. JBS.)
	Fullner Press and Tank installed.
	Arrangement made with H. Allnutt & Sons to share expenses over country travellers owing to termination of arrangement with Spicer Bros. Extension to Salle proposed (i.e. 3 storey building).
June 14th, 1900	Roland Green re-appointed Secretary but at a salary of £50 per annum.
Nov. 21st, 1900	Talk of electric light in mill.
Jan. 23rd, 1901	Preference Shares (£1,200 worth) issued at a premium of £75.
May 18th, 1901	Salle extension completed.
May 20th, 1901	A.B. Russell's fee as Auditor 40 guineas per annum.
May 20th, 1902	Only expenditure of any importance during the year was installation of a superheater (probably cost about £250, JBS).
	Reduction of 5% made to workpeople for 12 months owing to bad results.
	Esparto now £2.15.0. against £3.8.9.
May 30th, 1902	Consumption of Coal per 1 H.P.
	Saturated steam 1.96 lbs.
	Superheated steam 1.70 lbs.
	$12\frac{1}{2}$% saving in favour of superheated.

Dec. 17th, 1902	Superheat being successful in the Atalanta will be applied now to the Lorna and super-calender engine with a view to scrapping the gas engine.
Jan. 13th, 1903	Bleach £4.7.6. per ton.
May 27th, 1903	Fullner Filter installed. (First of its kind in this country. I looked after it during its trials. Not really satisfactory. JBS.)
	5% wages cut returned.
	Esparto £3.0.0. per ton.
	Art Cover Paper series started.
	Considering further steam engine and beaters.
	Electricity may be used for both light and power. (!!)
	Debentures to be increased to £20,000.
May 29th, 1903	Crohard adjoining mill bought for £450. Increased room taken in London Warehouse.
Jan. 4th, 1904	Gas Engine Producer scrapped. 250 H.P. Adeline Engine and generator added, also beaters (Two in old Clay House) and superheaters added.
May 27th, 1904	Rag breaker added.
	Esparto £3.2.6. C.I.F.
	Wood Pulp seriously advanced to £8.15.0. C.I.F.
Nov. 20th, 1904	Depreciation on Buildings increased from $2\frac{1}{2}\%$ to $2\frac{3}{4}\%$
	Depreciation on Machinery increased from $3\frac{1}{2}\%$ to $3\frac{3}{4}\%$
	and an additional $\frac{1}{4}\%$ in the following six months.
July 5th, 1905	Old water turbine scrapped and new one being put in.
	Larger Evaporating oven being put in also induced draught at steam boilers.
July 5th, 1905	Two Tidcombe cutters being replaced by a West End.
	Electric lighting throughout the mill and some electric driving.
	Wood Pulp £8.9.6. per ton (13/- below last contract).
	James Thomas ⎫
	Herbert Green ⎬ Appointed Directors
	W.A. Kershaw ⎭
	John Thomas ⎫
	Roland Green ⎬ Appointed Managing
	W.A. Kershaw ⎭ Directors
July 5th, 1905	Ordinary Directors (other than Managing Direc-

tors) to be paid £50 per year divided between them as they like.

Managing Directors to be paid £1,500 per year to be divided between the three of them as they agree.

W.A. Kershaw appointed Secretary at £50 per annum.

(Note. JBS. Up to this date the only directors attending Board Meetings were John Thomas and Roland Green.)

Feb. 12th, 1906	A. Wells appointed country traveller.
May 25th, 1906	New water turbine working.

Twelve electric motors working but no saving on coal. Induced draught a failure and returned to makers. Another West End Cutter ordered (this time duplex).

New Evaporator ordered at total cost of £2,000. New Guillotine ordered.

Ordinary Directors' fees refixed at twenty guineas per year, divided between the two.

Nov. 14th, 1906   Addition of Bank and Bond series.

(Note by JBS. I think this was not the commencement of this series but an expansion by the addition of extra colours etc.)

Short time worked.

July 17th, 1907   After considerable discussion it was agreed to show the Company's Balance Sheet to the Income Tax Surveyor (!!!) who had asked to see it.

Feb. 5th, 1908   Depreciation on Plant to be increased to 5%, next year to $5\frac{1}{2}$% and thereafter 6%.

Rotary Roaster ordered.

New steam boiler 30 ft. × 8'3" (No. 11) ordered.

New Goebel slitter to be ordered.

May 13th, 1908   Coal 16/6$\frac{1}{2}$d. per ton delivered.

Coal 14/-$\frac{3}{4}$d. per ton delivered the year before.

New value of paper stock £16,825.

July 30th, 1908   The Directors held between them—

223 out of the 323 Preference Shares.

224 out of the 229 Ordinary Shares.

July 30th, 1908   Decided to give notice to terminate the Colonial Agency with J. Dickinson & Co. Ltd.

Card Index started.

Feb. 6th, 1909   French Agency given to Douvet.

New Zealand Agency given to D.S. Cattanach.

May 17th, 1909   Some short time worked early in the year for seven weeks.

New roof put on No. 2 Machine House.

288 Ledger Wove and Wipe Off added.

27 lbs. Large Post added to Bonds.

30 lbs. Demy to Pamphlet Covers.

Sfax £3.8.0. per ton delivered.

Sulphite Wood Pulp £8.11.9. delivered.

Soda Wood Pulp £7.15.0. delivered.

Additional Goebel slitter bought.

South African agent Karl Schwartz (not taken up).

Jan. 3rd, 1909   Foreman's House in Orchard to be built.

Apl. 11th, 1910   J. Hadden & Co. appointed South African agents.

May 18th, 1910   Four days short time worked during the year.

Record Sales for year— £73,798.

H.M.S.O. buying stock Card Index.

Further 23½″ Goebel slitter ordered.

New set Plate Glazing Rolls.

T. W. Catly agent in Canada and British Columbia.

A. B. Russell's fee now 40 guineas and expenses.

Nov. 11th, 1910   Mr J. Thomas to see Bank re temporary loan of £9,000 to enable mortgage to be paid off and pending issue to replace mortgage.

Depreciation to be raised from 6% to 7½% by ½% steps each half year.

Goodwill £3,500 to be written off next Balance Sheet.

Question of dumping sludge in big field adjoining allotments discussed but no decision.

W. A. Kershaw to visit Switzerland with Mr J. B. Green to endeavour to open up business.

New steam boiler ordered 30 ft. × 9 ft. 2¼″ for 125 lbs presure.

Steam boiler house galavanised iron roof to be replaced with slate roof.

General offices and Directors' Offices to be rebuilt.

Standby electric generator to be bought.

Gold Medal obtained from the Brussels Exhibition.

Also exhibited at Printing and Stationery Exhibition, Amalgamated Hall.

Feb. 3rd, 1911   Formal notice received that £9,000 Mortgage would be called in on April 13th, 1911.

Discussion on building proposed Web Stock Room (Welfare Room) at estimated cost of £3,000.

May 22nd, 1911	Mentioned that the original possession of the mills had been taken on June 25th, 1860, so that they had now been in their possession for 50 years.
	Record profit at £8,385.
	H.D. Catty & Co. of New York appointed agents for Canada.
	Herr Caro appointed German agent in Hamburg.
	Esparto £2.15.0. into barge Thames.
	Old iron frame of steam boiler house to be re-erected at end of Mechanic's shop for additional Pulp and Esparto Store.
	Buying steam tractor and two trailers for sludge.
	Mortgage £9,000 now paid off.
May 22nd, 1911	New Web Stock Room (Welfare Room) contract placed.
Sep. 14th, 1911	Proposed purchase of Claptons Farm.
Nov. 15th, 1911	That 15% in place of 10% be written off Paper Stock waiting orders.
	Third stack of Plate Glazing Rolls purchased second-hand from University Press Oxford.
	Report on unsatisfactory nature of Foreman's work (W. Glisbey).
Jan. 4th, 1912	Transfer from W. Glisbey of shares held by him. (Presumably he had now been discharged and J. Tait engaged.)
May 13th, 1912	Record Profit £9,004.
	J. Hadden gave notice to terminate S. African agency.
	War in Tripoli causing difficulty with Esparto supplies.
	New 90″ slitter ordered.
	Claptons Farm purchased.
	Tractor House built.
	Women's Mess Room built (now Electricians' shop).
	New roof on No. 1 Beating House. (Note—this was put on the old principals which by 1920 were full of dry rot and whole roof had later to be re-built. JBS.)
	Chief Clerk, R. Loosemore retires. W. Hollis succeeded.
	Two days extra pay given to the workpeople at Christmas.
July 1st, 1912	Colonial Paper Co. appointed Australian Agents.
Nov. 11th, 1912	Old steam engine and chests No. 1 scrapped.

New Ashworth and Parker engine and White's drive installed on this machine, also longer wire frame.

Up to 37/6d. per ton paid for coal during the strike.

Agreed in future not to start until 6 a.m. on Monday and to pay the same full week's money.

W. Dawson & Sons appointed South African Agents.

May 15th, 1913   Bleach £5.15.6. per ton.

Exhibited at the Manchester Printing and Stationery Exhibition April 17th–May 1st, 1913.

Goebel Tube Making Machine bought.

New road made from settling ponds to main road at a cost of £463.

Railway siding to be renewed inside the weighbridge.

Offices to be extended by adding new Sample Office, Telephone Office and Typists' Room.

Re-valuation of Mills arranged by Rushton Son & Kenyon.

Oct. 22nd, 1913   Revaluation considered and accepted and Auditor instructed to incorporate in Balance Sheet as on September 30th, 1913.

Decided that—

(1) Increased value of land £2,097 be credited to reserve account.

(2) £2,000 part of the increased value of Buildings and £13,464 increased value of Machinery be capitalised by declaring a bonus of £18,344 payable to the Ordinary Shareholders in proportion to their holdings and that the issued Capital of the Company be increased by that amount. Authorised Capital to be increased to £100,000

£50,000 Ordinary ⎱ and that the shares be
£50,000 Preference ⎰ issued in £1 units instead of £100 units.

Nov. 12th, 1913   Depreciation on Buildings reduced to 1%. (Presumably owing to the fact that valuation had shown that previous rate was unnecessary—JBS.)

Dec. 2nd, 1913   Shortness of working capital noted owing largely to increased manufactured stocks.

Jan. 5th, 1914   Arbitration Award against Arbib for £987 and costs on some grass dispute settled in T & G's favour. Arbib applied to the High Courts who confirmed Arbitrations' Award.

227

Feb. 18th, 1914	Death of Mr James Thomas (Director) on February 11th.
May 15th, 1914	Olivier (Esparto suppliers) were sued by us for breach of Contract, £2,198 and costs. Large Rag Breaker replaces smaller one. Drum pumps on No. 1 Machine. Office extension completed. Siding renewed. Employers' Federation formed. Cost of Unemployment Insurance was £147. Sir John Thomas resigns Managing Directorship on becoming 80 years of age. W.A. Kershaw and Roland Green to be paid £650 per year each. No third Managing Director to be appointed. Sir John Thomas to be paid £100 per year as Chairman. Other Directors £50 per year. F.J. Thomas appointed Director.
Sept. 7th, 1914	Case against Olivier won.
Nov. 13th, 1914	£25 per year to be written off Claptons Farm property to be charged to settling ponds A/c.
Jan. 11th, 1915	Dissatisfaction with Mr Wells as Country Traveller. Letter written urging him to increase turnover. (Birmingham had been taken off his district and given to Mr Brough—JBS.)
June 7th, 1915	Forty six men had enlisted by this date. Joined the Employers' Federation.
Sept. 13th 1915	F.J. Thomas engaged as Assistant Manager at £400 per year. Sprinklers to be installed at £1,945.
Nov. 29th, 1915	Foreman's salary increased to £350. Managing Directors' salaries increased to £1,500 per year between the two. One week's wages given as gratuity to each man who had worked for more than a year with the Company at Christmas. Proportionately smaller amount for shorter services.
Jan. 17th, 1916	New Economiser bought. Discussion of Profit Sharing following a paper read on the subject by Mr Russell at the request of the Directors. Profit sharing further discussed and postponed till end of War.
May 27th, 1916	Cost of sprinkler installation written off against Insurance and not charged to Plant.

£1,000 to be put to Reserve for Repairs delayed by the War. Further £1,000 next year.

F.J. Thomas's salary increased to £450.

Agreed that minimum wage for adult males should be 30/– per week (!!! JBS).

Wood Pulp now between £30 and £40 per ton. Esparto £8.5.0. delivered mill.

Cameron Slitter ordered.

Commenced using straw again owing to shortage of Esparto.

Waste Paper Pulper bought.

July 24th, 1916	Two days' holiday and one day's pay given at August Bank holiday.

W. Hollis (Chief Clerk) leaves.

J. Walker appointed in his place.

New Railway Truck Weighbridge put in.

Sep. 18th, 1916	A. Wells engagement as representative terminated by mutual consent.
Nov. 27th, 1916	Bonus of £500 divided between Managing Directors and Assistant Manager, F.J. Thomas's salary raised to £500.

Still talking about Profit sharing.

Mar. 19th, 1917	Preliminary discussion re New Boilers and Turbine.

Exhibited at the British Industries Fair.

June 6th, 1917	Controlled by Ministry of Munitions as from April 23rd, 1917.

Apparently a Steam Tractor was ordered.

£5,000 put to Reserve for Steam Turbine.

Depreciation on Plant raised to $12\frac{1}{2}\%$ on account of impossibility of adequate maintenance.

£1,000 to Special Reserve for Repairs.

F.J. Thomas appointed Managing Director.

Bonus of a week's wages to be paid as at Christmas 1916.

Managing Directors' salaries increased

Roland Green	£950
W.A. Kershaw	£900
F.J. Thomas	£700

Wood Pulp costs £62.10.0. per ton delivered.

Tinted Writings 7d per lb, Pre-war 3d.

Between 80 and 90 men had joined the Army.

Water Tube Boiler ordered from John Thompson.

A.B. Russell's fee advanced to 60 guineas plus expenses.

July 31st, 1917	Still Profit Sharing!!
	Women's Welfare Supervisor appointed.
	Decided on Parsons' make of Turbine.
Oct. 15th, 1917	P. Cooke (Chief Order Clerk) having died as a prisoner of war in Germany, agreed to make an allowance to widow up to £5 per month until son was 18.
	Order of Parsons' Turbine authorised.
Nov. 26th, 1917	L.C. & Westminster Bank offer overdraft up to £15,000 without further security for purchase of Turbine.
	Week's wages at Christmas as before.
Mar. 18th, 1918	"Lowood" house purchased for use of Chief Clerk for £500.
May 28th, 1918	"Moorlands" house purchased for use of Mr F.C. Tew for £300.
May 28th, 1918	Week's pay to workpeople at Whitsuntide.
	£5,000 more to Reserve for Turbine.
	All kinds of raw material being used, waste paper, straw, waste cane, grasses, reeds, mats off foreign bales and any bamboo lying in this country.
	Wood Pulp £45 per ton.
	Straw £4.12.0. per ton.
	Stock Papers Pre-war selling at 3d now at 8d per lb.
	70% to 80% of production going to Government Departments.
	Major Bernard Green's allowance while on service increased to £250 per year.
June 10th, 1918	Major B. Green M.C. appointed Director. Articles altered to increase number of Directors to seven.
Sep. 30th, 1918	Proposed to capitalise Reserves.
Nov. 27th, 1918	Proposed to increase Capital from £100,000 to £200,000.
	F.J. Thomas's salary increased to £900.
	Roland Green appointed Deputy Chairman.
Dec. 18th, 1918	Share Capital increased to £200,000.
Jan. 22nd, 1919	Decision to capitalise reserves taken. Four new Ordinary Shares issued for each seven held.
	Smith, Stone and Knight appointed agents for West of England and South Wales.
June 5th, 1919	Turbine now in course of construction.
	Mr Harris, Chief Engineer, leaves.
	P. Webster appointed Chief Engineer.

	House to be built for Chief Engineer in the orchard.
June 18th, 1919	Directors' fees increased to £100 per year. Chairman's fee to £150. Two guineas given to London Hospital Fund.
July 21st, 1919	Donation £260 to Local War Memorial. Decided to exhibit at the British Industries Fair in 1920.
Sep. 24th, 1919	Fire reported in No. 2 Esparto Shed. Loss £7,629. Sir John Thomas gives five acres of Recreation Field to workpeople. Additional eight acres bought by the Company at £100 per acre. Mention made of Blockmaking Plant. Illuminated Address presented by the Workpeople to the Directors.
Dec. 3rd, 1919	Bernard Green appointed Managing Director. Salaries of Managing Directors to be £5,350 per annum divided as they see fit. Claim paid £7,185 for fire.
Jan. 5th, 1920	Proposal to issue another series of Bonus Shares. Later dropped. Agreed to buy a Refiner from Bertrams Ltd. (This was hopeless from the first and was thrown out in four or five years. JBS.)
Mar. 17th, 1920	E. McEwan appointed Secretary at a salary of £450. Engineer's House finished (£1,605) and Bridge over stream built (£500). Staplegrove House bought (£700). Proposal to put in new machine. Proposal to increase capital.
Apl. 8th, 1920	Consideration of formation of New Co. Proposal to change to C.J. Smith & Hudson as Solicitors if New Company was formed. (I have never been able to fathom why. Godden, Holme & Ward were very annoyed and reasonably so. JBS.) Rushton, Son & Kenyon instructed to proceed with new valuation, fee to be 250 guineas or 500 guineas if used for Prospectus purposes. Staplegrove House to be sold.
Apl. 27th, 1920	Sir John Thomas died on April 15th, 1920. New Company to be deferred. 86" Machine to be ordered at once before financial arrangements are made, subject to agreement with the Bank.

Apl. 27th, 1920	J.B. Sedgwick elected Director.
	Roland Green appointed Chairman.
May 12th, 1920	Wood Pulp £56–£68 per ton.
	Esparto £18 per ton.
	Turbine Generator switchboard, new shafting etc. all in hand.
	Lovells given contract for Machine House.
	Three shift system started.
	Riker lorry bought and garage built.
	Production 3,172 tons—61 tons per week.
	Concrete blockmaking going on a loss of £390.
July 20th, 1920	J.B. Sedgwick appointed General Manager at salary of £1,500 and house.
	Roland Green and W.A. Kershaw ask for salaries to be reduced to £1,000 as they want to gradually ease up working.
	F.J. Thomas to have £1,600 per year.
	Bernard Green to have £1,100 per year
	and in addition a gratuity of £500 to each, conditional on their taking up 500 Ordinary Shares to be allotted to each at par.
	Audit fee fixed at 100 guineas.
	Size House and Pump House and fire pump house ordered with Y.J. Lovell & Sons.
	Wedding present of £25 to E. McEwan and salary raised by £50.
	F.J. Thomas appointed Deputy Chairman.
	Proposed that Capital should now be £500,000
	£200,000 Ordinary Shares and
	£300,000 Preference Shares.
	Some of Ordinary Shares to be workpeople's shares.
	The above to be considered.
July 22nd, 1920	Staplegrove House to be sold to Wiggins, Teape.
	Godden, Holme & Ward to be associated with C.J. Smith & Hudson in any flotation issue if any to be underwritten.
	More talk of Bonus shares.
Aug. 20th, 1920	Proposed Capital be £400,000 in place of £500,000.
	Proposal to alter Preference Shares to 8% and cut out the clause giving them "Priority in distribution of Assets".
Oct. 26th, 1920	Land bought from F.J. Thomas for house for J.B. Sedgwick and contract placed.
	C.J. Smith & Hudson tender their resignation as Solicitors.

(I do not know how they were brought in by F.J.T. but Godden, Holme & Ward were very annoyed and I fancy the resignation was a bit forced. JBS.)

Commencement of Weekly Cost Sheets.

Nov. 24th, 1920   Depreciation reduced from $12\frac{1}{2}$% to 10% and discount on papermaking materials from 5% to $2\frac{1}{2}$% and Repairs Materials from 30% to 20% on the advice of the Auditor.

Feb. 23rd, 1921   Profit for half year to Sept. 30th, 1930 £27,549.

Request from Mr B. Green and J.B. Sedgwick to be allowed to buy shares.

Agreed to allot not more than 5,315 shares at 25/- (Cannot remember the reason for the odd number but probably to round off the capital to an even amount—JBS.)

Resignation of Mr D. Hutcheson, London Manager, who was given a pension of £100 per year. A.H. Starling appointed at £526 per year.

Economiser (Lowcock) agreed on at £1,510.

No decision as to capital (later deferred).

Apl. 8th, 1921   Commencement of trouble with the Westminster Bank.

May 12th, 1921   Memorandum presented by JBS to Board on Sales Agreements (previously given by JBS to F.J. Thomas but he preferred it to go to the Board as a whole.)

Decided to drop F.J.T.'s idea of preferential treatment to Wholesale Trade—circulars to be started.

June 15th, 1921   Report by W.A. Kershaw and J.B. Sedgwick on meeting with Norwich Union re proposed loan.

J.B.S. authorised to approach National Provincial Bank to take over our account, failing that accept the Norwich Union's offer.

Special discount of $3\frac{3}{4}$% to be given to certain firms.

Proposal to discontinue the office of Managing Directors deferred.

June 29th, 1921   Short time started on June 12th, 1921 and still continues.

Esparto dropped from £18 to £7 per ton.

Wood Pulp dropped from £68 to £20–£25.

Steam Turbine started August 1920.

No. 1 Water Tube Boiler started August 1920.

No. 2 Water Tube Boiler in hand.

Total write down of stocks £25,000.

A.B. Russell 100 guineas and expenses.

Sept. 21st, 1921 — Death of Mr W.A. Kershaw on August 28th, 1921.

No progress made with negotiations with National Provincial Bank.

Reid Bros. debt £2,307 written off as bad.

Mr Alan B. Green appointed Director.

Nov. 10th, 1921 — Bernard Green's salary increased by £300

J.B. Sedgwick's salary increased by £200 on account of extra work due to Mr Kershaw's death.

Secretary's salary increased by £50.

F.J.T. reported that a clerical error had been made in a tender to H.M.S.O. for a large quantity of paper (actually half price quoted, JBS) but that he hoped to get a settlement.

Dec. 14th, 1921 — Loss over mistake in H.M.S.O. tender was £489 when they had accepted debit for additional £328.

Agreed to issue 20% more Ordinary Shares at par, offered in first place to existing shareholders and those not taken up to be placed by the Directors.

Further attempt to be made to fix loan with Westminster Bank.

Jan. 19th, 1922 — Westminster Bank agree to loan of £40,000 secured by second Debentures.

Godden, Holme & Ward instructed to break off negotiations with Norwich Union.

Allotment of shares as authorised, December 14th, 1921.

Feb. 28th, 1922 — F.J. Thomas stated that he could not accept any responsibility for the Sales of the Company.

May 3rd, 1922 — Mr Roland Green resigns Chairmanship.

Mr Herbert Green appointed Chairman.

$3\frac{3}{4}$% discount cancelled and scheme of Quantity Rebates started.

Lovells instructed to start reconstruction of No. 2 Beater House roof.

Proposed reorganisation of Management.

May 24th, 1922 — Letter from Bank indicating willingness to help over redemption of Debentures shortly due for payment.

Letter from F.J. Thomas read objecting to certain proposals including his resignation as Managing

Director and the appointment of a new Director.

F.J. Thomas removed as Deputy Chairman.

F.J. Thomas removed as Managing Director.

J.S. Peacock appointed Director with salary of £1,200 as Sales Manager and Organiser of Sales.

F.J. Thomas offered three months' salary as Managing Director—refused.

June 8th, 1922	Memorial tablet to be erected to employees killed in the War.
June 28th, 1922	Very nearly full time reported.
	New water tank in operation.
	No. 3 Machine working.
	1,700 shares issued to certain employees.
	Position of Presse Pate to be altered.
	Secretary's salary increased by £50 per year.
Dec. 7th, 1922	New lease of London Warehouse for 21 years from 29th September, 1922 at rent of £355 to Sept. 1924 and after £500 per year.
	Depreciation reduced from 10% to 7½%
	£850 paid to F.J. Thomas on termination of his appointment.
	Twelve second hand beaters bought at £60 each (about £85 each including dismantling and carriage) eight more to be bought if available (subsequently bought).
	Tower Bleachers to be installed.
	Reported that New General Manager had been appointed at Westminster Bank—J.B.S. to call and see him.
Feb. 2nd, 1923	3,100 shares to be allotted to employees at 22/- each.
	Reported that new General Manager of Westminster Bank was not inclined to carry out intention expressed by them in their previous letter. (i.e. re Debentures). J.B.S. to re-open negotiations with National Provincial Bank Ltd.
Feb. 22nd, 1923	National Provincial Bank Ltd agree to give overdraft £55,000, £40,000 at once, balance as and when Debentures are redeemed. Security second Debentures—up to redemption of first Debentures and then first Debentures pari passu with ordinary first Debentures.
	Directors, other than Mr Herbert Green to give guarantee for—
	£20,000 jointly and severally. Mr Herbert Green to deposit £2,500 Debentures and Life Policy for

235

£2,000—agreed.

Transfer of banking account agreed.

Apl. 24th, 1923   A.B. Starling's engagement renewed at salary of £650 per year.

June 5th, 1923   J.B. Sedgwick appointed Deputy Chairman.

Bank account reported transferred to National Provincial Bank.

Transfer of £10,000 to General Reserve agreed.

Purchase of land from W.H. Ford in Heavens Lea.

Special bonus of 7,500 francs to Basiaux Freres.

June 25th, 1923   James Barr & Son authorised to claim for refund of E.P.D.

No. 1 Beater House to be re-built.

No. 1 Beater floor to be raised to same level as No. 2.

July 17th, 1923   New first Debentures agreed on at $6\frac{1}{2}\%$ per annum for twenty years.

One day's pay to workpeople for holiday.

Mr Bishop gives up Midland Agency. Mr Tyler takes this over.

Oct. 1st, 1923   Completion of cancellation of old Debentures and issue of new ones. Result, £17,200 new Debentures placed.

Nov. 15th, 1923   Mill on short time.

Nov. 20th, 1923   Commencement of attack on J.B. Sedgwick and to a lesser degree on J.S. Peacock.

Demand for Committee of Enquiry by Mr Bernard Green, subsequently waived in favour of Arbitration. Arbitrators, Mr W. Godden and Sir Stanley Johnson. £500 to be paid by the Company towards Costs.

May 31st, 1924   Report of Umpire on Arbitration (Mr Thesiger) read.

See Page 188

Mr Bernard Green asked time before tendering his resignation as Managing Director.

Mr McEwan's appointment as Secretary terminated.

June 4th, 1924   Mr Bernard Green refuses to carry out his undertaking to resign his position as Managing Director or to resign as Director until the Annual Meeting.

W.A.J. Handscomb appointed Secretary.

June 30th, 1924   Mr Bernard Green's resignation as Managing Director accepted.

July 2nd, 1924	Owing to the withdrawal of Mr Bernard Green's resignation as Managing Director, his appointment is revoked.
July 11th, 1924	Mr Bernard Green advised that no claim for salary would be entertained. Copy of Award to be sent to all shareholders.
July 23rd, 1924	Bernard Green does not offer himself for re-election. Number of Directors increased to seven. H.E. Austin and A.J. Clarke elected Directors.
July 24th, 1924	Carl Basiaux asked to attend Meeting. Bernard Green appointed Mill Manager at £750 per year, subsequently increased to £850. A.B. Russell's fee raised to 200 guineas inclusive.
July 25th, 1924	Cheques to be signed by two Directors or one Director and the Secretary. £230 voted to Basiaux Freres (i.e. half loss made by them in under-estimating crop.)
Sept. 10th, 1924	Board do not agree to insure Steam Turbine. "Lowood" house to be sold. R. Jennison (Chemist) to have new house built on land bought from Ford. West End Cutter to be bought. No. 1 Beater House roof to be re-built. Suggested that House on Clapton's Farm be sold.
Nov. 5th, 1924	In future dividends on Ordinary Shares to be paid less tax. Claptons Farm (part) sold.
Dec. 14th, 1924	H.E. Austin sells his holding and ceases to be a Director.
Dec. 16th, 1924	Death of Mr Laurence Green (once a Director) reported.
Feb. 11th, 1925	Three Directors a quorum. Consideration of purchase of H. Allnutt & Son, Lower Tovil Mill.
Feb. 19th, 1925	Rushton to value Lower Tovil at a fee of forty guineas and that the business to be bought. Capital of New Company to be £5,000 in 5,000 Ordinary Shares. Mr K. Barcham Green to be Manager at £300 per year. Management to be under control of Thomas & Green Ltd. Purchase—Cash payment of £1,000 and £10,000 Debentures for twenty years or life of Mrs Laurence Green, whichever is longer, 4½% first year, 5% for 2nd year and afterwards 5½%

	Debentures guaranteed by Thomas & Green Ltd.
Apl. 3rd, 1925	Purchase of H. Allnutt & Son completed.
	Capital to be altered to £10,000 (5,000 issued).
Apl. 21st, 1925	Valuation of H. Allnutt & Sons—

Buildings	£9,976
Plant	11,457
Two houses	1,000
	£22,433

Roland Green asks to buy part of Heavens Lea property. Agreed.

June 4th, 1925 — New stack of Calenders to be added to No. 3 Machine.

E.P.D. refund amounting to £13,782 agreed. £1,262 allowed as counterclaim. Of balance J. Barr & Son paid £1,461.

Reserve for Income Tax on Claim £2,754. Balance used as to two-thirds to reduce value of buildings and one-third to reduce value of plant.

July 8th, 1925 — J.B. Sedgwick appointed Managing Director. J.S. Peacock appointed Managing Director. Both with seven years' agreement.

Salary of Secretary raised £50 per year.

Nov. 25th, 1925 — Liquid Chlorine to be used.

Esparto Boilers to be converted to cutting out. Two Leith Walk strainers to be bought for Half Stuff Mill.

Jan. 6th, 1926 — Directors consider adding further Esparto Boiler.

Feb. 17th, 1926 — Negotiations to be opened to buy some of the farm garden (20 ft frontage).

Apl. 13th, 1926 — Secretary's salary raised to £550.

Loss of Profits Insurance on Fire Risk to be taken out.

Cost figures to be kept more private.

Loan to Tennis Club to build a hard court.

Consideration of new Grass Potcher.

June 2nd, 1926 — Letter of thanks to be sent to G. Hinchliffe & Sons for attention to us during the Coal Strike.

£50 placed at the disposal of the Managing Directors as a Compassionate Fund to help cases of sickness etc.

Authority given for ordering Bleaching Towers etc. (presumably also Grass Potcher).

Profit now to include interest on Preference Shares.

	Six beaters started in No. 1 Mill.
	Half Stuff Mill being modernised.
July 10th, 1926	Miss W. Bell engaged as Belfast Agent.
Oct. 13th, 1926	Two second-hand Esparto Boilers bought.
	7½ ton Crane to be put in yard.
	Half Stuff Mill extension to be completed.
	Overhead Electric Travelling Crane to be put in for Grass.
	Chain Grate and Lixiviating plant on old Roaster.
	New Mixing House and Bleach Plant to be considered.
	New Standard Pattern Book to be produced.
	Mr Bishop re-appointed Northern Agent.
	Mr Harrington takes over Scottish agency due to the retirement of Mr Strathie.
Feb. 9th, 1927	New Effect to be added to the Evaporators.
	Purchase of an Embossing Machine authorised.
May 10th, 1927	Neckar Water Softening Plant not entirely satisfactory but taken over.
	Consideration of putting in "Delthirna" Size Plant.
	£500 put to Pension Reserve.
	Duplex Cutter (?angle) and small cutter to be bought.
July 20th, 1927	New Causticising and Bleach Plant to be put in, including New House.
	"Delthirna" Size to be adopted.
Oct. 13th, 1927	Siding to be altered.
	1% to be written off Buildings allocated to such buildings as the Managing Directors think fit.
Nov. 9th, 1927	Settling Ponds account to be written down to £1.
	General Reserve to be increased to £30,000 from £20,000.
	64″ Koebig Cutter to be bought.
	Week's holiday with hourly pay but no bonus to be given to all employees in the Company's service for four years or more. One day's pay with average bonus to those not entitled to the payment before mentioned.
Jan. 18th, 1928	Mr Roland Green died on December 31st, 1927 after about 55 years service with the Company and its predecessor.

Director	1890–1905
Managing Director	1905–1927
Chairman	1920–1922

————————————

	New Cover Pattern Book submitted to the Board.
Jan. 23rd, 1928	W.B. Stone appointed Director, also appointed Assistant to Managing Directors at £250 per year.
Mar. 7th, 1928	Black Liquor Tanks approaching completion. General lay-out of mill for future discussed and approved.
Apl. 18th, 1928	Two new Esparto Boilers started, also new West End Cutter and part of the Causticising Plant. Chain Grate would be working at Whitsuntide. New brick chimney stack to be ordered. Order for new boilers to be placed with Stirling or Thompson. Mill car bought (15.9 Morris). Mr Stone employed continuously at £750 per year.
May 23rd, 1928	Chimney stack ordered from Chimneys Ltd. £2,294 Steam Boilers ordered from Stirling at £19,750. £500 additional to be placed to Pensions Reserve.
Aug. 29th, 1928	Mr Webster (Chief Engineer) to be given notice as not competent to handle new steam plant. J.B.S. authorised to terminate the contract with Basiaux Freres on the secession from the partnership of Mr Carl Basiaux.
Oct. 24th, 1928	H.G. Montey appointed Chief Engineer. Contract with Basiaux Freres terminated. New contract for 4,000 to 5,000 tons entered into with Basiaux Freres through Price & Pierce as their agents at £4.1.4. C.I.F. London. J.S. Peacock to visit New Zealand, Australia and India owing to the death of our agent in New Zealand, Mr Pitt Snr.
Oct. 24th, 1928	Mr Bernard Green to carry on at the London Warehouse.
Nov. 21st, 1928	Six more Beaters to be put in.
Jan 30th, 1929	First steam boiler expected to start about March 31st. Agreement made with G.W. Railway for alteration and extension of siding.
Mar. 20th, 1929	New Bleach Plant working. Insurance against Loss of Profits through breakdown of Turbine placed. Present market price of Esparto £5.10.0. but we

were covered by the contract mentioned on 24th October 1928.

New spring water tank to be ordered.

May 8th, 1929   F.H. Exley has been appointed New Zealand agent.

Colonial Paper Co.   Australia

Titaghur Paper Co.   India

Thanks of Workpeople for Entertainment given on April 27th to celebrate opening of new Steam Boilers.

Cottage to be built for Salle Foreman.

£250 honorarium to J.S. Peacock for his journey.

May 17th, 1929   Formation of S.A.T.A. for production of Esparto supplies in Tunisia.

May 29th, 1929   J. Tait (Foreman) to be pensioned.

Sept. 26th, 1929   Agreement with Carl Basiaux to act as Technical Adviser at salary of £750 per year.

Directors of S.A.T.A.   J.B. Sedgwick
                                   J.S. Peacock
                                   A. Picard

Capital   1,250,000 fcs.

Dec. 4th, 1929   J.B. Sedgwick authorised to appoint Price & Pierce Ltd as Selling Agents for S.A.T.A.

New Agreement with J.B. Sedgwick and J.S. Peacock.

Commencement of Adhesive Lagging negotiations.

Apl. 1st, 1930   Foundations of new Roaster to be commenced.

May 28th, 1930   J.B. Sedgwick had visited Germany to report on the Soda Pulp Mill at Regensberg at the request of the English Shareholders. As a result of this the Company was soon afterwards put into liquidation.

£250 to be invested as the nucleus of a fund to build a recreation room later in place of the Welfare Room. This investment was made.

£500 additional to Reserve.

H. Allnutt & Son advised to terminate Mr T.L. Green's engagement.

July 9th, 1930   First mention of proposed Sewage Farm adjoining the mill.

Roaster to be ordered.

Letter minuted from Secretary of the Workers' Committee thanking the Directors for having kept the works so fully employed.

Nov. 26th, 1930	Ruling Machine working.
	Morris Isis bought.
Feb. 20th, 1931	Reduction in prices of Stock Papers.
	Mr Tyler's Agreement extended.
June 10th, 1931	Workers' holiday and pay reluctantly cancelled owing to bad trade.
Sept. 30th, 1931	Reduction in Directors' fees, also in salaries of Directors and Staff.
Nov. 4th, 1931	Mill on short time for past six months.
Dec. 3rd, 1931	No interim dividend on Ordinary Shares.
	No day's pay at Christmas to workpeople.
Jan. 27th, 1932	Report on visit of J.S. Peacock and J.B. Sedgwick to Germany and order of Embossing Machine and rolls.
May 4th, 1932	Mr May appointed Scottish Agent in place of Mr Harrington who resigned.
Aug. 3rd, 1932	£5,000 to be placed to Reserve.
Nov. 23rd, 1932	Second Universal Embossing Machine to be ordered.
	No Interim Dividend on Ordinary Shares.
Feb. 15th, 1933	New Embossing Department to be built.
June 1st, 1933	Sewage Scheme still under consideration.
	Sturtevant Plant to be installed on No. 3 Machine.
	£250 to be transferred from Pension Reserve to meet cost of Pensions.
Aug. 2nd, 1933	Association of Paper Mills in Wye Valley formed to watch the Sewage Scheme.
Nov. 22nd, 1933	New final settling ponds constructed for Waste Water.
	No Interim Dividend on Ordinary Shares.
	No day's pay at Christmas.
Feb. 14th, 1934	Third bay to be built of Embossing Dept.
	A.B. Starling's salary cut to be restored.
June 6th, 1934	£250 taken from Pension Reserve Fund to meet cost of Pensions.
	H.C. Montey, Chief Engineer, leaves.
	Day's pay to workpeople at Annual Outing.
	New roof to be built over No. 2 Machine House.
	New issue of Debentures to be put in hand.
July 10th, 1934	Mr A. Thomson appointed Chief Engineer.
	Directors' fees re-instated.
	No. 3 Machine House to be lengthened, by about 35 ft and No. 2 also to same length.
Aug. 22nd, 1934	Mr J.B. Sedgwick and Mr J.S. Peacock given new Agreements.

Mr B.S. Stone and Secretary's salaries reinstated. General salaries are to be dealt with by the Managing Directors.

$6\frac{1}{2}$% Debentures to be endorsed for further twenty years at $5\frac{1}{2}$% from April 1st, 1935.

Nov. 28th, 1934   £10,000 to be written off Buildings and Plant in consideration of the following—

(a) that much work had been paid for at inflated prices after the War.

(b) that certain otherwise good buildings would have to be demolished in the scheme of reconstruction decided upon.

Further Debentures to be transferred from the Bishopsgate Nominees Ltd at £105 each.

No Christmas pay to workpeople.

Reconstruction of No. 1 Machine House.

Web Stock Room put in hand.

Dec. 7th, 1934   Thirty Debentures of £100 each transferred at £105 each.

Jan. 30th, 1935   Further stack of Calanders to be put in on No. 3 Machine.

Further Debentures to be transferred at £110.

Completion of Web Stock Room and Cutting House authorised.

May 15th, 1935   H. Allnutt & Son Ltd, to discontinue depreciation but to transfer £300 per year to Reserve.

June 26th, 1935   Reconstruction of Salle authorised. Also third Press Rolls and Extra cooling rolls on No. 3 Machine.

Oct. 2nd, 1935   Report on Turbine breakdown.

The Loss of Profits should be covered by insurance in connection with this breakdown.

1936   Conditioning Machine.

Secondhand Turbo Generator.

New Pay Office.

First Aid Room.

Laboratory.

Reconstruction of Salle and covered Loading Bay (rail and road).

Construction of an intermediate floor in the Clay House, with an area of 1,500 sq ft to provide for a new ream stock paper stock room, authorised by the Board.

1937   Further bay added to the Embossing Department.

New small stores.

1938	Concreting of Yard finished as far as the Fitters Shop.
	New Fitters Shop.
	Heavy Stores.
	Clay House floor finished and racks almost completed.
	Foundations of Carpenters Shop completed and plans passed.
	Dismantling work in connection with Export Packing Shed now started.
	Printing and Tipping Machine purchased.
	Installation of the Turbo Generator and weir.
1939	Concreted banks of Wye Stream as far as upper bridge to "The Orchard".
	Note: Seybold Guillotine purchased.
	25 h.p. Morris second car.
Sept. 1939	Building work generally suspended during the period of World War II (September 1939 to 1945)
1941	Ministry of Works requisitioned an area of land of approximately 235 ft × 180 ft adjoining our Railway Sidings, on which a building was subsequently erected for food storage purposes. An Agreement was entered into with the Ministry of Food for Thomas & Green Limited to manage this building (to be known as Buffer Depot 148) See Report Book No. 1 pages 390/393.
Apl. 1942	An extremely low tender received for building a new Esparto Shed over and larger than the existing one. Subject to obtaining the necessary permit, which the Paper Control will support, the Board decided to accept same.
July 1942	Permit received for the erection of this larger Esparto Shed and it is estimated it will be completed in three months.
Nov. 1942	Permit received for repairing the Yard outside the Offices.
Sept. 1944	Messrs Cook & Son Ltd tender for a new roof over the Half Stuff House was accepted and the work is to be carried out as soon as a Ministry of Works Licence is granted to us.
Nov. 1945	The Esparto Boiler House roof is now in a serious condition and Messrs Cook's tender for £1,363.15/- has been accepted for the renewal of this roof and the work will be proceeded with as soon as possible.

Sept. 1952   Power House extension built to house the Danks Boiler.

Dec. 1956   Outer shell of the large double roof over No. 3 Beater House was replaced.

PLANT

THE FOLLOWING SCHEDULE SETS OUT ITEMS OF
PLANT OBTAINED BY PERMIT FOR INSTALLATION
AND OR/WORKING DURING THE PERIOD OF WORLD
WAR II (SEPTEMBER 1939–1945),
and
ORDERS PLACED FOR ITEMS OF PLANT FOR DELIVERY
AND INSTALLATION IN POST WAR PERIOD.

Mar. 1942	2 Fordson Tractors purchased, one for hauling Esparto Grass/Straw to the Mill, the other for shunting purposes in our private sidings to take the place of horse haulage.
Apl.	Further Tractor purchased and two trailers for use with the tractors.
May	Permit obtained for the purchase of a 3½ ton Morris Van, the existing one having worn out—it has covered some 120,000 miles.
June	Priority obtained for a pressed steel tank for the storing of Black Liquor (This released a considerable quantity of scrap metal for the War effort).
Aug.	Priority has been given for three more points for our private rail sidings, thus enabling us to by-pass the turntable, by laying rails to form a shorter route to the coal bunkers and line to the Ministry of Food Buffer Depot 148.
Sept.	Applied for priority for a Concentrator, the application is supported by the Paper Control and when it is eventually installed it will do away with the Press Pate, with consequent saving in labour and manpower. *Note:* This was not installed as originally planned.
Feb. 1943	Priority obtained for three more turnouts for our private railway siding.
Aug.	Order placed with A. Edmeston for a Duplex Cutter—estimated cost £3,925. Subsequently delivered and installed and in operation in 1951.
July 1944	Order placed for a Vicery Dirtec Separator for No. 3 Papermaking Machine at a cost of approximately £916. Licence was refused at this time, but subsequently obtained and delivery was made in January 1946.

May 1945	12 cwt Good Lift.
Jan. 1946	2 ton Morris Hoist ordered—in operation in 1947.
Jan.	Automatic control equipment for our Sterling Water Tube Boilers—cost approximately £1,273 ex Geo. Kent Limited.
June	3 ton Crane ordered for the new and enlarged Esparto Shed. This came into operation in 1948 at a cost of approximately £1,014.
July 1947	200 kW Generator purchased for £400 and two Diesel Engines of 135 h.p. each for £550 per engine.
Nov.	54 kW Cummins Diesel Generating set purchased from Ministry of Supply. Cost approximately £1,157 to date—installed and working satisfactorily.
Feb. 1948	Electric Automatic Pumping set ordered. Delivered and installed. In operation October 1949 at a cost of £1,000 approximately—ex the Automatic Sprinkler Co. Ltd.
Apl.	J. W. Cubbage & Son carried out work on the Esparto Duster and dust extraction plant installed to minimise dust problems and improve the working conditions generally of the dustermen. Cost around £700.
July	Ford Prefect Car MPE 728 purchased.
Oct. 1949	5 ton Fordson Van delivered and in operation. Cost around £1,000. This will enable deliveries by road to the Midlands, West Country and the North.
Easter 1953	Scheme 5 First Phase of power re-organisation Scheme D.C. to A.C., Electricity Sub-Station, Rectifier, etc.
May	Fleming Pulper ex Frasers (London) Ltd. £1,180. In operation February 1954.
Aug.	Danks 12,000 lb Super Economic Boiler £10,030.
Aug.	New liquid pipe feed system to Beaters, including re-siting and improvement of Press Pate and Strainers. Estimated cost £11,000.
Oct.	Aquamist Spray for No. 1 Machine ex Watford Engineering—£658.
Apl. 1954	New Rotary Roaster Shell ordered from Ernest Scott—in operation 1956. Cost £3,151.
May	Ordered Avery 5301 Combined road and rail Weighbridge—in operation 1956. Cost £1,071.
July	Radcliffe Saveall for No. 3 Papermaking Mach-

		ine—in operation 1955. Cost £955 plus £400 for tank and piping.
July		Jagenberg two drum high speed Slitter delivered and in operation Sept. 1955. Cost £5,673.
Oct. 1954	Scheme 12	Second Phase of power re-organisation. Metropolitan Vickers 500 kW. Turbo-Alternator Set and control equipment. (In consultation with and via National Boiler and General Insurance Company Limited) In operation August 1955.
Mar. 1955	Scheme 7	No. 3 papermaking machine alterations:

Projection Slice

Alteration to	In operation
Wire part	September
Press part	1955
Dry part	

Apl.	Radcliffe Saveall for No. 1 Papermaking Machine installed and in operation in 1956. Cost £808.
July/Aug. 1956	Masson Scott Midget Refiner—Cost £1,114. 10s.

OFFER DOCUMENTS
for the acquisition of

Y. TROTTER & SON LIMITED

Directors:
Gordon G. Ruffle (*Chairman*)
J.M. Hay
Grahame Stoddart
J.M. Askew
W.B. Swan
T.B.S. Gladstone
G.T. Mandl

Registered Office:
Chirnside Bridge Paper Mill,
Duns,
Berwickshire.
18th August, 1967.

To the Members of Y. Trotter & Son Ltd.:

Dear Sir(s)/Madam,

I am now in a position to submit to you details of the proposed merger with Thomas & Green, Ltd. ("Thomas & Green") and there are enclosed the various documents in that connection.

The scheme falls into two phases and, although the second phase does not directly affect you, it does form an integral part of the scheme. The proposals are:

1. The Fourstones Paper Mill Company Ltd. ("Fourstones") offers to acquire the whole of the issued ordinary share capital of Y. Trotter & Son Ltd. ("Trotter") and, as a separate offer, the whole of its preference share capital in exchange for a total of 12,213 of the Ordinary shares of £1 each of Thomas & Green which Fourstones owns.
2. Thomas & Green will acquire from Fourstones the shares of Trotter agreed to be sold to Fourstones.

The result, assuming that all shareholders agree, will be that Trotter will be a wholly owned subsidiary of Thomas & Green.

As mentioned in my letter to you in May the company's affairs are at a most critical period and the position has unfortunately shown no indication of improving. Your directors have been seeking a solution whereby, instead of placing the company in voluntary liquidation and thereby being forced to sell assets at break-up values, it would be possible to merge our business with another comparable concern so as to achieve considerable economies which would enable your company to survive in the present extreme pressures in the

Industry. The opportunity for achieving this was suggested by Mr. G.T. Mandl who, as you know, joined our Board in May, and the scheme now submitted to you has been formulated in conjunction with the Boards of Thomas & Green and Fourstones.

Your directors take the realistic view that, in the event of a Liquidator being appointed and forced to sell the assets—in such circumstances Balance Sheet values have little relevance, particularly in the case of papermaking mills, which cannot conveniently or profitably be altered to other uses—the likelihood of there being anything left for shareholders after meeting all liabilities and allowing for the costs and expenses of liquidation would be extremely problematical.

All your directors, independently of Mr. Mandl (who has not, of course, voted as a director of Fourstones, Thomas & Green or your company in regard to these transactions), consider the terms of the offers fair and reasonable and they intend to accept them in respect of the holdings which they own or control. They strongly recommend their acceptance by all other shareholders.

You will appreciate that it is not easy to forecast the prospects of Thomas & Green after merging with your company but it is felt that there is considerable potential in the rationalisation of the two companies following the merger. In the meantime papermaking at Chirnside has been suspended although it is intended to continue and develop there the finishing of traditional papers and also the engineering side of activities. The principal operating mill will be Thomas & Green at Wooburn Green.

PROCEDURE FOR ACCEPTANCE

To accept the Offers relating to your holding, you must complete and sign the enclosed Form of Acceptance and Transfer or, if you are a holder of both classes of shares, both the red and grey forms enclosed should be completed in accordance with the conditions thereon, and return them, together with the relative Share Certificate(s), to the Secretary, Y. Trotter & Son Limited, Ayton, Eyemouth, Berwickshire, as soon as possible, but in any event so as to arrive not later than 11th September, 1967.

No acknowledgment of receipt of these documents will be given, but if the documents which you have forwarded are in order, certificates for fully paid Ordinary Shares of Thomas & Green will be sent by post at your risk within 28 days after the Offers become unconditional.

In the event of either Offer lapsing, the appropriate Share Certificate(s) forwarded by you or on your behalf will be returned by post at your risk, together with your Form of Acceptance and Transfer, within 14 days. If your Share Certificate(s) is/are not readily available or has/have been lost, you may nevertheless complete the

250

Form of Acceptance and Transfer and forward it in accordance with the above instructions. Fourstones may, at its discretion, treat acceptances as valid notwithstanding any irregularities or that they are not accompanied by the relative Share Certificate(s), but no allotment will be made until any irregularity in the Form of Acceptance and Transfer has been resolved and the Share Certificate(s) or acceptable indemnity has been delivered.

ADDITIONAL INFORMATION

No payment or other benefit is being made to any of your Directors as compensation for loss of office or as consideration for or in connection with their retirement from office. Mr D.A. Huckle, the present General Manager of your Company, is to join the Board of Thomas & Green.

Except as set out in Appendix B of the Offers your Directors know of no material change in the financial position or prospects of your Company since 2nd July, 1966, being the date of the latest published accounts other than in the normal course of trading.

Excepting Mr G.T. Mandl (in connection with the Agreement between Thomas & Green and Fourstones referred to in the enclosed Letter of Offers) none of the Directors of Trotter has any interest in any contracts entered into by Fourstones.

There is set out in Appendices A and B of the Offers further general information regarding Thomas & Green and your Company respectively which has been provided by the Directors of each Company.

Yours faithfully,
GORDON G. RUFFLE,
Chairman

OFFERS
by
THE FOURSTONES PAPER MILL COMPANY LIMITED
for the
PREFERENCE AND ORDINARY SHARES
of
Y. TROTTER & SON LIMITED

THE FOURSTONES PAPER MILL COMPANY LTD

Directors:
G.T. Mandl (*Chairman*)
A.E. Harris
R.R. Rudd

South Tyne Mill,
Fourstones,
Hexham,
Northumberland

To the Members of
Y. Trotter & Son Limited

18th August, 1967

Dear Sir(s) or Madam,

Following the recent discussions with your Board, The Fourstones Paper Mill Company Limited ("Fourstones") hereby offers to acquire, free from liens, charges and encumbrances and with all rights attached thereto the whole of the issued Share Capital of Y. Trotter & Son Limited ("Trotter") on the following terms and subject to the following conditions:–

BASIS OF EXCHANGE

(1) *Ordinary Shares.* For every 4 Ordinary Shares of £5 each of Trotter which you hold, Fourstones will transfer to you One fully paid Ordinary Share of £1 of Thomas & Green, Limited ("Thomas & Green").

(2) *Preference Shares.* For each Preference Share of £5 of Trotter which you hold Fourstones will transfer to you One fully paid Ordinary Share of £1 of Thomas & Green.

The Ordinary Shares of Thomas & Green will be transferred free from all charges, liens and encumbrances.

Any holder entitled to a fraction of a £1 Thomas & Green share will have the right to elect either:–

(a) to have paid to him 5s., 10s. or 15s. cash for each quarter, half or three quarters of a share respectively; or

252

(b) upon paying the cash necessary to make up 20s. per share to have transferred to him an additional Thomas & Green Ordinary Share held by Fourstones.

AGREEMENT WITH THOMAS & GREEN

An Agreement made the 17th August, 1967, between Thomas & Green and Fourstones provides for the transfer to Thomas & Green of the shares in Trotter in respect of which acceptances are received. The Agreement is conditional upon these Offers becoming unconditional and acceptances in respect of not less than ninety per cent of the issued shares of each class of Trotter being received.

CONDITIONS OF THE OFFERS

The Offers, which are to be treated as being made separately in respect of each class of Share Capital of Trotter, are subject to the following conditions:-

(a) In the case of the Offer for Ordinary Shares acceptances being received on or before 11th September, 1967 (or such later date, not being later than 21st September, 1967, as Fourstones may decide), in respect of not less than 90% (or such lesser percentage, if any, as Fourstones may decide to accept as sufficient) of the issued Ordinary Shares of Trotter;

(b) In the case of the Offer for Preference Shares:-

(i) acceptances being received on or before 11th September, 1967 (or such later date, not being later than 21st September, 1967, as Fourstones may decide), in respect of not less than 90% (or such lesser percentage, if any, as Fourstones may decide to accept as sufficient) of the issued Preference Shares of Trotter; and

(ii) The Offer for the Ordinary Shares of Trotter becoming unconditional.

(c) No change taking place in the issued share capital of and no special resolution being passed by Trotter before the latest date for acceptance whether original or extended.

THOMAS & GREEN

The information in the following two paragraphs has been supplied by the Directors of Thomas & Green.

(1) *Business*. The business established in 1860 was taken over by the Company on its incorporation in 1890. Although its shares are not quoted on any Stock Exchange, it is a Public Company with approximately 200 shareholders. Its business is operated from an established paper-mill at Wooburn Green, Buckinghamshire, specialising in the production of coloured papers, plain and embossed Cover Papers, Embossed Box Coverings and other speciality papers. The mill is well equipped, with two Fourdrinier Papermaking Mach-

ines 84″ and 63″ wide, of which the 84″ machine is at present in production. It includes a Converting Department with Embossing, Laminating, Impregnating and Coating equipment. The mill has recently been extensively modernised with the installation of capital equipment which inludes an oil-fired boiler; an entirely new pulp preparation plant; and moisture control equipment on the paper machine.

The production is complementary to the papers produced by Trotter and there is therefore considerable potential in the rationalisation of the two companies following the merger.

Sales and purchasing are combined with its subsidiary H. Allnutt & Son, Limited, of Maidstone, Kent, and Fourstones and joint Sales Offices are maintained in London, Birmingham and Manchester. These arrangements will continue following the merger.

(2) *Current trading position and prospects.*

The accounts for the year ended 31st March, 1967, are not yet completed but preliminary figures suggest that the loss for this period after depreciation will be in the region of £89,000. This estimated loss is calculated after charging exceptional amounts totalling approximately £32,000 including an ex gratia payment; exceptional depreciation on the disposal of certain fixed assets; a consultancy fee; and a drastic writing down of 365 tons of sub-standard paper stocks built up over past years. The bulk of the operating losses for this period took place in the first half of the year to September, 1966, and for the second half of the year to March, 1967, these losses were substantially reduced.

During the year to 31st March, 1967, two major reorganisations took place within the mill resulting in the operating staff being reduced by almost a half with the result that for the first quarter to June, 1967, there is estimated to be a small operating profit before depreciation. Heavy annual depreciation charges of approximately £17,000 will continue but the Company on its own was already on its way to return to operating on a virtual break-even position for the year. Considerable acceleration of this trend is expected from the merger in the absence of unforeseen circumstances. However, the paper industry continues to pass through a period of deep depression which is bound to affect future profits and makes it impossible to make far reaching forecasts. Every effort will continue to be made to develop production of speciality papers so as to assure the Company's future place in the industry when trading conditions improve.

(3) *Share Capital.*

In the last three years the issued Ordinary Share Capital of Thomas & Green was increased as follows:—

Year ended 31st March, 1965, from 114,169 to 121,669 Ordinary Shares.

Year ended 31st March, 1966, from 121,669 to 127,752 Ordinary Shares.

Year ended 31st March, 1967, from 127,752 to 147,752 Ordinary Shares.

Save as aforesaid there has been no change in the Share Capital of Thomas & Green in the last three years.

MARKET IN SHARES

Only isolated transactions are recorded for the Thomas & Green and Trotter Shares during the past six months. Apart from one sale of 6,000 Thomas & Green Ordinary Shares of £1 each at 7s. per share there have been a few transactions for Thomas & Green Preference and Ordinary Shares at 10s. per share. In the same period there are only two transactions recorded in Trotter Ordinary Shares of £5 each at 20s. 3d. and 12s. 6d. per share respectively. There were no transactions in the Trotter Preference Shares of £5 each during this period.

ADDITIONAL INFORMATION

No payment or other benefit is to be made or given to any Director of Trotter in connection with the Offers as compensation for loss of office or as consideration for, or in connection with, his retirement from office. Excepting the appointment of Mr D.A. Huckle to the Board of Thomas & Green no agreement or arrangement exists between any Director of Trotter, Thomas & Green or Fourstones and any other person in connection with or conditional upon the outcome of the Offers. Other than the Agreement dated 17th August, 1967, referred to above, there is no agreement or arrangement whereby the beneficial interest in any shares acquired by Fourstones or Thomas & Green under the Offers will or may be transferred to any other person.

The emoluments of the Directors of Fourstones and Thomas & Green will not be increased as a result of the Offers becoming unconditional.

DOCUMENTS AVAILABLE FOR INSPECTION

Copies of the following documents will be available for inspection at the offices of Messrs Godden, Holme & Co., 7a Laurence Pountney Hill, London, E.C.4, and at the registered office of Y. Trotter & Son Limited, Chirnside Bridge Paper Mill, Duns, Berwickshire, and Messrs Robertson & Maxtone Graham, C.A., 33/34 Charlotte Square, Edinburgh 2, during normal business hours on any weekday (except Saturday) until the Offers become unconditional or lapse:—

(a) The consolidated accounts of Thomas & Green and its subsidiary and the accounts of Trotter for each of the last three financial years for which accounts have been published.

(b) The Memoranda and Articles of Association of Thomas & Green, Trotter and Fourstones.

Yours faithfully,
By order of the Board,
R.K. DUNN,
Secretary.

PARTICULARS OF THOMAS & GREEN

The Directors of Thomas & Green have provided the following information:—

SHARE CAPITAL

Authorised		Issued
No. of Shares		No. of Shares
50,000	6 per cent Non-cumulative Preference Shares of £1 each	40,000
150,000	Ordinary Shares of £1 each	147,752

Of the 147,752 Ordinary Shares in issue 127,752 are fully paid up and 20,000 partly paid up.

The Preference Shares confer the right to a fixed non-cumulative preferential dividend at the rate of 6% per annum. On a winding up the surplus assets are divisible first in payment of the capital paid up or credited as paid up on the Preference Shares, the surplus in repayment of the capital paid up or credited as paid up on the Ordinary Shares and the balance being divisible equally and rateably between the holders of Preference and Ordinary Shares as one class according to the number of shares they hold respectively. At a general meeting every member present in person has one vote on a show of hands and on a poll one vote for every Share held by him but the holders of Preference Shares have no right to receive notice of or to be present or to vote either in person or by proxy at any general meeting by virtue or in respect of their holding of Preference Shares unless it is determined at a general meeting of the Company not to pay the full dividend on such Preference Shares for the financial year then last past or unless a resolution is proposed affecting the rights or privileges of the holders of the Preference Shares.

Thomas & Green has loans outstanding secured by way of fixed and floating charges on its undertaking, property and assets (including Bank borrowing) which on the 10th August, 1967, totalled in the aggregate £156,888.

ASSETS

The Net Assets of Thomas & Green, as appearing in the balance sheet as at 31st March, 1966, the latest date to which accounts have been published, are summarised as follows:—

			£	£
Fixed Assets as independently valued in 1940, or at Cost, less amounts written off:—				
Freehold land and buildings	.. ..			122,332
Plant, machinery, fixtures, fittings and motor vehicles	.. .. ..			179,900
				£302,232
Trade Investments at cost	.. ..			2,410
Life Endowment Policy	.. ..			9,103
				313,745

Deduct: Excess of Current Liabilities over Current Assets viz:—

Current Liabilities:			
Bank Overdraft (Secured)	.. ..	£150,727	
Trade Creditors and accrued expenses	..	77,654	
Hire Purchase Agreements	.. ..	2,887	
Bills payable	.. ..	31,178	262,446
Current Assets:			
Stocks at cost or lower realisable value	..	142,633	
Debtors (less provision for doubtful debts) and prepayments	.. .. ..	90,228	
Income Tax recoverable	.. .. ..	13,545	
Cash in hand	.. ..	214	246,620
			15,826
			297,919
Secured Loan	.. ..		32,550
Net Tangible Assets	.. ..		265,369

NOTES ON ASSETS

(1) Attention is drawn particularly to the fact that the value of the fixed assets is based on a valuation in 1940 with subsequent additions at cost. The present freehold land and buildings include 40 acres of land and 26 residential properties, the latter were valued this year by an independent firm of Estate Agents at £83,000.

(2) There has been excluded from the above summary the investment in the subsidiary company H. Allnutt & Son Limited, because arrangements are being made for its disposal simultaneously with the Offers becoming unconditional.

(3) Since 31st March, 1966, the Company has sold 8.3 acres of land, the net proceeds of which were £82,500. This land appeared in the Company's books at approximately £1,300. Expenditure during the year to March, 1967, increased the book value of plant and machinery to approximately £193,000 after depreciation. Much of this plant and machinery was acquired on Hire Purchase terms which will increase this item in Current Liabilities to approximately £26,500. Since 31st March, 1966, the Company recovered £20,919 on the Life Endowment Assurance Policy included in the above summary at £9,103; this and the proceeds of sale of some premises

of the company was used to reduce the Secured Loan above to £10,731.

Arrangements have been made for a loan of £20,000 from Forward Trust Limited secured by way of Second Legal Charge on certain of the residential freehold properties of the Company—this will be reflected in the accounts for the current year ending 31st March, 1968. Save as aforesaid there has been no material change in the financial position of Thomas & Green since the last Balance Sheet and Report relating to the year ended 31st March, 1966, laid before the Company in General Meeting other than in the normal course of trading as referred to in the letter of offer.

LOSSES

The Losses of Thomas & Green (excluding its subsidiary company H. Allnut & Son Limited) and dividends paid for the last three years for which accounts have been presented are as follows:—

Year ended	Loss before charging depreciation	Depreciation	Loss after charging Dividend depreciation	Preference Dividend gross	Preference Dividend net	Ordinary Dividend gross	Ordinary Dividend net
	£	£	£	%	£	%	£
31st March, 1964	21,289	13,013	34,302	6	1,470	3	2,098
31st March, 1965	20,690	12,306	32,996	6	1,440	nil	nil
31st March, 1966	51,124	13,188	64,312	6	1,410	nil	nil

The dividends do not include distributions from capital profits made on the Ordinary shares in respect of the years ended 31st March, 1964, of 7½d. per share, and 31st March, 1965, of 1s. per share.

The loss figures in Column 3 above are calculated after deducting all trading expenses including depreciation but before deducting taxation. However:—

(1) The figure for 1965 is after deducting certain adjustments for previous years amounting to £3,400.

(2) The figure for 1966 is before taking credit for a dividend received from a subsidiary from previous years profits of £14,058 net.

DIRECTORS' INTERESTS

The Directors of Thomas & Green hold or are beneficially interested in the following shares in Thomas & Green and Fourstones:—

	Thomas & Green		Fourstones	
	£1 Ordinary Shares	£1 Preference Shares	£1 Ordinary Shares	£1 Preference Shares
R.P. Clarke, The Heights, Henley Road, Marlow, Bucks	2,775	—	—	—
R.P. Clarke and another	2,382	350	—	—
MacA. Bexon, 32 Amersham Road, High Wycombe, Bucks.	4,000	150	—	—
A.G.W. Freeman, 21 Baltimore Court, Hove, Sussex	1,593	425	499	—
A.G.W. Freeman and another	—	—	1,496	500
G.T. Mandl, 45 Westbourne Terrace, London, W.2.	15,729	594	26,370	150
R.A. Purssell, 3 Chiltern Terrace, Wooburn Green, Bucks.	500	—	—	—
R.K. Green, 11 Green Road, High Wycombe, Bucks.	500	—	—	—

Excepting Mr G.T. Mandl (whose holding is set forth in Appendix B) none of the Directors holds or has any beneficial interest in any shares in Trotter and Thomas & Green holds no shares or has any beneficial interest in any shares in Trotter. Thomas & Green holds 1,750 Ordinary Shares of Fourstones. Fourstones before the merger holds 32,250 Ordinary Shares in Thomas & Green. Other Companies in which Mr G.T. Mandl has a controlling interest, hold a total aggregate of 2,325 Ordinary and 1,700 Preference Shares of Thomas & Green. In addition to the above the Directors' families hold a total of 2,250 Ordinary and 666 Preference Shares in Thomas & Green.

APPENDIX B
PARTICULARS OF TROTTER

The Directors of Trotter estimate that the company incurred a trading loss, after charging depreciation, for the year to 1st July, 1967, of approximately £37,900.

At 1st July, 1967, the estimated Assets of Trotter can be summarised as follows:—

	£
Fixed Assets at cost less amounts written off:	
Heritable Property	14,217
Plant and Machinery and Motor Vehicles	127,004
	141,221
Trade investment at cost	100
Excess of Current Assets over Current Liabilities	8,733
	150,054
Less: Short Term Loans to Company	17,700
	£132,354

It should be emphasised that the fixed assets appear at their book values and, as stated in the accompanying letter from the Chairman of the Company, it is most unlikely that these values would be realised on liquidation.

DIRECTORS' INTERESTS

The Directors of Trotter hold or are beneficially interested in the following shares in Trotter:

	Ordinary Shares	Preference Shares
Gordon G. Ruffle	49	39
J.M. Hay	600	100
Grahame Stoddart	300	55
J.M. Askew	—	50
W.B. Swan	5	51
T.B.S. Gladstone	55	—
G.T. Mandl	50	—

Excepting Mr G.T. Mandl (whose holding is set forth in Appendix A) neither Trotter nor any Director of Trotter holds or has any beneficial interest in any shares in Thomas & Green. None of the Directors of Trotter (excepting Mr G.T. Mandl) holds any shares in Fourstones. Fourstones holds no shares in Trotter.

ADDITIONAL INFORMATION

There has been no material change in the financial position or prospects of Trotter since 2nd July 1966 being the date of the last

261

balance sheet laid before the Company in General Meeting, other than in the normal course of trading and as shown above.

It is not the intention of the Directors of Trotter to pay the dividend on the Company's Preference shares for the year ended 1st July 1967, but the dividend for the six months to 30th June 1966, payment of which was approved at the Annual General Meeting held on 29th September 1966, is included in the Current Liabilities referred to above, and payment will be made in due course to the shareholders registered at the last named date.

OFFER DOCUMENTS
for Thomas & Green Ltd

OFFERS

by

THE FOURSTONES PAPER MILL COMPANY LIMITED

for

6% NON CUMULATIVE PREFERENCE SHARES

and

ORDINARY SHARES

of

THOMAS & GREEN LIMITED

THOMAS & GREEN LIMITED

Directors:
R.P. Clarke CBE MA BCL
(*Chairman*)
G.T. Mandl (*Deputy Chairman*)
R.A. Purssell
G. Egermayer

Registered Office:
Soho Mills,

Wooburn Green,
High Wycombe,
Bucks.

To the members of Thomas & Green Limited   28th February, 1972

Dear Sir or Madam,

OFFERS BY THE FOURSTONES PAPER MILL COMPANY LIMITED

A preliminary announcement was circulated to you on the 10th December, 1971 informing you that your Board had received from The Fourstones Paper Mill Company Limited ("Fourstones") notification that it was proposing to make Offers to acquire the balance of preference and ordinary shares in your Company which it did not already hold. Since that date Fourstones has decided to amend the Offer for Ordinary Shares to include a cash alternative of 50p per ordinary share. Fourstones is now making the Offers as amended and full details are given on the following pages.

Your Company is already a subsidiary of Fourstones which at present holds 50.4% of its ordinary share capital. Mr G.T. Mandl owns 96% of the equity in Fourstones and also owns directly 7.9% of the equity in Thomas & Green. Trading by Thomas & Green for the past three years has been profitable in contrast to the catastrophic losses of the immediately preceding years but there has been a downward trend in trading profits since 1969 which has been compensated only partially by a rise in income from letting surplus property. No ordinary dividend has been paid since 1964 and, due to the continuing need for substantial capital expenditure, the directors are unable to forecast when any dividend on the ordinary shares might be expected.

Although your Company's mill and ancillary properties have a substantial potential value, progress in obtaining planning permission for even small parts is attended by very much difficulty, and although some progress is currently being made in a plan for building some industrial warehousing in 4 acres at the rear of the mill, there seems little likelihood in the immediate future of any significant increase in either rental income or capital funds from this source. Moreover any developments which would result in the sale of a substantial part of the land or would interfere with the continued operation of the mill would not be acceptable to your present Board, whose firm policy of continuing paper making at Soho Mill has been demonstrated throughout all the difficulties of recent years.

As Mr Mandl is a director and controlling shareholder of Fourstones and one of its subsidiaries, I have asked Turquands Barton Mayhew & Co., Chartered Accountants, to examine and report on the terms of the Offers. Their report, which is reproduced in Appendix IV, states that in their opinion the Offers would appear fair and reasonable.

In view of the foregoing, having carefully considered the terms, your directors are unanimously of the opinion that the Offers provide better prospects for the minority shareholders than they have at present. Each director intends to accept or to procure acceptances of the Offers in respect of the holdings shown in Appendix IV paragraph 3 of the Offers document and the Board recommends all shareholders to accept in respect of their own holdings.

Yours faithfully
R.P. CLARKE
Chairman

THE FOURSTONES PAPER MILL COMPANY LIMITED

Directors: South Tyne Mill
G.T. Mandl   Fourstones,
G. Egermayer   Hexham,
                                        Northumberland

To the Members of Thomas & Green Ltd.   28th February, 1972

Dear Sir or Madam,

OFFERS FOR THE PREFERENCE and ORDINARY SHARES of THOMAS & GREEN LIMITED

A preliminary announcement was made by circular letter on the 10th December, 1971 of the terms upon which The Fourstones Paper Mill Company Limited ("Fourstones") would make offers to acquire the balance of the issued share capital of Thomas & Green Limited ("Thomas & Green") which it does not already own.

You will see from your Chairman's letter which is set out on the previous page and forms part of this document that the Directors of Thomas & Green unanimously recommend you to accept the Offers which they intend to accept in respect of their own holdings.

1. *The Offers*

    Fourstones hereby offers, subject to the terms and conditions set out below, to acquire all the 40,000 6% non cumulative preference shares of £1 each in Thomas & Green ("the Preference Shares") and the remaining 73,242 ordinary shares of £1 each in Thomas & Green ("the Ordinary Shares") it does not already hold at the date hereof on the following terms and conditions:—

Shares in Thomas & Green	Consideration
For each £1 6% Preference Share	£1 unit of 7% Preferred Unsecured Loan Stock 1996–2002 in Fourstones ("the 7% Stock")
For each £1 Ordinary Share	£1 unit of 5% Deferred Unsecured Loan Stock 1996–2002 in Fourstones ("the 5% Stock")

    Ordinary Shareholders who accept the offer for their shares not later than 3 p.m. on 21st March, 1972 may elect, as an alternative to taking 5% Stock, to be paid cash at the rate of 50p per share ("the Cash Alternative").

    The election for the Cash Alternative can only be exercised in respect of the whole and not a part of the Ordinary Shares in

265

question. The Cash Alternative will in no event be extended beyond 3.00 p.m. on 21st March, 1972.

The 7% Stock and the 5% Stock will be allotted and issued credited as fully paid up on the day following the relevant offers becoming or being declared unconditional pursuant to a resolution of the Directors of Fourstones to be passed.

Payment of interest on the 7% Stock and the 5% Stock (less income tax) will be made annually on the 31st March 1973 in respect of the period from the date of issue of the Stocks to that date.

The offers which are separate offers for the Preference Shares and Ordinary Shares, are subject to the following terms and conditions:—

(A) The Preference Shares and the Ordinary Shares Will be acquired free from all liens charges and incumbrances together with all rights attaching thereto, including the right to all dividends and other distributions declared, made or paid here after except that Preference Shareholders will be entitled to receive the dividend on their Shares in respect of the year ended 31st March 1972.

(B) The enclosed forms of Acceptance and Transfer in respect of the offer(s) shall be deemed to be part of the offer(s).

(C) Irrevocable acceptances being received (and not withdrawn in the circumstances mentioned in paragraph 2 (f) of Appendix IV.) in manner prescribed in paragraph 8 below not later than 3.00 p.m. on 21st March, 1972 or such later date as Fourstones may determine being not later than 26th April, 1972 in respect of not less than 90% of the Preference Shares and 90% of the Ordinary Shares in the Company in respect of which those offers are made or such lesser percentage of either or both as Fourstones may decide.

(D) The additional terms contained in paragraph 2 Appendix IV.

2. *Particulars of the Loan Stocks*

The Loan Stocks will be created by a resolution of the Directors of Fourstones and will be constituted by separate Trust Deeds for each stock. The Trustees of both stocks will be the Midland Bank Executor and Trustee Company Limited.

The Loan Stocks will be issued on the basis that, on a winding up of the Company or other return of assets, no repayment of capital or interest then due on the 5% Stock will be made until the capital and interest on the 7% Stock has been fully paid. However, apart from this and the different rates of interest, the Stocks will be issued on identical terms, which are summarised in Appendix I.

266

3. Information Relating to Fourstones

Fourstones was incorporated in 1924 to continue the business of paper making at South Tyne Mill, Hexham carried on for 160 years previously and this business, with that of paper convertors, it has continued since then. It has two active wholly owned subsidiaries, Paper Mills Sales Company Limited and Lamboss Limited which act as sales agents for the products of both Fourstones and Thomas & Green. Appendix II contains information regarding the share capital, profits, dividends, net tangible assets and current financial position of Fourstones.

4. Reasons for the Offers

Since 1966 when Mr G.T. Mandl and Fourstones first acquired substantial interests in Thomas & Green and, particularly since 1969, when control of Thomas & Green was acquired, the mills of the two companies have been operated with an increasing degree of co-operation including the transfer of products between mills to absorb manufacturing capacity more efficiently, the sharing of a sales organisation through Paper Mills Sales Company Limited and the sharing of engineering services. It is intended that this co-operation should be intensified and extended to other fields. The present divided ownership of Thomas & Green is likely to cause increasing difficulties in allocating the benefits of the joint operations between the two mill companies

5. Proposed Group Structure and Management

If the Offers are declared unconditional it is intended that Fourstones' manufacturing business and the mill property, together with the benefit of all contracts and subject to all liabilities, shall be transferred to a wholly owned subsidiary at present dormant. The assets will be transferred at book value and the sale consideration will remain, for the time being, on loan account. Upon completion of this transaction Fourstones will change its name to "Thomas & Green Holdings Limited" and the subsidiary will change its name to "Fourstones Paper Mill Company Limited". By these means Fourstones will become a holding company owning two paper manufacturing companies, two sales agency companies and certain surplus land at Fourstones. The Loan Stock will be issued in the name of Thomas & Green Holdings Limited.
It is also intended that the Board of Fourstones (renamed "Thomas & Green Holdings Limited" as mentioned above) will be:—

    G.T. Mandl (Chairman)
    R.P. Clarke, C.B.E., M.A., B.C.L.
    G. Egermayer

The Board of Thomas & Green will be:—
   G.T. Mandl (Chairman)
   R.A. Purssell
   G. Egermayer

It is not contemplated that there will be any change in the number or status of any of the present employees of Thomas & Green and Fourstones resulting from these Offers being succesful.

6. *Effects of Acceptance*
   A Preference Shareholders
      (i) The gross annual income of an accepting shareholder will increase from 6% to 7%, i.e. by 16½%. Arrears of income, should these arise, would be recoverable whereas the present preference shares are non-cumulative, meaning that no claim can be made for arrears should a dividend for any year not be paid.
      (ii) The 7% Stock, if not redeemed previously, is to be repaid at par on 31st March, 2002 whereas the Thomas & Green preference shares are only repayable in the event of a winding up or similar return of assets.
   B Ordinary Shareholders
      Accepting shareholders who do not elect to take the Cash Alternative will receive a future annual income (subject to tax) of 5% of the par value of their shares or 10% of the price (50p per share) at which the most recent recorded share sales have taken place. The last dividend declared and paid on the ordinary shares was 3% in respect of the year ended 31st March, 1964. The 5% Stock, if not redeemed previously, is to be repaid at par on 31st March, 2002 whereas a capital repayment in respect of the Thomas & Green ordinary shares would only be obtainable in the event of a winding up or similar return of assets.
   C Taxation—Both Classes
      Acceptance of the Offers for 7% Stock or 5% Stock should not itself give rise to any Capital Gains Tax liability. Acceptance of the Cash Alternative or the subsequent disposal of either of such Stock may give rise to liability to tax on any capital gain depending on the particular circumstances of each individual Shareholder. If any Shareholder is in doubt as to his position regarding taxation he should consult his tax adviser.

7. *Opinion of Turquands Barton Mayhew & Co.*
   Chartered Accountants

Turquands Barton Mayhew & Co. were requested to consider the terms of these Offers. In a letter dated 28th February, 1972 (reproduced in Appendix IV paragraph 6) they have expressed the view that the offers would appear to be fair and reasonable.

8. *Acceptance and Settlement*

    (a) Preference Shareholders

        To accept the 7% Stock you should complete the YELLOW Form of Acceptance and Transfer in accordance with the instructions on page 1 of that Form.

    (b) Ordinary Shareholders

        To accept the 5% Stock you should complete the GREEN Form of Acceptance and Transfer in accordance with the instructions on page 1 of that Form. To accept the Cash Alternative you should complete the PINK Form of Acceptance and Transfer in accordance with the instructions on page 1 of that Form.

These Forms duly completed together with the relevant share certificate/(s) for your Thomas & Green Preference and/or Ordinary Shares and/or other document(s) of title should be returned in the enclosed pre-paid addressed envelope as soon as possible but, in any event, so as to arrive at the Registered Office of Thomas & Green Limited, Soho Paper Mills, Wooburn Green, High Wycombe, Bucks. NOT LATER THAN 3.00 p.m. on 21st March, 1972.

Acceptance may at the discretion of Fourstones be treated as valid if not accompanied by the relative share certificate(s) but no purchase consideration will be sent until the relevant share certificate(s) or other acceptable documents of title for your shares or a satisfactory indemnity in respect thereof has/have been received. Fully paid Definitive Certificates in respect of the Loan Stocks in Fourstones to which you become entitled if you accept the Offer or a cheque for the cash payable to Ordinary Shareholders electing the Cash Alternative will be sent to you or your agent within 28 days after 21st March, 1972 or the date of the receipt of your documents whichever is the later. No other acknowledgement will be sent.

All documents will be despatched by ordinary post at your risk.

9. *Additional Information*

Information regarding the Share Capital, profits, dividends, net tangible assets and current financial position of Thomas & Green is set out in Appendix III.

Additional information relevant to the Offers is set out in Appendix IV.

Yours faithfully
G.T. MANDL
Chairman

PARTICULARS OF THE 7% PREFERRED UNSECURED LOAN STOCK 1996–2002 ("7% STOCK") AND THE 5% DEFERRED UNSECURED LOAN STOCK 1976–2002 (5% STOCK") OF THE FOURSTONES PAPER MILL COMPANY LIMITED

(in this Appendix only called "the Company").

Although the 7% Stock and 5% Stock will be created by separate Trust Deeds the particulars set out below are, excepting priority inter se on a winding up and interest, applicable to each. Accordingly unless otherwise expressly stated the phrase "Stock" in these particulars means each of the said two Stocks.

The Trust Deeds will not contain restrictions on the disposal of or creation of charges on the assets of the Company or any of its subsidiaries or the making of a change in the nature of their respective businesses. Stock-holders will be deemed to have notice of and will be bound by the terms of the respective Trust Deeds as amended from time to time.

The Trust Deeds will contain inter alia provisions to the effect set out below.

1. *Priority on a Winding Up*

The Trust Deeds will provide that in the event of a winding up of the Company, the claims of the holders of the 5% Stock will be received by the Trustees for the time being of the 5% Stock on trust to apply the same

First in payment or satisfaction of the cost, charges, expenses and liabilities incurred by such Trustees (including any unpaid remuneration);

Secondly in payment in full of the claims of the holders of the 7% Stock outstanding at the commencement of the winding up to the extent that such claims are admitted in the winding up and are not satisfied out of the other resources of the Company; and

Thirdly towards payment of the amounts owing on or in respect of the 5% Stock.

2. *Interest*

The 7% Stock will carry interest at the rate of 7% per annum and the 5% Stock will carry interest at the rate of 5% per annum.

270

In both cases interest will be payable annually in arrears on the 31st March each year.

3. *Redemption and Purchase*

   (a) The Company will be entitled on or at any time after 31st March, 1996, upon the expiration of not less than three months' notice in writing, to redeem the whole or any part (to be selected by drawings) of the Stock for the time being outstanding at par together with accrued interest Provided that none of the 5% Stock shall be redeemed so long as there remains any part of the 7% Stock outstanding.

   (b) The Stock unless previously repaid or purchased will be repaid at par together with interest accrued up to the date of repayment on the 31st March, 2002.

   (c) The Company may at any time purchase Stock either by tender available to all Stockholders alike at any price or by private treaty at a price not exceeding £100 per cent (exclusive of interest but inclusive of expenses) but not otherwise.

   (d) All Stock repaid or purchased in accordance with any of the foregoing provisions shall be cancelled and shall not be available for reissue.

4. *Limit on Borrowing*

   (a) The aggregate principal amount (together with any fixed or minimum premium payable on final repayment) at any one time outstanding in respect of all monies borrowed by the Company and all its subsidiaries (excluding except as mentioned below amounts for the time being borrowed by the Company from and for the time being owing to any subsidiary or by any subsidiary from and for the time being owing to the Company or any other subsidiary) shall not without the sanction of an ordinary resolution of the Stockholders exceed an amount equal to one and three quarter times the aggregate of the amount paid up on the share capital of the Company and the amount standing to the credit of the Capital and Revenue Reserves of the Company and its subsidiaries (including any Share Premium Account and the balance on profit and loss account) all as shown by the latest audited consolidated Balance Sheet of the Company and its subsidiaries but adjusted as may be necessary to reflect any variation since the date of such Balance Sheet in the amounts of such paid up share capital and reserves and to exclude any sums set aside for taxation and any amounts attributable to outside shareholders in subsidiaries.

   (b) For the purposes of the foregoing:—
       (i) the Share Capital and the amount standing to the credit of

271

revenue reserves of the Company and its subsidiaries shall not include any amount arising from a revaluation, subsequent to 31st March, 1971, of any of the fixed assets of the Company or its subsidiaries Provided that it shall be permissible to include any credit to consolidated reserves arising from an independant professional revaluation of any freehold or leasehold property of the Company or its subsidiaries for which planning consent for development has at any time thereafter been obtained; and

(ii) monies borrowed shall be deemed to include the following (except in so far as otherwise taken into account):—

(A) the principal amount for the time being outstanding in respect of any debenture within the meaning of section 455 of the Companies Act, 1948, of the Company or a subsidiary but so that in the case of a debenture issued by way of collateral security the amount to be taken into account shall be the principal amount thereof or the amount of the borrowing collaterally secured whichever shall be less;

(B) the principal amount raised by the Company or a subsidiary and for the time being outstanding by acceptances under any acceptance credit opened on its behalf by any bank or accepting house;

(C) the nominal amount of any share capital and the principal amount of any borrowed monies together in each case with any fixed or minimum premium payable on final repayment, the repayment of which is guaranteed or secured by the Company or a subsidiary and the beneficial interest in which is not owned by the Company or a subsidiary;

(D) the nominal amount of any redeemable share capital of a subsidiary owned otherwise than by the Company or another subsidiary; and

(E) the proportion of monies borrowed by the Company and its wholly owned subsidiaries from any partly owned subsidiary which is equivalent to the proportion of its Ordinary Share Capital not attributable to the Company; but shall not include:—

(F) an amount equal to the monies borrowed or raised by a company which becomes a subsidiary (being monies outstanding on the date on which it becomes a subsidiary) until whichever is the later of the date six months from the date of it so becoming a subsidiary and the date of the publication by the Company of the first consolidated Balance Sheet issued after the end of the financial period in which it so becomes a subsidiary;

(G)   amounts borrowed for the purposes of repaying within four months the whole or any part of the monies borrowed by the Company or a subsidiary (other than from the Company or a subsidiary and other than monies borrowed falling within paragraph (F) above) for the time being outstanding (together with any fixed or minimum premium payable on final repayment) pending their application for such purpose within such period; and

(H) the proportion of monies borrowed by any partly owned subsidiary which is equivalent to the proportion of its Ordinary Share Capital not attributable to the Company.

5. *Issue of Further Stock*

In the event of the Company creating or issuing additional unsecured loan stock which is identical in all respects (save for the first payment of interest thereon) with the 7% or 5% Stock respectively such additional unsecured loan stock shall be constituted by a Deed expressed to be supplemental to the Trust Deed concerned and shall form a single issue with the 7% or 5% Stock as the case may be.

6. *Transfer*

The Stock will be registered and transferable in amounts and multiples of £1.

7. *Modification of Rights*

The Trust Deed constituting the 5% Stock will provide that the provisions referred to in paragraph 1. above may in no circumstances be modified. The other provisions of the Trust Deeds and the rights of the Stock-holders will be subject to modification abrogation or compromise in any respect with the sanction of an Extraordinary Resolution of the Stockholders as provided in the Trust Deeds. In addition the Trustees will be entitled at any time and without the consent or sanction of the Stockholders to concur with the Company in making any modification in such provisions which in the opinion of the Trustees it shall be expedient to make, if the Trustees are of the opinion that such modification will not be materially prejudicial to the interests of the Stockholders concerned.

8. *Indemnification of Trustees*

The Trust Deeds will contain provisions for the indemnification of the Trustees and for their relief from responsibility in certain events. Any consent given by the Trustees may be given on such terms and conditions, if any, as they think fit.

THE FOURSTONES PAPER MILL
COMPANY LIMITED
Hexham, Northumberland

1. *Share Capital*

The authorised and issued share capital of Fourstones is as follows:

	Authorised	Issued and fully paid
	£	£
7% Redeemable cumulative preference shares of £1 each	10,000	9,800
Ordinary shares of £1 each	40,000	35,000
	£50,000	£44,800

Preference Shareholders may require the Company to redeem their shares at any time after 31st December, 1973 at the rate of 100p per share or if not so redeemed such shares may be redeemed by the Company at any time on or before 31st December, 1983 at the rate of 110p per share subject to six months prior notice. All arrears of cumulative dividend due on the date of redemption is thereupon payable.

2. *Profits and divisions*

The profits of Fourstones for the period of three and a half years ended 31st March, 1971, based on the audited accounts, were as follows:

	30.9.68 (12 mos.)	30.9.69 (12 mos.)	31.3.70 (6 mos.)	31.3.71 (12 mos.)
Turnover	£299,256	£302,731	£174,531	£310,033
Profit before depreciation or interest	35,855	29,128	19,255	38,256
Depreciation of fixed assets	10,010	11,998	6,220	14,379
	25,845	17,130	13,035	23,877
Interest payable	6,699	6,477	3,895	6,503
	19,146	10,653	9,140	17,374
Preference dividends-gross	350	529	343	686
Retention	£18,796	£10,124	£8,797	£16,688

No taxation has been payable due to relief for prior year losses. No ordinary dividends have been declared or paid in respect of the period.

The above figures exclude the results of subsidiaries. The profits of Thomas & Green and its subsidiary for the three years ended 31st March, 1971 are set out in Appendix III. Profits and losses of

274

the other subsidiaries throughout the same period have been negligible.

3. *Net tangible assets*

Based on the audited balance sheets of Fourstones and its subsidiaries (excluding Thomas & Green and its subsidiary) at 31st March, 1971 the net tangible assets of the group were as follows:

Net assets employed in trade

	£	£
Fixed assets—at cost	178,085	
at valuation by directors in 1964	19,850	197,935
Less Depreciation		69,395
		128,540
Current assets		
Stocks	51,111	
Debtors and prepayments	76,352	
Investment grants receivable	16,244	
Bank balances and cash	226	
	143,933	
Current liabilities		
Bank overdraft (secured)	66,289	
Creditors and accrued charges	79,718	
Due to Thomas & Green	4,818	
Bills payable	13,511	
Preference dividend—gross	686	
	165,022	
Net current liabilities		21,089
		107,451
Loans (£5,863 secured)		45,585
		61,866
Shares in Thomas & Green at cost		58,072
Net tangible assets		£119,938

NOTES:
1) Stocks are stated at the lower of cost and net realisable value. Cost of finished paper includes a proportion of mill overheads,
2) The Directors of Fourstones are of the opinion that the market value of land and buildings exceeds the amount (£19,850) stated in the balance sheet but they are unable to estimate the difference.
3) At 31st March, 1971 commitments for capital expenditure amounted to £17,400; no further capital expenditure had at that date been approved by the board.
4) At 31st March, 1971 Fourstones had accumulated tax losses of approximately £18,000 available against future profits.

5) Loans comprised:

Repayable by instalments extending to 1984	3,301
Repayable on demand (including £30,000 subsequently deferred at to date of payment)	42,284
	£45,585

4. *Current financial position*

Save as disclosed herein and other than in the normal course of business, there have been no material changes in the financial position of Fourstones or its subsidiaries since 31st March, 1971.

THOMAS & GREEN LIMITED
High Wycombe, Buckinghamshire

1. *Share Capital*

The authorised and issued share capital of Thomas & Green is as follows:

	Authorised	Issued and fully paid
	£	£
6% non-cumulative Preference shares of £1 each	50,000	40,000
Ordinary shares of £1 each	150,000	147,752
	200,000	187,752

2. *Profits and Dividends*

The consolidated profits of Thomas & Green and its subsidiary and the dividends paid for the three years ended 31st March, 1971, based on the audited published accounts, were as follows:

	1969	1970	1971
Turnover	£630,045	£651,663	£681,856
Trading profit before depreciation ..	61,676	57,876	47,984
Depreciation of fixed assets	25,733	25,733	40,750
	35,943	32,143	7,234
Net rental income	1,249	8,527	14,716
	37,192	40,670	21,950
Interest payable	19,567	18,239	21,195
	17,625	22,431	755
Preference dividends (gross)	2,400	2,400	2,400
Retention	£15,225	£20,031	£(1,645)

No taxation has been payable due to relief for prior year losses. No ordinary dividends have been declared or paid in respect of the period.

3. *Net tangible assets*

Based on the audited consolidated balance sheet at 31st March, 1971, the net tangible assets of Thomas & Green and its subsidiary were as follows:

	£
Fixed assets at cost or valuation	664,320
Less Depreciation	297,081
	367,239

Current assets

Stocks	..	..	..	196,340
Due from Fourstones		..	..	14,701
Debtors and prepayments	..	..	..	191,360
Investment grants receivable		..	..	18,981
Bank balances and cash	..	..	..	717
				£422,099

Current liabilities

Bank overdrafts (secured)	..	..	..	95,985
Creditors and accrued charges		..	..	157,936
Due to fellow subsidiaries of Fourstones		..	9,883
Hire purchase accounts	..	..	..	14,497
Bills payable ..	..	..	..	38,271
Preference dividend (gross)	..	..	..	2,400
				£318,972

Net current assets	..	..	..	103,127
				470,366
Loans (£115,550 secured)	..	..	..	116,948
Net tangible assets	..	..	..	£353,418

NOTES

1) Fixed assets comprise:

Assets valued in 1940	..	..	..	..	136,954
Subsequent additions at cost	..	..	..	527,366
					£664,320

2) The directors' report for the year ended 31st March, 1971 stated that the board was of the opinion that the market value of the group's land and buildings exceeded the amount (£128,832) stated in the balance sheet but that the board was unable to estimate the difference.

3) Stocks are stated at the lower of cost and net realisable value. The cost of finished paper includes a proportion of mill overheads.

4) At 31st March, 1971 commitments for capital expenditure amounted to £35,000 and capital expenditure approved, for which no contracts had been placed, amounted to £8,000.

5) At 31st March, 1971 Thomas & Green had accumulated tax losses of approximately £185,000 available against future profits.

6) Loans comprise:

Repayable by arrangement beginning not earlier than 1974—secured	90,000
Repayable by December, 1975 in quarterly instalments—secured	23,750
Repayable on demand	1,398
Repayable on or before 22nd January, 1974—secured	1,800
	£116,948

4. *Current financial position*

Save as disclosed herein and other than in the normal course of business there have been no material changes in the financial position of Thomas & Green and its subsidiary since 31st March, 1971.

GENERAL INFORMATION

1. *Responsibility for Statements*

This document has been approved for issue by the Boards of Fourstones and Thomas & Green. The Directors of each Company present at the relevant meetings have considered all statements of fact and opinion contained in the documents and accept collectively and individually, responsibility for the accuracy of all such statements of fact so far as relating to their own Company or its subsidiaries or its Directors and for the bona fides of any opinions expressed herein by or on behalf of their Company or its Directors and confirm that to the best of their knowledge and belief no material factors or considerations have been omitted which ought properly to be disclosed herein by their Company.

2. *Additional Terms of the Offers*

(a) Any extensions of the last date for acceptance of the offers (as provided in paragraph (1) (C) of the Offer Letter) will be announced on or before the working day next following the day on which the offer would otherwise have closed.

(b) On the working day following the expiry of the acceptance period (as from time to time extended) ("the relevant day") Fourstones shall announce, in relation to the offers for each class of shares separately, the total number of Ordinary shares or as the case may be Preference shares (as nearly as practicable):

    (i) for which acceptances of the relevant offer have been received;

    (ii) acquired or agreed to be acquired during the course of the relevant offer; and

    (iii) held before the offer.

(c) In computing the number of shares represented by acceptances there may be included or excluded for the purposes of the announcement acceptances not in all respects in order or subject to verification.

(d) References herein for the making of an announcement include (should this prove necessary) the release of an announcement by advertising agents to the press.

(e) No revision of the offers is intended.

(f) If, having declared the offers unconditional, Fourstones shall fail to give by 3.30 p.m. on the relevant day, the remaining information required under paragraph (b) above, such declaration shall be void, and immediately thereafter and pending a further such declaration (which must be accompanied by the information required under paragraph (b) above and may not be made before the expiry of eight days after the relevant day) any person who has already accepted the offers shall be entitled to withdraw his acceptance by notice in writing to The Secretary, Thomas & Green Limited, Soho Paper Mills, Wooburn Green, High Wycombe; Bucks. An acceptance may also be withdrawn at any time after 12th April, 1972, unless and until the offers have become or been declared unconditional. Save as provided above acceptances will be irrevocable.

(g) If the offers become or are declared unconditional (subject only as aforesaid) they will remain open for acceptance for at least fourteen days thereafter unless they become or are declared unconditional on an expiry date and Fourstones has given not less than ten days' prior notice in writing that they will not be open for acceptance beyond such a date. If in accordance with the above provisions an unconditional declaration becomes void and is subsequently reinstated such period of fourteen days will run from the date of the second declaration.

(h) While no revision of the offers is contemplated
  (i) if the offers should be revised, any revised offers will be kept open for at least eight days from the date when the document communicating such revised offers is posted and
  (ii) in any case where the revised consideration represents on such date (on such basis, taking market values where available, as Fourstones may consider appropriate) an improvement in value on the consideration previously offered, the benefit of the improved offer will be made available to acceptors of such offer in its original or any previously revised form and for such purpose acceptance of the offers in any such form shall constitute authority to Fourstones to authorise any person to sign on behalf of any such acceptor an acceptance of any such improved offer. Such authority shall be irrevocable if and so long as the original acceptance remains irrevocable, but any acceptance signed in pursuance of such authority shall be revoked automatically if the original acceptance becomes revocable and is duly revoked.

3. *Material Interests*
  (a) (i) The Directors of Fourstones and their families are interested in the shares of Fourstones as follows:—

	Beneficial Interests		Other Interests	
	Preference Shares	Ordinary Shares	Preference Shares	Ordinary Shares
G.T. Mandl ..	150	33,733	—	—
G. Egermayer ..	—	—	—	—

(ii) Fourstones own 74,510 (50.43%) of the Ordinary Shares of Thomas & Green. It owns no Preference shares.

(iii) Except for 410 Ordinary shares of Fourstones acquired by Mr. G.T. Mandl in November, 1971 and 690 Ordinary shares of Thomas & Green acquired by Fourstones in May and September, 1971 at 50p per share in each case none of the interests of the Directors or of Fourstones in (i) and (ii) above have been acquired within twelve months prior to the date of this document.

(b) (i) The Directors of Thomas & Green and their families are interested in the following shares of Thomas & Green:—

	Beneficial Interests		Other Interests	
	Preference Shares	Ordinary Shares	Preference Shares	Ordinary Shares
R.P. Clarke ..	—	2,775	2,216	1,191
G.T. Mandl ..	880	11,766	—	—
	(and see paragraph (a) above)			
R.A. Purssell	—	500	—	—
G. Egermayer	—	—	—	500

(ii) Excepting Mr. Mandl's interest in Fourstones (see paragraph (a) none of the Directors of Thomas & Green have any beneficial interest in the share capital of Fourstones.

(iii) Except for 350 Preference Shares of Thomas & Green acquired by Mr G.T. Mandl in May and July 1971 at 50p per share none of the interests of the Directors of Thomas & Green in paragraph (i) above has been acquired within twelve months of the date of this document.

(c) The total of interest free loans outstanding and due from Fourstones to Mr G.T. Mandl and his associated companies as at 31st March, 1971 were as follows:—

Mr G.T. Mandl	£12,243
London Boxboard Co. Limited	£ 4,500
G.T. Mandl & Co. Limited	£18,673

By an agreement dated 28th February, 1972 referred to in paragraph 7 (ii) below, repayment of £30,000 of these loans was deferred and this amount is now repayable by equal instalments over a ten year period commencing on 31st March, 1973. The balance of these loans remains repayable on demand. No interest is payable on any of the loans. Apart from this, there has been no material change in the amount or the terms of repayment of the loans due from Fourstones to Mr Mandl or his associated companies from 31st March, 1971.

(d) There is no agreement or arrangement between Fourstones and any other person or any Director of Thomas & Green having any connection with or dependant upon the offers except as disclosed elsewhere in this document.

(e) None of the Directors of Fourstones has a service agreement with Fourstones. None of the Directors of Thomas & Green has a service agreement with Thomas & Green.

(f) No agreement or arrangement exists whereby any shares of Thomas & Green acquired by Fourstones will be transferred to any other person.

(g) There will be no variation in the emoluments of the existing Directors of Fourstones as a consequence of the offers.

4. *Pro-Forma Statement of Consolidated Assets*

The following is a pro-forma statement of the net tangible assets of Fourstones and its subsidiaries based on the consolidated balance sheet of Fourstones and its subsidiaries as at 31st March, 1971, adjusted to allow for:

(i) full acceptance by shareholders in Thomas & Green of the Loan Stock Offers now made and the consequent issue of loan stock;

(ii) the acquisition, since completed, of an outstanding minority interest in Paper Mills Sales Company Limited for a cash consideration of £836.

(iii) the completion of the agreement deferring £30,000 of the loans due by Fourstones to Mr Mandl and two of his associated companies referred to in paragraph 3 (c) above and 7 (ii) below.

	£	£
Fixed assets at cost or valuation		862,255
Less Depreciation		366,476
		495,779
Current assets		
Stocks	247,451	
Debtors and prepayments	267,712	
Investment grants receivable	35,225	
Bank balances and cash	943	
	551,331	
Current liabilities		
Bank overdrafts (secured)	163,137	
Creditors and accrued charges	237,625	
Hire purchase accounts	14,497	
Bills payable	51,782	
Preference dividends	3,086	
	470,127	
Net current assets		81,204
Carried forward		576,983

283

Loans

5% deferred unsecured loan stock 1996/2001	73,242	
7% preferred unsecured loan stock 1996/2001	40,000	
Repayable by instalments extending to 1984 secured	3,301	
Repayable by ten equal annual instalments from 31st March 1973	30,000	
Repayable by arrangement, beginning not earlier than 1974—secured ..	90,000	
Repayable by December 1975 in quarterly instalments—secured ..	23,750	
Repayable on demand or within the years 1972 or 1973 (£3,960 secured) ..	15,482	275,775
Net tangible assets		£301,208

5. Market in Shares of Thomas & Green

Only isolated transactions are recorded for the Thomas & Green Preference and Ordinary Shares during the past twelve months. All these transactions record that such shares have in each case been transferred at the rate of 50p per share.

6. Letter from Turquands Barton Mayhew & Co.

The following letter has been received by the Directors of Thomas & Green:—

The Directors
Thomas & Green Limited

28th February 1972

Gentlemen,

In accordance with your instruction we have considered the offers dated 28th February, 1972 made by The Fourstones Paper Mill Company Limited for all the 6 per cent non-cumulative preference shares and the balance of the ordinary shares in your company which it does not already own.

We report that in our opinion such offers would appear in the circumstances to be fair and reasonable.

Yours faithfully
TURQUANDS BARTON MAYHEW & Co.
Chartered Accountants

7. General Information

(i) Except as disclosed elsewhere in this document no share or loan capital of Fourstones or Thomas & Green has been issued since 31st March 1971 and no such capital is proposed to be issued and no commission discounts, brokerage or other special terms have been granted in connection with the issue or sale of any capital of Fourstones nor any of its subsidiaries been put under option or agreed conditionally or unconditionally to be put under option. The authorised and issued share capital of Thomas & Green has not varied from that shown in Appendix III in the past three years.

(ii) On the 21st December 1971 Fourstones acquired from Mr G.T. Mandl the whole of the issued share capital of a dormant company, Goodall Young & Co. Limited, for £1,500 satisfied in cash and on the same date acquired from G.T. Mandl & Co. Ltd the remaining 836 shares of £1 each of Paper Mill Sales Limited it did not then own at par satisfied in cash.

On the 28th February, 1972 by an agreement under seal

   (i) Mr G.T. Mandl, London Boxboard Co. Limited and G.T. Mandl & Co. Limited agreed to defer £30,000 of the sums due to them and then payable on demand (see (paragraph 3(c) above) to equal annual payments over a ten year period commencing on the 31st March, 1973. These loans to continue interest free; and

   (ii) Mr Mandl agreed, subject to these offers becoming unconditional to subscribe in cash at par for such number of Ordinary Shares of Fourstones (taken at par) as were equal to the amount payable by Fourstones to Ordinary Shareholders of Thomas & Green who accept the Cash Alternative. Apart from these neither Fourstones nor Thomas & Green have entered into any contracts which are or may be material in the two years preceding these offers.

(iii) The expenses incidental to these offers including stamp duty are estimated to amount to £3,000 and will be paid by Fourstones.

(iv) The information regarding Thomas & Green contained in this document has been supplied to Fourstones by the Board of Thomas & Green.

(v) Turquands Barton Mayhew & Co. have given and have not withdrawn their written consent to the inclusions in the offer document of the reference to their statement of opinion in the form and context in which it appears.

(vi) If sufficient acceptances are received Fourstones will apply the powers conferred by Section 209 of the Companies Act 1948 to acquire any outstanding shares but such powers will be applied only in respect of each class of shares separately.

8. *Documents Available for Inspection*

Copies of the following documents will be available for inspection at the offices of Messrs Godden, Holme & Co., 7a Laurence

Pountney Hill, London, E.C.4. during usual business hours on any week day (excepting Saturdays) during which the offers remain open for acceptance:—

1. Memorandum and Articles of Association of Fourstones and Thomas & Green.
2. Published Accounts of Fourstones and Thomas & Green for the last two financial years.
3. The letter from Turquands Barton Mayhew & Co. and the consent of Turquands Barton Mayhew & Co. referred to in previous paragraphs.
4. A proof (subject to modification) of the Trust Deeds constituting the 7% Stock and the 5% Stock.

G.T. MANDL
Publications in Paper Trade Press
1970–1985

MARKETING IN RELATION TO THE PAPER INDUSTRY 1970*

(Reprinted from *The Paper Maker*, June 1970.)

Mr George T. Mandl examines some well-known existing definitions

The word "marketing" has come very much to the forefront in discussions and numerous publications in recent years but many people are not clear in their minds of its true meaning and it would be interesting to examine some of the well-known existing definitions in relation to the paper industry.

The first and best known definition of "Marketing" is the fulfilment of a market demand at a profit. Looking back over the past ten years, we have certainly fulfilled the former without, however, meeting the latter.

A second more detailed definition of "Marketing" defines it as consisting of the following three points:

(1) *Assessment of the market*
   Under this category comes the analysis of statistics, market research, forecast of future trends and generally the knowledge necessary for the producer to estimate with reasonable accuracy from the quantity required by the market the anticipated volume he can expect to supply.
(2) *Stimulation of the market*
   Here the supplier has to assess the form of promoting his product—whether by quality, service or other means—in order to persuade a buyer to give him a share of his particular business.
(3) *The sale*
   This is an automatic consequence of the first two points provided these have been carefully considered and prepared.

Once again, looking back in retrospect on the sales policies and financial results of our industry, we come across—with very few exceptions—a total lack of these fundamental marketing methods and find only an over-production due to absence of the assessment of the market and price cutting as the only stimulation.

A more widespread understanding of the fundamental concept of

* Text of a paper presented on 8 May 1970 at a meeting on marketing organised by the Northern District of the BP & BMA. The meeting was held at the Manchester Club.

marketing would therefore appear to be extremely important for the future well-being of our trade and it is for this purpose that this meeting has been organised.

ROOT CAUSES OF ECONOMIC PRESSURE

The Spring Conference of the Technical Section last year was entitled "Technical Changes Resulting from Economic Pressure on Paper Mills". The two-day conference discussed a wide variety of subjects, how the industry could best meet economic pressure, which has gradually been building up over the past ten years.

I should like to examine here some of the circumstances which have led to this economic pressure which threw our industry into one of its deepest depressions during 1967 and which led to the closure of over 30 paper mills in this country.

This depression was not confined to this country but due to the international nature of the paper trade had world-wide repercussions, embracing all the major pulp and paper producing countries of the world.

The root causes of the trouble lie in the structure of our industry. From the smallest one-machine paper mill to the largest of the pulp-producing giants, the problem of capital intensity is common to all, whereby the capital employed by each unit is as a rule turned over only once a year. In such circumstances it is relatively easy for production oriented management to pursue very aggressive sales policies, based on lower cost of additional production being squeezed out of each unit. This policy has led to what is known as marginal costing, whereby only the direct costs of the additional capacity are calculated in order to secure substantial additional business.

The production oriented management which, in the Nordic countries, was almost entirely technical, was unaware of the disastrous consequences of such policies, carried out without any attempt at fundamental marketing.

MARGINAL COSTING

Prices calculated on marginal costing soon became ruling market prices and the production oriented management then proceeded to defend their policies as being "The survival of the fittest" and the elimination of excess capacities by bankruptcy and closure of the smaller and weaker economic units.

Although price levels expressed in terms of the cost of living index had reached an all-time low throughout the world, capital investment continued, regardless of return on capital employed, as long as companies were able to borrow substantial funds based on their previous profit records and the first-class security of their fixed assets.

The inevitable consequences soon followed; both shareholders and bankers realised that the profits earned on the new investments did not cover depreciation and interest. We were fast moving towards a situation where insufficient funds were being generated for the replacement of existing plant. Further fund raising became difficult and the industry was obliged to take stock of its situation and begin to change its policies to an adequate return on capital employed and a sound concept of marketing.

This is the phase into which we are now gradually entering after more than a decade of self-destruction, which was as incredible as it was unnecessary. For it was in this decade that the growth of pulp and paper consumption throughout the world has experienced one of its greatest booms and it is tragic that, through lack of co-operation, this boom has brought the industry to the edge of disaster.

Let us examine a little more closely some of the criteria which have led paper and pulp producing industries as varied as those of Scandinavia, the UK, the Common Market and North America into the same situation of overproduction.

RETURN ON CAPITAL EMPLOYED

The British paper industry produces paper on some 500 machines, of which 50% are more than 50 years old. These machines were written down on the books and it was possible for a limited period of time to produce increases in capacity at very low investment costs.

Due to marginal costing, no new units could compete. This became increasingly evident from the loss figures being returned by mills with substantial new capital investment. The return on capital employed fell to levels at which no investor was willing to risk his money and the price of pulp and paper mill shares throughout the world continued to fall far below net asset values, until a level of yield was reached which brought them in line with other industries. This situation was helped by the very low nominal capital structure of the industry, which had changed little in recent years in spite of world-wide inflation. A situation not dissimilar to investment in pre-war gilt edged securities occurred to those who, quite rightly, foresaw the exploding demand for future consumption of paper and board and put their money into pulp and paper industry shares.

Do not let us be misled by the relatively good performance of some of these equities when compared with others within the industry or indeed the stock market indexes. The exploding consumer boom of pulp and paper since the war should have put our industry amongst the leaders and certainly not at the bottom of the list. It is an incredible fact that shareholders were finding themselves in a situation whereby the value of their shares in real terms dropped far below previous levels after a very extensive investment and modernisation of their mills.

As a result of all this, new thoughts began to emerge. The late Mr William Tait, the well-known Scottish paper maker, put this into a nutshell when addressing the Technical Section in London last year. "Many of you think you are in business to make paper. You are wrong, you should be in business to make money."

Quite apart from our interest in forestry, we have failed to see the wood for the trees.

At long last some of the production oriented technocrats, who have so disastrously ruled the world's principal pulp and paper industries in the past, are gradually being replaced by younger men who have come from more progressive industries with the specific task of improving profitability.

STILL GETTING AN EXTREMELY CHEAP PRODUCT

Those critics of high paper prices amongst our customers should compare present prices based on the cost of living index, as well as the index of wages and salaries, with those of 15 years ago. They will realise that they are still getting an extremely cheap product even after the recent increases and will have to suffer a number of further increases before we reach a truly economic level.

It was most unfortunate that the guilty and innocent suffered alike in this war of excess capacities which we have just experienced. Our two mills did not increase their capacity and, on the contrary, now produce less in terms of tonnage than they did before the war; yet the depression hit us as hard as the rest of the industry and it was a miracle that we survived the losses of the middle '60s.

Our investments have been aimed at specialisation and rationalisation rather than increase in capacity and this must be the right policy for any small mill wishing to remain in business and to remain independent. However much we specialise, we cannot escape the general economic trend of our industry and we must therefore strive towards greater co-operation, better communications within and amongst the companies belonging to our industry in order to earn the profits necessary for the maintenance of our mills in the future.

Paper machines which have lasted 50 years will certainly not last for another 50. The capital cost of replacing them is astronomical in proportion to the size of every unit. Nobody else will help us. No subsidies from Governments can be expected because the world needs paper.

THE THREE MAIN FACTORS

The three main factors which have brought about the present un-happy situation and should be very seriously investigated are, in order of importance, the following:

The continuing over-production has led to marginal costings and resulted in a low return on capital employed throughout the indus-try. It is an established fact that the lowering of selling prices has stimulated no increased demand for paper and it can therefore be safely assumed that consumption cannot be stimulated by price. Once we accept this fact, we should be able to discard any attempt to increase an individual market share based on the mistaken belief that this can be achieved by price cutting. Instead of calculating the return on capital employed based on costs of production and current selling prices, we should make a calculation in reverse whereby the selling price should be calculated on a realistic return of capital employed plus adequate provisions for the replacement of existing plant.

Once this new costing has been confirmed by all the major prod-ucers, it should be introduced as the new basic minimum selling price for each grade of paper by the major producers in all countries participating in any particular market. I am sure that the provisions of the Restrictive Trade Practices Act are directed towards the safe-guarding of the public against excess profits through price rigging but not against the maintenance of a minimum return on capital employed necessary for the maintenance of the industry. We have an example in the Bell Telephone Company of the USA who hold a virtual monopoly and whose charges are judged on the above criteria.

I do not say that this step is an easy one, both in view of the mistrust which has for many years existed within our industry, as well as from the provisions of the Restrictive Trade Practices Act but it is an avenue which must, in my opinion, be fully explored if the in-dustry is not to be faced with virtual extinction in the coming decade.

AN EXAMPLE OF RATIONALISATION UNDER PRESSURE

The second point we should look at is the rationalisation through product swaps, of which a very good example has recently been given by the Swiss paper industry. Too many grades per mill causes a great deal of loss of production and streamlining of these through swap arrangements would clearly benefit all concerned. The Swiss mills, who have, for many years, enjoyed tariff protection and high carriage charges to their home market, have been forced into this step by the duty-free importations from EFTA countries including both Scandinavia and Austria. This is a very good example of rationalisation of an industry under pressure.

293

The third is an entirely domestic question and concerns the substantial additional costs incurred by mills stocking their output.

Very substantial tonnage of paper consumed in this country has to bear the cost of double handling: first into mill stock, then out of mill stock into merchant stock and finally to the consumer. We know from inter-firm comparisons how high the costs of putting paper in and out of stock are to a merchant. It has so far not been assessed that similar costs are being incurred by the mills putting the paper into their own stock. There is virtually no price differentiation between a making order and a delivery from mill stock, although the on-cost absorbed by the mill could well be in the region of up to 15%. If the product is to be distributed to the consumer without a very substantial increase in price, allowing for the double stocking operation, an elimination of one of the stock operations is clearly necessary. The resulting saving could then be equitably shared between the mill and the merchant, resulting in an improvement of extremely poor profitability of both parties. This will inevitably mean that merchants will carry fewer lines with a larger and faster turnover to allow only making orders to be delivered to their warehouses. Where the mill, for reasons of type of product, is still obliged to stock, the upcharge for the stock should go to the mill that carries such stock and delivery should, wherever possible, be arranged mutually between the merchant and the mill direct to the consumer so that double handling is eliminated.

These are some of the outlines which could lead to an improvement of our position. They presume a very much closer co-operation between companies within the industry and indeed between different paper producing countries throughout the world and very much better horizontal communications than we have at present. Also, within individual companies and groups, vertical communication must be improved, as large numbers of responsible executive personnel are unaware of some of the major problems facing the industry. Without this improvement, the great technological advances and skills of our industry will continue to be wasted.

PRIMARY FUNCTION OF MARKETING IN THE PAPER INDUSTRY (1971)

(*The World's Paper Trade Review*, 28 January 1971.)

By G.T. Mandl

Most concepts of marketing are directed, quite properly, at the end consumer, and most statistics are based on annual consumption figures relating to per capita consumption. There is, however, a vast difference between a marketing effort aimed at the consumer, where demand is, to a large extent, stimulated by price, and marketing of an industrial raw material, where price, as a rule, does not have the slightest influence on demand.

The ultimate aim of marketing should be the fulfilment of a demand at a profit. Thus, all consumer aimed marketing anticipates a higher profit in the end, even though lower prices may be charged in anticipation of a higher volume which, in turn, would produce the higher profits.

Our industry has, for more than a decade now, attempted to stimulate demand by price, although everyone must have been aware that the reduction in price would not be accompanied by an increase in volume to compensate for the price reduction. The inevitable result was an uneconomical selling price, with which our entire industry is faced today with only very few exceptions.

This is borne out by the wholesale indices published by the Central Statistical Office. In order to emphasise my point, I will take the year 1954 = 100 and give you the index figures for 1967. The figure for all industrial manufactured goods is 135%, while for paper and board it is 115%.

Do not let us be misled by the fact that raw materials, power and fuel costs, making up the major constituents for paper and board manufacture, had a lower index figure than the rest of industry. This is not the case—the figure is actually higher, highlighting an incredible pressure on margins for paper and board manufacturers.

The raw material index for all manufactures amounts to 110%, while for paper and board it amounts to 114%. If one were to compare this with the general index for the cost of living and wages and salaries, the index based on 1955 = 100 was in 1967 equal to 195–196 for salaries and wages, and 151 for retail prices (see tables 1–3).

I have no suggestions how the UK consumption of paper and board in general could be stimulated, and I do not really believe that it can; paper and board consumption figures have always been closely related to the general standard of living level, and consumption tends to fluctuate with the state of the economy, just as the strength of the paper market seems to follow the stock market indices in the Western world. If we therefore accept this situation as fact, we must also accept that demand cannot be stimulated by price of paper, board and pulp—with the exception of household tissues and possibly a few other specialities in the disposables field aimed directly at the consumer.

If we assume that UK paper and board consumption will continue to grow at the present rate, we are faced with a consumption figure of some 10 million tons by 1980, compared with the 1969 figure of 7 million tons.

It would be unrealistic to assume that two-thirds of this quantity will be manufactured in the UK, which would bring the present production of just under 5 million tons in 1969 to just short of 7 million tons in 1980. The bulk growth is clearly going to be in areas in which the UK paper industry does not have the basic economic advantages enjoyed by integrated mills in Scandinavia and North America.

I would therefore advocate a totally different statistical concept, ie percentage of the market expressed by value rather than by tons, as is the case at present.

The present import share of 34% in 1969, expressed in tonnage, dwindles to 27% expressed in terms of value, and I would consider that the maintenance of this value percentage, projected over the next 10 years, showing 65/70% home produced and 30/35% imported, is not only more realistic, but also more profitable, for it is only on sales on profit and not on volume that the British paper industry need not only survive, but could actually prosper in future.

AWARENESS OF INDUSTRY'S PROBLEMS

In order to achieve this object, a very much greater awareness of the industry's problems within the industry is essential. The large corporations, who dominate the scene, are decentralised to such an extent that their sales staff are unaware of the appalling low return on capital employed and are fighting for the maintenance of market shares by volume rather than concentrating on sales by profitability. This is where professional marketing should come in, with an educational function in the first instance, and which should only be changed to a marketing function when the first pressing need has been fulfilled.

We are also faced, as an industry, with the provisions of the

Restrictive Trade Practices Act which has had, in our climate of overproduction, a tendency to depress prices below an economic level instead of preventing excess profits to the detriment of the consumer, which was the object of the legislators.

Certain representations have already been made for the need to amend RTP in Britain as far as the paper industry is concerned, but as our industry is international, a wider application would be necessary. If, for instance, all monopolies' restrictions were to cease against any industry whose average return on capital employed had fallen below 10%, there would be an immediate upsurge in profitability, productivity, employment and investment incentive, with a resulting healthy industry paying substantial amounts of corporation taxation to their respective governments.

Once the 10% return on capital figure has been reached, the restrictions would immediately reapply to protect the consumer and the profitability of the industry would ultimately fall below 10% and thus the cycle would be repeated. Dare we hope in the common sense of our legislators to adopt such a policy?

Table 1 *Indices of wholesale prices of paper and all manufactured goods*
(1954 = 100)

Year	All	Paper
1954	100·0	100·0
1955	102·6	104·5
1956	107·0	109·1
1957	110·4	110·6
1958	111·1	110·8
1959	111·5	108·8
1960	113·0	108·6
1961	116·0	109·8
1962	118·6	109·6
1963	119·9	109·9
1964	123·9	112·4
1965	129·6	115·0
1966	133·2	115·4
1967	134·9	115·2
1968	140·9	124·4

Source: Central Statistical Office.

Table 2 *Changes in prices of basic raw materials of the paper industries and all manufacturing industries except food, drink and tobacco*
(1954 = 100)

Year	All	Paper
1954	100·0	100·0
1955	103·0	106·3
1956	106·7	110·8
1957	107·4	111·1
1958	100·8	107·4
1959	101·7	104·1
1960	101·8	105·2
1961	100·6	108·4
1962	100·6	105·8
1963	103·0	106·5
1964	107·1	110·3
1965	107·5	114·6
1966	110·9	114·4
1967	110·1	114·3
1968	119·7	121·6

Source: Central Statistical Office.

Table 3 *Indices of wages and salaries and general index of retail prices*

(1955 = 100)

Year	Wages	Salaries	Gen. retail price index
1967	196·0	194·7	151·0
1968	211·2	206·9	158·0

Source: Ministry of Employment and Productivity.

Table 4 *Profitability of 10 representative companies in the UK paper and board industry*

Year	Per cent return on capital employed
1956	22·7
1957	17·6
1958	13·5
1959	15·0
1960	17·0
1961	15·5
1962	13·0
1963	11·0
1964	11·7
1965	12·7
1966	10·5
1967	7·2
1968	8·1

Source: IRC Report April 1968. Calculations have been based on net profit before interest and tax, and net capital employed.

DIM PROSPECTS

If we continue in the present situation, the prospects are very dim indeed. The borrowed money, on which much of the industry has been living in recent years, cannot be repaid from present profits; nor can new funds be raised economically at present-day costs of money. New investments will be restricted to political rather than economic motives and an industry with such a healthy growth as ours will continue to languish.

The remedy is to a large extent in our own hands.

G. T. MANDL CELEBRATES ITS
FIRST 25 YEARS (1972)

(Reprinted from *Paper*, 20 December 1972.)

Guests from West Germany, Denmark, Belgium and The Netherlands, as well as from the United Kingdom, attended the 25th anniversary dinner of G. T. Mandl & Co, held recently at the Stationers' Hall in London.

George Mandl, chairman of the company, who presided, recalled that the "virile child" of the 1950s and 60's became of age with a coming-out party in 1968, and now, at 25 was far from being sedate.

It had a holy trinity of three fathers, the first being Mr De Pooter, who was in his 80th year and had come over specially from Brussels.

"He introduced me to everybody connected with board when I first went to Belgium in 1949 and together we organised an export consortium of Belgian board makers, who shipped a substantial tonnage of board to Britain in the early 50s. When import duties and exchange rates brought this business to a standstill, he stood at the cradle of what is now our Brussels office, with sales of kraft linerboard on the Belgian market. Even now, he still works part time having changed very little and certainly lost none of his energy, since I first met him.

"The second is Dr Beukema, sometimes known as Mr Frog after the well known trade mark of his mill, which in its day produced the finest strawboard (starch pasted, specially treated, of course) in Holland. I will not tell you his age, but it is a well known fact that he is as old as his mill, which was built in 1899.

"This was the new Beukema mill,* the first, now operated by the Hooites-Beukema Co-operative, was founded by his grandfather in 1866 and who was one of the early pioneers of strawboard manufacture in the province of Groningen."

Having been the first to produce strawboard, Dr Beukema saw sooner than most its decline, after more than 50 years, as classical commodity. While more than half a dozen of the Groningen mills closed down, Beukema mill prospered on other products, and finally abandoned strawboard, with a full order book, and a new machine, three years ago.

The third father, Mr Mandl continued, was, understandably,

* This book is bound in Eskaboard, made by Beukema Mill.

Scandinavian. "I am deeply sorry to say *was*—for Mr Sten Lundberg* died on 25 October, having accepted my invitation to attend this dinner. He gave me the first opportunity ever to be given to a newcomer by a major Scandinavian mill since the war, in giving me the Brusafors-Hällefors agency in 1955.

"I gained a great deal of practical experience in pulp and paper making from him and was very sad when he left Brusafors to become managing director of Munksjö in 1960. Our business connection was, however, not severed for long. Our Vienna office were appointed agents for Munksjö and when in 1962 I applied for the Strömsnäs agency, he wrote to Sten Rasch: 'There is no question whether you should take him—I greatly regret that I cannot have him myself'."

What started out as a one man band, assisted by Jack Ulot, and under the guidance of these three fathers, grew very fast, particularly under the impact of Scandinavian agencies after 1958. Harold Gould joined the company 10 years ago, soon followed by Sandy White, who has contributed so much to the continued success of the packaging papers business through a period of upheaval, which closed down a large number of paper agencies that were household names long before G. T. Mandl was started.

"I could clearly see the gathering clouds in the early 60s which spelt doom for the independent agency business from Sweden," Mr Mandl went on. "The growing concentration of the industry meant more and more mill sales offices in London and I often told my Swedish friends that my stuffed effigy would one day be exhibited in the Nordiska Museum in Stockholm, as the last UK agent for a Swedish mill.

"There were other problems: Rising wages and salaries and static paper prices on a fixed commission, which called for a constantly increasing turnover with the same personnel, coupled with increasing marketing demands from the mill.

"My thoughts turned to vertical integration—a captive market—not to control a customer, as some agents did, but to own a British mill and integrate its sales with the agency.

"The depression which spelt the end to so many agents, also brought about the closure of many mills—over 50 in Britain alone. It was therefore not difficult to get a mill, the difficulty was to keep it running. Here again I was very fortunate in having an excellent team with the happy result that this rather daring experiment succeeded and we are today marketing the products of our two paper mills together with those of our British and overseas agencies, profitably through the same selling organisation.

* The illustrations in this book are printed on Silverblade, made at the Silverdalen Mill of AB Brusafors-Hällefors (now part of MoDo), of which Mr Lundberg was Managing Director from 1946 to 1960.

"This year we have repeated this exercise and integrated our ailing Dusseldorf agency with a board mill in Southern Germany.

"I am not going to complain and lament over the loss of some 60,000 tonnes of agency business we have built up and lost to mills' own sales offices, in some cases with our own personnel. A business is like a living organism, and even if lightning strikes a main branch, the tree goes on growing.

"Today, our five sales offices cover the principal European markets and represent a large number of mills. Our own three mills produce some 26,000 tonnes of paper and board and provide long term security to our main activities in the UK and Germany. Our widespread connection has enabled us to diversify further in to market research and advisory services, which appear to grow as a healthy third division of our activities.

"None of this could have been achieved without the support of our customers and I am very happy to welcome so many here tonight. Without them, we would not be in existence. Together with the mills represented here tonight, we drink their health, for many more years in what we hope will be more prosperous times for our trade."

Dr Beukema, who attributed Mr Mandl's success to his great interest in people, was the first of many of those present to pay tribute to Mr Mandl and his organisation, and to express the hope that the second 25 years would be even more successful than the first.

Among the guests were executives from mills represented by G. T. Mandl, representatives from the NAPM Strawboard Section, from paper bag and paper sack manufacturers, exporters, and fellow agents and merchants.

THE ECONOMIC PROSPECTS OF THE BRITISH AND EUROPEAN PAPER INDUSTRY (1973)

(Reprinted from *Paper Technology*, April 1973.)

SYNOPSIS

The paper industry in Europe has been passing through a severe economic crisis in recent years. The possible motivation of those responsible for this situation is discussed, as well as alternatives for defence and prospects for the future.

1. INTRODUCTION

Looking around the paper industry in Europe today is reminiscent of a battlefield scene where neither side has won and both sides have suffered very heavy casualties. The area is littered with the dead and wounded.

In human terms it is a relatively harmless situation, for instead of blood only money flows into the ground, but like human resources the dead cannot be revived and the rehabilitation of the wounded is a very long and costly process. We may well ask ourselves the question why it happened and whether it was really necessary in an industry that is far from declining, but involving a production for which demand is rising at a higher rate than most other industrial commodities in the western world.

It is well known that the basic reason for this situation is that more paper was produced than the market was able to consume. Although consumption has risen steadily, the increases have not taken place in regular annual steps and they have been tied to the growth of the western European economy in general.

Following the recession of 1967, we had a rather sharp increase in consumption during 1968–1969 followed by a levelling-off and an actual minor decline in 1970–1971. This is now being caught up by another sharp increase during this year. All appears therefore to be set fair for 1973, but we can already forecast the next recession, based on the cyclical experience of previous years, to take place some time in 1975.★

If, as individuals and indeed individual companies and mills, there is very little, or nothing, we can do about this highly unfortunate situation, we can at least try and analyse the reasons behind it and the motivation of those who bring about the consequences.

★ The 1975 Recession was correctly forecast in 1972.

302

2. MOTIVATION

In theory, the responsibility is wholly collective and rests squarely on the shoulders of the pulp and paper industries of the world.

Basically, the individual motivation is aimed at achieving a profit for the company, but the ways to this rather desirable end are extremely strange.

The first of these is the assumption that new units installed at very high capital cost, but low labour cost, would out-compete older written-off units operating their mills on a low capital but high labour cost. The initial calculation shows a loss on account of high depreciation, interest and capital charges in spite of low labour costs but anticipates a reversal of the situation when, through the passage of time, the depreciation will have been reduced and the low labour cost will win over the older unit, thus producing a profit.

The second motivation is one of strength and power of the big corporations and those who lead them. We have a situation very similar to that in politics, where the interests of the shareholders (in politics, the electorate) are thrown overboard in favour of winning a great victory over their opponents and after they have forced them into closing their mills, profit will be their ultimate end result.

The third motivation is one of pure technology without marketing, utilisation of natural resources and subsequent conquest of markets through price.

The immediate result of all three motivations described above is very clearly a net loss. They have one thing in common—no marketing, ignorance of the basic fact that demand cannot be stimulated by price. In each case, however, there is a justification.

In the first instance, the ultimate strength of the modern unit with its lower labour costs over the older mills; in the second, the greater market share after eliminating the competition through forcing it to close; in the third, the ultimate victory of the technologically perfectly sited units basing their output on enormous resources of raw materials and cheap power. As in politics these promises are hardly ever fulfilled. In the last few decades, no war has ever left a nation better off than it was before it started and no electorate would have voted voluntarily in favour of going to war unless in sheer defence of their lives and freedom.

The same applies to our industry. The war which has now been raging for some 10 years has involved all those mills who were not prepared voluntarily to close down their production and hand over their orders to their competitors. The electorate, that is, the shareholders, were never consulted and certainly would never have agreed to the rather irresponsible course that our industry has taken, although it is all supposed to be for their good in the long term. I totally fail to see any advantage to any shareholder coming as a result of all this and I would gladly challenge any company boss who has been largely responsible for this over-production to prove me wrong.

3. POSSIBLE MEANS OF DEFENCE

We can next ask ourselves what defence a mill, region or country has against this situation—what lessons can be drawn from past experience?

The possibilities of a company's defence depend entirely on its size, production and location. A newsprint mill, for example, can survive in Southern Germany, close to the scarce forest resources in continental Europe and far away from the ports that bring in cheap Scandinavian and North American imports. A similar company situated, for instance, in the Netherlands or in the UK would be facing the greatest difficulties. A de-inking waste mill has failed in Sweden, but has succeeded in the UK and the processing of waste is generally the best defence in a market with a high density of population and far removed from the forest resources of integrated mills. A small speciality mill can survive in a large market, but it would soon be out of business if it exported its entire output of speciality papers. Retreat into specialisation can only take place, therefore, for a limited number of mills in a limited number of large markets, otherwise overproduction of specialities will result with the same disastrous consequences that have already overtaken the rest of the industry.

Defence can also be taken on a national basis through the active intervention of trade associations, such as in France, or governmental intervention through tariffs, such as in Spain or the Republic of Ireland. These usually have very severe repercussions, as most advanced nations have substantial bilateral trade and any restrictions on imports, or trade tariffs for any commodity bring with them immediate reciprocal disadvantages from their trading partners. Therefore, this is a rather difficult course to follow for any of the highly developed countries, such as the enlarged EEC, and the matter rests, as it always has done, collectively on the industry as a whole.

Many companies still operating today do so in an economically much weaker position than they did 10 years ago, having been depleted of their resources and reserves and unable to borrow any more money to maintain their mills at an efficient level. Many machines are still being operated at a direct loss, although the majority of these have now been closed down. Unfortunately, most of the closures took place after involving the mill in very substantial losses that could have been foreseen as all cost factors and selling levels were known. Yet, incredibly, the obvious step of closing *before* the losses had piled up was, in many cases, not taken, perhaps in anticipation of some miracle that did not materialise. When they finally closed down, the losses involved often exceeded the book value of the machine. Therefore, the cost of hanging on is extremely high and a closure before the loss is clearly preferable to a closure after the loss.

4. THE FUTURE

What is going to be the future pattern? The old school of thought that this or that country or region is *our* market is clearly no longer viable. Amongst the free trading nations, pulp, paper and board is one market and each unit must take a detached and highly critical look at itself and ask itself the questions—*how* viable is it? How profitable is it now? How much money is being generated to *maintain* that profitability? How should any funds, either generated or borrowed, be invested in the mill? Clearly not in increasing the output unless this is backed by a tangible demand for the product, for any increase under present circumstances, based on reducing production costs without existing demand, worsens the situation and reduces overall profitability to the industry.

Whichever way is chosen, whether rationalisation or diversification, or ultimately capitulation, that is, closure, the reason must have been clearly analysed beforehand rather than left to luck or providence, or a combination of both.

We must also recognise that we cannot make paper without employing people. These employees are not in the least concerned with the resources, or power politics, or technological advantages of certain companies that have brought about a collapse of the price structure to levels that no longer bear any relation to costs. Whilst the price of most commodities is based on costs but subject to the law of supply and demand, the price of labour is not. There is now almost one million unemployed in the UK. Yet the cost of labour continues to rise. We can expect, therefore, all our costs to go on rising however much governments may try from time to time to put a brake on inflation. It is not my objective here to go into the economics of inflation, but to point out the necessity of charging those who use our products a realistic cost for paper and board as indeed we are being charged for whatever we purchase or consume.

If, as a result of all this, we can one day achieve a balance between supply and demand, then we can look forward to a happier future. For it will only be then that we will be able to sell our products at a price reflecting a true relation to our costs and start slowly and laboriously to replenish our reserves and to repay the debts for which we are at present barely earning the interest.

G. T. MANDL OPEN NEW PLANT IN DENMARK

(Reprinted from *Paper*, 5 September 1973.)

The Union Jack and the Danish flag were flying side by side when G. T. Mandl & Co A/S officially opened its new factory at Otterup, near Odense, Denmark.

Mr G. T. Mandl welcomed the guests in Danish and outlined the company's development, which started with the export of filter paper from Fourstones 10 years ago and lead to the establishment of a wholly owned sales company four years later.

The first converting machine was installed in Mr Grønbech's coffee warehouse in Odense in 1967 and the business moved to rented premises in Otterup a year later. By 1971 some 40 people were employed and the need for more space brought further expansion plans.

A two acre site was bought from the Otterup Council on a new industrial trading estate and construction of the new 10,000 sq ft factory started in January. The new factory was in full production during the first week of August.

"Our mills in England can look back over almost three centuries of tradition in paper making," Mr Mandl continued, "but one cannot make a living out of history. This new, modern building is an example of new development based on old tradition. From hand made paper, and blotting to filter and other speciality paper was the way small independent paper makers had to go if they wanted to compete with large groups which dominate the paper industry of to-day. Scandinavia is Europe's largest paper producer and yet we succeed in exporting most of our filter paper to Scandinavia."

Among the guests were representatives of the local authorities, the Danish Press, and building contractors. Some of the new machinery was supplied by Joseph Winterburn and Scapa Engineering, who were also represented. The project was designed and supervised by Mr G. Egermayer, from Thomas & Green, who was also present.

A number of presents were given to the company by the employees, neighbouring firms, customers and suppliers and telegrams and good wishes were received from the sister companies in Britain, Germany, Belgium and Austria, and John T. Langebæk, managing director of De Forenede Papirfabrikker A/S, in Copenhagen.

The official opening ceremony was followed by a luncheon for the employees of the company, at which Poul Grønbech and Lennart

Hansen wished Mr Mandl a happy 50th birthday on behalf of the staff, which coincided with the opening of the new plant. Mr Mandl thanked all concerned for the efforts they had made. He added that the company was very happy to provide such agreeable working conditions in a new building, which brought about the unique situation of more applicants than vacancies at a time when Denmark was importing foreign labour.

SWISS MILL IS SAVED FROM CLOSURE

(Reprinted from *Paper*, 3 July 1974.)

Vereinigte Papierfabriken Netstal AG recently announced the closure of their two mills at Netstal, near Glarus, Switzerland. The two mills produced approximately 12,000 tonnes of mechanical printings and MG wrapping, and employed about 150 persons. The main reason for the proposed closure was shortage of labour necessary to operate both mills, and the declining profitability of the low grade packaging and printing papers.

The proposed closure would have meant that a large number of employees with many years service would have had to be retrained for other industries, and the closure would also have represented a substantial economic loss to the region.

Negotiations therefore took place with the view of continuing at least one of the two paper mills, and these have been successfully concluded. A new company has been formed, which has taken over the production facilities of the larger of the two mills equipped with a 220 cm Fourdrinier machine and employing 100 persons.

Mr G. T. Mandl has been invited to join the board as director of marketing and will be responsible for the introduction of a completely new programme of creped speciality and filter papers, intended for both the Swiss and export markets.

While the machinery is being adapted to the new programme, the mill will continue in the short term to manufacture coloured part mechanical printings, and all sales will be handled through the offices of the G. T. Mandl & Co. organisation in the UK, West Germany, Belgium, Austria and Denmark.

British Paper & Board Industry Federation

TECHNICAL DIVISION ANNUAL DINNER 1978

After Dinner Speeches at the Annual Dinner of the Technical
Division, on the Occasion of the Spring Conference 1978, by Mr
G.T. Mandl, Principal Guest, and Mr G.H. Nuttall, Chairman of
the Technical Division (1978)

(Reprinted from *Paper Technology and Industry*, May/June 1978.)

In his letter of invitation, your Director, Mr A. G. Marriott informed
me that the organizing committee for the Spring 1978 Conference
had suggested that "one of the Captains of our industry" be asked
to address this Dinner. He added that "my special position within
the industry makes me an ideal choice for this task". I therefore set
out to try and define a "Captain of our industry". It is obviously
someone, who like a captain at sea, is in charge of some kind of
vessel; I agree with Mr Marriott that, right now, all captains of our
industry are at sea, regardless of the size of their vessel.

As I have always paddled my own canoe, I came to the conclusion
that I must also be a Captain, albeit with a crew of one and therefore
partially qualified for the criteria set out in Mr Marriott's letter.

Having established my status of Captain, and position at sea, I
gave some thought on how one becomes a Captain of industry.
There appear to be a number of choices:

1. You carefully choose your parents; if your date of birth falls some
time before 1930 and you had the right parents who owned large
industrial interests, you are in.
2. Having failed in the choice of your parents, you can still make it
by choosing the right type of wife (or, rather, parents-in-law). For
their qualifications see point 1.
3. You wait until family-owned industry is virtually eliminated,
pack your Field Marshal's baton carefully into your old kit bag,
work hard, pull all possible strings and perhaps you will make it,
first trembling with fear whether you will ever get there, and then
continuing to tremble in order to stay there.

Well, the first alternative is clearly the easiest one. I qualified by
my date of birth and my parents did actually own a paper mill.

There was, however, a big snag. It was located in Czechoslovakia
and, after only a brief period of three years following my father's
death, the Communist régime kindly relieved me of all further worry

309

and responsibility by confiscating the mill without compensation, under the guise of nationalisation.

And so, in 1949 I came to England with a capital of two pounds ten shillings.

Having after all failed in choice (1), and in the firm belief that remaining a bachelor was preferable to attempting alternative (2), I immediately discounted my chances under alternative (3) for the following reasons:

Why should a foreign gentleman (however westernised—even if not necessarily oriental) succeed in climbing the difficult ladders in large UK organizations? Moreover, I was undisciplined, impetuous, un-punctual and altogether the type of person I should never have employed myself.

I very soon had to learn the hard way; that if you are looking for a helping hand, you will find it at the end of your right arm.

Instead of investing my earnings as a Paper Mill Agent in raising a family, I bought the majority of Fourstones Paper Mill shares in 1962 for less than you would spend today on a three bedroom semi in the seedier parts of London's sprawling suburbia.

The odds were certainly not very favourable: Fourstones had a 60 inch machine dating back to 1860. At speeds in excess of 150 ft/min it tended to crash through the sound barrier. With some 80 people, it produced 20 tons of blottings and antiques a week, and was losing at the rate of £15,000 a year.

There had been virtually no investment since 1908 and the esparto plant had just been closed down. Coal was shovelled by hand into a Lancashire Boiler, and it was the last UK mill to send out its invoices hand written with a special ink which copied into an invoice book with the aid of a turnscrew press.

In 1963, I bought a second hand cellulose wadding Yankee machine for £3,000, and Fourstones proudly became a two-machine mill in its bi-centenary year!

Thus I qualified as a Captain of industry and the only thing that mystified the paper trade (sometimes me included) was why I did not go down with the 50 out of 200 mills that have closed down since then.

With more than generous help from the bank, and a few good years in the paper agency business, we were able to buy a large shareholding in Thomas & Green (that was about to go into liquidation at that time).

This mill was equipped with a *giant* 84 inch modern (1922) paper machine capable of a staggering speed of 300 ft/min, and we proceeded to close down its two 100-year-old 60 inch machines and concentrated on the production of specialist papers on the one machine.

Then, finally, the two mills were merged in 1972 and I became that last and only individual owner in the paper industry in Britain.

I believe that profit, not turnover, is the key to success. Some of you may remember the late Willie Tait addressing the Technical Section at Caxton Hall some years ago when he said, "You think you are in business to make paper—you are wrong—you should be in business to make money."

In my company we now make less in tonnage than we did before the War. This is probably the main reason why we continue to make profits and did not join the 50 mills on the way down the drain (although most of them had far better and more modern equipment than we did).

You may ask, what has all this to do with the Technical Division? We are, after all, concerned with process control, engineering, computerisation and so on.

I am trying to highlight the importance of marketing, management and financial control as part of the paper-making process which, in the recent past, have all too frequently been disregarded or even ignored.

The equal importances of commerce, labour relations and technology are now reflected in the new structure of the British Paper & Board Industry Federation, and show not only how a trade association should be run, but how a successful paper industry should be structured.

But it was not always so in the past; the Technical Section used to be very much the Cinderella in the old BPBMA, and was at one point threatened with extinction.

A group of young rebels got together in what was called the Systems Engineering Committee—it had nothing to do with either systems or engineering and consequently changed its name, in 1971, to Management Sciences Committee. This was Geoff Nuttall, the late Tony Truman, Keith Bridge and Alan Marriott. When I was supposed to join the Committee in conjunction with my attempt to introduce marketing discussion groups to improve communications within the industry, the Committee was forcibly disbanded in 1973 and re-formed under what subsequently became known as the Technical Seminars Committee.

Now the poachers have become gamekeepers and I hope they continue to enjoy Lady Chatterley's favours for many years to come.

The very fact that my old *ex* Systems Engineering Committee friend Geoff Nuttall is Chairman of the Technical Division and that, of all "Captains of industry", I should be proposing this toast reflects many changes that have occurred in our association. It is no longer a club where regimental or school ties formulated policies whilst our industry staggered from crisis to crisis, and when many of us were beginning to wonder whether the UK would have any paper industry left at all.

The few brave voices of common sense were lost in the wilderness

311

until 1975 left us staring at the shambles of a 3·5 m ton production in a 7 m ton market whilst, at the same time, Germany was able to increase its output from 4 to 6 m tons (and will soon be producing 7 m).

It was no fun to view the going down of some very fine old ships from my little canoe. Sometimes it looked as though it might be sucked down in the wake of some of the sinking vessels nearby.

It is not altogether surprising that, according to a recent survey, no less than 34 per cent of qualified technologists, scientists and technicians have left the UK paper industry since 1973.

The reason is clear: No technology without profits—or no profits without technology. What came first the chicken or the egg?

This brings me to the present economic situation of the paper industry. It is clearly in a terrible mess, particularly in Europe. After a continued rise of 4 per cent consumption fell sharply by 20% during the second half of 1974, and has since been rising at approximately 3%. This means that it will take seven years, or up to 1981, to recover to 1973 levels. These figures vary from grade to grade but, on average, the situation looks like remaining pretty grim for some time to come.

We have some examples, particularly in Sweden and Finland, of very bad results in spite of advanced technology, high productivity and closeness of raw material supplies. A party of visitors being taken around a brand new paper mill recently were told that everything worked under push button control, except for the sales.

Competition on equal terms is prevented by continuous changes in the rates of exchange which have replaced the previous establishment of defensive trade barriers. Vast government subsidies further distort the picture. I cannot help feeling that private enterprise is coming to an end and that we are moving into an era of government-controlled economies. The fact that this has been tried in the Soviet Union for 60 years with the resultant standard of living some 80% below the so-called capitalist countries does not appear to deter anyone. In my opinion, wealth created by private enterprise expressed in terms of high standard of living cannot be replaced by any other system. It is, moreover, an integral part of a free and democratic society. Government subsidies, however welcome in times of recession, do not compensate for government interference with industry and free enterprise, or for fiscal measures which make me feel that careers such as mine will no longer be possible in future.

In the short term, we shall have to learn to run our industry on a shoestring and establish break-even points far below capacity levels that would have been thought feasible a few years ago. Closures of large units are unlikely in any of the major European countries because of the need to preserve employment; bankrupt companies will continue to manufacture paper under the management of

312

government receivers. This has already happened in France and Italy, and will certainly also happen in Scandinavian countries. Our very great skills in technology will now have to be concentrated on efforts of rationalisation and maximum utilisation of existing resources.

I do not believe that, because of the present situation, we can do without the high skills of our technologists just because we cannot afford to pay them. On the contrary, I feel that we must direct our efforts at improving communications between the three vital divisions of our industry and try to out-wit our competitors even if we cannot out-compete them. This will call for much more flexibility on the part of the trade unions than has been the case in the past.

More unemployment means a greater drain on the meagre resources of the remaining population and more mill closures mean more imports in foreign currencies we can ill afford.

It would appear that over-production is a situation with which papermakers have had to live since the Middle Ages. As I can see from the affluent faces around me, they have survived in spite of it!

Let me therefore hope that, with the skilful assistance of our Technical Division, we will continue to survive and to make paper in the future.

THE CHAIRMAN

It was with considerable reluctance that I invited George Mandl to speak tonight. You see, I have heard George talk before, and I know he is almost impossible to follow—follow *after*, that is. Few people are gifted like George with the ability to speak so fluently especially when one remembers that English is not his native tongue. But a small matter like that would never deter him from expressing his highly individual views, one of the few outlets left to the ageing rebel who has been sucked into the Establishment.

My reluctance also stemmed from knowing that George would take no notice of what I asked him to talk about. I suggested "The Place of the Technologist in the Changing World of Industry", or some such stirring theme, and George simply telexed back (being, as usual, abroad) that he would stay on his own ground rather than delve into "possibly controversial areas". Well, it was a great pleasure to listen to his assessment of the economic situation and what the future holds in store. Whenever I hear you speak, George, I always feel like picking up a banner and marching off to some glorious and rational goal—the fact that the direction in which you would send me changes from time to time is less important than the great uplift it gives to the soul.

Now one of the problems for me of speaking again tonight is that I have already talked in my Annual Report this morning about how I feel we are progressing in the Technical Division. I decided, however, that it would be appropriate to enlarge a little on one of my favourite themes; this question of status both of the Technical Division and of technical men themselves in our industry. I have said many times before, not least on this occasion in the past year, that I consider one of the deep-rooted problems in industry in the UK— not only ours but others—lies in the lack of respect accorded to the technologist and engineer for the talents they can bring to bear. I have tried in a modest way to remedy this by taking every opportunity, when talking to Chief Executives and in committees, of emphasising the importance of technology to the future of the paper industry. Appreciation of this point is not a measurable quantity, but I hope maybe that in one or two cases I have kicked the door ajar a bit.

One small consolation in this is that I have discovered, somewhat to my surprise, that many of our technical colleagues abroad feel at a similar disadvantage. Certainly this has been voiced to me recently in Canada and also, as a result of my growing contacts with EUCEPA, I have heard concern expressed by technical people in several European countries. It is perhaps significant that this view is not, so far as I can tell, held in the States (where, indeed, many more Chief Executives seem to have a technical or production background), nor in Germany, France and Sweden, where technical aptitudes are accorded considerable prestige.

Returning nearer to home, I think the magnitude of our own problem is highlighted by one telling statistic for which I am indebted to the Industrial Training Board (it's almost the only thing I am indebted to them for!). This appeared in an analysis of employment trends in paper industry technical staff over the two years 1974 and 1975, resulting from a specially commissioned survey. We are talking here about technical people with appropriate qualifications at different levels, not craftsmen and instrument mechanics. The analysis showed that, compared to an overall reduction during that period in members employed in the industry of 9.9 per cent, the corresponding reduction in technical people amounted to 27 per cent. Within this, we find that people with degrees dropped 30 per cent, whilst those with HND or HNC dropped 21 per cent and those with A Levels dropped as much as 43 per cent.

Now one is led to ask, in the light of these quite astonishing figures, just what was the depth of thinking behind those who were responsible for making this happen? Was there any pause to question whether the future of the company concerned would be jeopardised by such a proportionately high reduction in the availability of technical skills? Or was it a straightforward matter of expediency in the face of a fight for survival?

I am afraid I am convinced that, in most cases, it was expediency pure and simple which lead to companies adopting this approach. I cannot believe that any Chief Executive would be so ignorant as not to realise that, for every qualified man made redundant, a little bit of the life-blood of his company's future is drained away. So is it surprising that, over the past year or two, there has been a strong move for the staffs of companies, especially those working on the technical side, to organize themselves in a union? Some may consider it regrettable that this has happened, but my own view is that, if it makes future redundancy of technical people as difficult as applicable to operatives, then the industry will at least be better protected against the folly of an easy course again being taken in the face of adversity.

The technical man is, in these matters; always at a disadvantage, for his work spans months and often several years before its value becomes realised. Any investigation, however closely directed to production, demands time to be completed thoroughly and effectively. Direct on-floor trouble-shooting, where technical skills are often of limited value in relation to the practical experience gained by long hours of working with equipment, can seem slow and relatively ineffective. So it is often felt that the technical man's contribution can, in an extreme situation, be sacrificed. And let it be said that the technologist is sometimes his own worst enemy because his whole training leads him to observe, measure, analyse, verify and deduce— all in a painstaking way—and the demand for a quick solution or 'playing a hunch' can appear to offend against this discipline. But, to the harassed production man, this smacks of pedantry and, even worse, ineptitude and ignorance of the relative importance of problems.

If one looks, however, at the areas where the technical man really can contribute; product quality improvement, equipment design, process modification, project engineering, product development, raw-material saving and, above all, sheer innovation; then one is looking at the level at which the production efficiency and product competitiveness of a company will stand two, five, even ten years hence. Sacrificing this aspect of a company is as serious and suicidal as many of the other symptoms blamed for UK industry weakness; lack of investment, adherence to over-manning, poor management incentive, and so on.

What really scares me is that we may be past the point of no return. The image of industry in the UK, and ours in particular, is probably lower than in any other industrialised country. The rewards are poorer than in the service sector. Security and pensions are worse even with the new Pensions Act. Personal status in the community is low. Just what attraction does the paper industry hold for any bright and qualified youngster? The technical people he will meet in the industry will all too often appear cynical about their position. Innovation and enthusiasm are squashed under the weight of day-to-day pressures and lack of management commitment to the future. And yet no-one disagrees, not least the Tripartite Sector Working Party, that the future of paper in this country depends on successful specialisation and on greater use of indigenous materials, especially of course, waste. And who is going to bring this about? The engineer and the technologist. So if they are of poor calibre, or defensive as a result of years of insecurity, or just not there at all—what, may one ask, are the chances of real success in this task?

We are now in the fourth year of recession. All the indications are that growth of demand for paper in the UK over the next five years will be negligible. The French and Germans are achieving a phenomenal rate of increase of imports. So, all the pointers are that today's conditions should be regarded as normal and it is going to get tougher. But, to date, we have done amazingly well as an industry; profits are by no means poor and probably the best overall in Europe where (as George told us) near chaos and panic reigns in many areas. Things are therefore not all black, and short-term gains and rationalisation have succeeded remarkably well. But, if we are to hold on, we must now be shaping our rôle in the European paper industry for the '80s. And within it, we must be defining the rôle of the technical man. Each company will chart its own destiny in this. I know the ones I would back.

Let me finish by relating to you the experience of a Technical manager who took up a new appointment. He arrived on his first day to find his predecessor just closing his brief-case preparatory to departing. The desk was clear, the walls bare, the bookshelves empty. He had expected at least a week to learn about the job from his predecessor and, naturally, he asked where all the information was.

"Everything you need is in the top left-hand drawer. All the best", and with that he departed.

So the new Technical Manager walked behind the desk, opened the drawer and inside were three envelopes with the instruction "To be opened when needed". He thought; well, I have to start somewhere, so he opened the first envelope, pulled out a single piece of paper and on it he read 'Say to everyone; I'm new here and I'm just learning".

So he went round the laboratory to meet his staff, and into the mill, and to talk to the buyer, and the salesmen, and production foremen, and wherever he went he said "I'm new here and I'm just learning". And he was absolutely appalled at what he saw. His laboratory was in a filthy condition, the assistants surly and uncooperative, equipment dilapidated and broken, the reports system chaotic, everything in a real mess. Then he went into the mill and found the men looked at him with suspicion, openly derided the laboratory, refused to disclose anything and laughed at the idea of running a trial.

After a couple of weeks of this, he began to get very depressed and wonder where on earth he could make a start to get some improvement. And he began to realise that he couldn't continue saying "I'm new here and I'm just learning", because people were asking when was he going to get something useful done.

So, after a bit of thought he decided he would look at the second envelope. When he opened this, again there was a single sheet of paper inside and on it he read: "Blame me".

And he thought what a good idea so, as he went about the mill, he told everyone what a mess his predecessor had left, how it was going to take a real effort to repair the damage he had done, and so on.

But things continued to go from bad to worse. He discovered that suppliers wouldn't come near the mill because it wasn't paying, there were continual crisis meetings as complaints flooded in, the managing director was hitting the bottle and staggering round the mill threatening to sack everyone (and, in particular, the Technical Manager). So, after a few more weeks of this he was reaching desperation point and finally he opened the drawer again, gazed at the last envelope, and realising this was his last hope to get on top of the situation, he opened it.

And on the bit of paper he read:

"Buy three envelopes".

INDUSTRIAL RELATIONS
British Paper & Board Industry Federation
TECHNICAL DIVISION, LONDON DISTRICT
ANNUAL DINNER 1979

Text of the Speech on Industrial Relations by Mr George T. Mandl,
Chairman of Thomas & Green Holdings Ltd

(Reprinted from *Paper Technology & Industry*, January/February 1980.)

The Technical Division's London District held its Annual Dinner at
the Mount Royal Hotel, London on Tuesday December 4 1979. The
Chairman of the District, Mr T. Bolton, was in the Chair for the
Dinner; introduced the main guests for the evening—including your
Editor—and the after-dinner speech by Mr George T. Mandl, Chair-
man of Thomas & Green Holdings Ltd.

Mr Mandl was his usual entertaining—yet erudite—self. He said,
"Technical Division Members are gluttons for punishment. Why else
have I been asked to speak to you again? To quote Malvolio in
Twelfth Night:
"But be not afraid of greatness;
Some men are born great
Some achieve greatness
And others have greatness thrust upon them".

"The previous time that I spoke to the Division, I attempted to
describe how one becomes a 'Captain of Industry'. Now I shall try
to define how one becomes great (in the paper industry this is sometimes referred to as notorious).

"First—it takes a very long time. Some of you may remember
Stewart Don, the lovable and somewhat absent-minded editor of the
Paper Maker—now retired many years ago. At one trade dinner, I
happened to be seated next to him; then a young man in my thirties.
When he saw the place card with my name, he turned to me and
asked, 'Are you Mr Mandl's son?' The question obviously startled
me, as it raised doubts about my legitimacy; which in those days was
still regarded as a necessary part of respectability. 'I hope so', I
answered, in turn startling Stewart Don. Only then did it dawn on
me that perhaps my reputation, even in that early stage of my career,
appears to have jumped over the generation gap (not to be confused
with the Generation Game!) and, having observed my youthful
appearance, Stewart Don came to the conclusion that mine must be
a family business and that I was the junior, having for once taken
the 'Old Man's place' at a trade dinner.

"Now, gentlemen, that was the first time I had an inkling what it meant to have greatness thrust upon me! Actually to achieve greatness took almost another 20 years when, for your 1978 Spring Conference, Alan Marriott wrote to me, in his letter of invitation, that your Committee had decided to invite one of the 'Captains of our Industry' to address the Dinner. The theme of my speech then was the definition of how one becomes a Captain of Industry (and, for those of you who have forgotten, or were unfortunate enough not to be present, may I refer to *Paper Technology & Industry*, volume 19, number 6, page 135 May/June 1978). Now, being great is not a full time job, nor a sufficient theme for an after-dinner speech, as much as I should love to dwell on this subject a little longer. Good speeches are like good pills; not to be indulged in too frequently, or to be administered except in case of necessity, and preferably provided with a sugar coating to make the bitterness a little more palatable.

"For tonight's theme I have chosen the question 'Does no end to confrontation mean confrontation without end?'.

"Yes, you are right; I refer to industrial relations, not necessarily in paper making but in the UK in general. For, unless it is solved, the problem will continue to erode further our falling standards of living and create untold misery to 'both sides of industry'.

"Let us ponder for a moment on these words 'both sides of industry'. I should like to quote from the recent CBI conference, in Birmingham, when it was said; 'why do we talk about "two sides of industry"?'. Has one ever talked about 'both sides of the Army' or 'both sides of the Navy'? In industry, we are fighting a war which, thankfully, has taken the place of previous wars without the involvement of bloodshed; but they are wars just the same. We hear of the fight for market shares and, in our industry in particular, our market share has dropped to about half of paper consumption in the country. 'Very well', you may say, 'we have all the disadvantages; first EFTA, then Duty-free Quotas with the Scans having all the integrated raw materials'. But what about the latest avalanche of imports from the EEC? Waste-based board? Or, to look a little further afield, motor cars; once a great export, now barely covering half of domestic consumption?

"It is not generally realised that 50% of all manufactured goods are now imported into the UK, whilst there are $1\frac{1}{2}$ million unemployed. The reason is simple; imports are better, or cheaper, or both. Workers who expect value for their money buy imported products, but are not always willing to provide equal value for the money they get in their wage packet. A vicious circle has developed, with low productivity causing a fall in profits which, in turn, has caused a fall in investment, making the plant less and less competitive.

"Profitable companies create employment, because of the demand for their competitive products. Conversely, loss-makers create unemployment, which cannot be solved by Government subsidies, workers' sit-ins, or what-have-you. It is the consumer who decides in the end whether an industrial unit is viable or not.

"It must be understood, of course—and this is particularly important for paper—that any major investment involving large new capacities must be made to meet an existing, and not anticipated or hypothetical, demand. Price wars result from badly-planned overcapacities without proper market research and lead to losses which are just as damaging to the economy as we are currently witnessing in Sweden and Finland. It is very clear to me that, on a number of fronts, the economic battle in this country is being lost, with all the unpleasant consequences. I am not an economist and there is a great deal of smoke screen when one listens to economic theoreticians, regardless of whether they come from the extreme left or from the extreme right. In order to understand the problem, one has to reduce it to its simplest common denominator, and then the smoke screen lifts and one begins to understand the problems reduced to elementary arithmetic.

"The earning power we obtain for our labour is represented by the purchasing power of money which is a means of exchange for goods and services. If all the people want more money for providing less work, they have to accept that the money they get will purchase less in goods and services; unless, of course, outside funds (such as external loans) prop up the difference. One really cannot expect other countries to pay up all the time! These loans are usually available short term, and the interest (via higher taxation, whether in the form of PAYE or VAT is immaterial) further erodes the money available to purchase goods.

"The inflationary flood of money is being syphoned away by government regardless whether Labour or Tory, for they both cook in the same kitchen with the same ingredients on the same stove. We have to accept the fact that more real money can only be earned by more productivity; and that does not necessarily mean more sweat and toil, just a little more common sense. The Unions blame the management, the management blames the Unions; but, in fact, the blame lies squarely and equally on both sides. Just as in government a real solution can only be achieved in a coalition between moderate Conservative and moderate Labour politicians, so in industry the 'us and them' has to go and the common objective must be reached by mutual understanding, good communications, and the abandonment of militant confrontations.

"Confrontations are the result of lack in communications. Unsolved minor grievances are permitted to escalate, questions of prestige and loss of face predominate over common interest and, in a short time, the gulf widens, often in the end leading to closure of whole plant. The creation of large, anonymous, conglomerates has greatly contributed to this problem which, I am glad to say, is almost unknown in small owner-managed companies such as mine. I am proud to say that *our* industrial relations have been such that we have not lost a single day in strikes (other than isolated national one-day stoppages) in the 20 years I have been involved in the paper industry in this country.

"We have always succeeded in hedging rising wage costs with investments; enabling higher productivity to pay for the cost, and leaving something over to provide for interest and depreciation and, yes, I do dare say it, *profit*, without which no company has any future. We have gained the respect and liking of our work-force, because they saw that, by supporting our policies, they also supported the security of employment and future earnings in two mills whose record 20 years ago gave them little hope for the future. We operate three plants in this country, as far apart as in Buckinghamshire, Manchester and Northumberland, and two still-further afield in Denmark and Switzerland, involving some 350 people in all, in widely varying economies, currencies, and climates of industrial relations. Yet—lo and behold!—the formula worked in all five regardless of location, nationality, size of market, or economic climate. 'Administration', being non-productive, has been cut to an absolute minimum; I am proud that we do not have any head office and the total number in 'management and administration' is well below 10% of the total work-force.

"It makes me shudder when I see four administrative staff for every six teachers or seven—yes, I repeat, seven—for every three medical or nursing staff in the health service. This is certainly *not* the way to reduce unemployment; it is, in fact, the fastest way of increasing it. Is there perhaps not, somewhere, a lesson to be learned? I have often asked myself, if the whole of British industry had been able to do likewise over the past 20 years; 'What would the economy be like; what standard of living would we enjoy today?' This is not *Utopia*—it depends on every one of us, who is in charge of a department, a production unit, a mill, or a whole company.

"Why should we accept that our currency has to go down all the time, when it is a well known fact that the countries with the hardest currencies and the lowest inflation rates enjoy the highest standards of living?

"May I quote from Michael Lambert's Gold Medal Speech at Stationers' Hall in November 1971; '... the negotiating table seemed, at times, to bear a surprising resemblance to the Mad Hatter's tea party—the conversation having a curious logic all its own. Here I was, in a world in which it seemed that people neither said what they meant, nor meant what they said; a world in which common sense was at a discount and nonsense at a premium; where everyone was unreasonable except oneself; where people rushed from one crisis to another.' This has ceased to be a game out of *Alice in Wonderland*; it's 'for real' now.

"Also, Tory and Labour politicians who address each other in perfect, sometimes even Etonian, English should start writing a mutually understandable Concise *English* Dictionary so that one Englishman, or Welshman, or Scotsman, or Irishman—or should I say person?—can understand another and do away with the need of an often poor and unqualified interpreter under the 'Conciliation Procedure'.

"As a foreigner, and I still am one even 40 years after my first arrival in this country, I have one enormous advantage; I do not belong to any class, and can therefore talk with equal ease to all those who appear to be unable to talk to each other. Perhaps this has enabled me to avoid the pitfalls of confrontation, to some extent, but I do not believe that British management and British workers really need a foreign interpreter to solve their problems. The tolerance and kindness of the people of this country have enabled me to find shelter, first from the Germans, later from the Russians. The same tolerance has given me the chance—not to be taken for granted in many countries—to create a business, without the trade converging on the newcomer to stifle him before he could become a dangerous competitor. I have attempted to repay like with like, and have helped the economy which had given me this chance; by creating employment through the restructuring of obsolete mills into highly specialised, viable, and productive units; by ploughing back the entire earnings year after year, and thus, incidentally, not having to pay too much in tax!

"The spread of products and locations had the object of spreading the risk, thus enabling the stronger units to help the weaker ones, depending on the different cycles involved. Job satisfaction has always been a major motivation for me, and I have attempted to provide it, all the way down the line, with all the means at my disposal.

"Looking back—to the days when I set up the paper mill agency in 1949, and then the purchase of the first 500 shares in Thomas & Green in 1958, followed by the daring step of taking on Fourstones Mill in 1962, and then the setting up of a coffee-filter plant in Denmark in 1967 to provide vertical integration, right up to participating in the third mill at Netstal in Switzerland in 1974—it has all been tremendous fun, motivated by the challenge to succeed against extremely difficult odds. As a third-generation papermaker, I have been rewarded by being able to celebrate, at the three mills; a centenary, a bi-centenary, and a ter-centenary, 'though, unfortunately, not in that sequence.

"I am glad to say that there is a large number of small firms such as mine in this country. Yes, even in paper making; I am sure you know most of them. They go unobtrusively about their work, they

322

are rarely seen and seldom heard, but everybody marvels when their results are published.

"Geof Nuttall accurately described me as 'the ageing rebel that had been sucked into the establishment'. What was it that I had been rebelling against? Has the rebel changed, or the establishment? I leave it to you to think of the answer!

"Well, I am not making a secret of it; anybody who wants to is heartily welcome to copy the formula and to imitate the system. I shall be delighted if, by talking about it the way I have been able to tonight, I have been preaching to the converted."

GEORGE MANDL AWARDED 1981 PAPER INDUSTRY GOLD MEDAL

(Reprinted from *Paper*, 19 January 1981.)

George T. Mandl, who, from nothing, has built up an international speciality paper making and converting group operating from six locations in three countries with sales in the region of £12m a year, has been awarded the 1981 Paper Industry Gold Medal, presented by Paper.

Mr Mandl becomes the 15th recipient of the medal since its inauguration in 1967. It will be presented to him, together with the honorarium that goes with it, by Timothy Benn, chairman–elect of Benn Brothers Ltd, publishers of *Paper*, at the annual dinner of the National Association of Paper Merchants in London on 15 April. Mr Benn becomes chairman of Benn Brothers Ltd, on 1 February.

The special Gold Medal Award Committee's citation says that Mr Mandl provided an outstanding example of what individual initiative and perseverance could achieve in a traditional industry and in a foreign country.

By his example and wide interest in all aspects of the paper and board industry he had shown that a man, without material resources, could achieve a remarkable place in the industry's affairs.

Born in Prague in 1923, Mr Mandl is the third generation of a paper making family and received his education in Czechoslovakia, Switzerland and England. He served with the Allied Forces from 1941–45 and was decorated for his war services.

After the war he became managing director of the family ground-wood and board mill, near Carlsbad, and held this post until 1948, when the mill was nationalised by the Communist regime. From 1946 to 1948 he was a member of the executive committee of the Czech Paper Makers' Association, representing the privately owned mills, and in 1947 he founded the London Boxboard Co, Ltd to handle the sale of boards and boxes in the United Kingdom and exports from his own mill. For a brief period after his mill was taken over he worked for the Nationalised Paper Corporation.

A NEW START

At the beginning of 1949 Mr Mandl arrived in England with a suitcase and £2 10s. in his pocket to start life all over again. He was employed by the Buckinghamshire Paper & Box Co, Ltd until the

Party at Paper Agents' Dinner at Park Lane Hotel London 1962. *l. to r.:* Mrs H. Ulot, Mrs M. Beukema, Dr T. R. A. Beukema, Mrs Alec Brown, G. T. Mandl, Alec Brown (Brown Brothers), J. Ulot (London Boxboard Co.)

25th Anniversary Dinner of G. T. Mandl & Co Ltd at Stationers' Hall in 1972

G. T. Mandl & Co Ltd, 25th Anniversary Dinner Stationers' Hall 1972
Left to right: A. De Pooter, Belgium; J. Sjögren, Germany; G. T. Mandl, UK; Poul
Grönbech, Denmark; A. Vandenbogarde, Belgium (European Offices)

G. T. Mandl & Co. Ltd. 25th Anniversary Dinner Stationers' Hall 1972
Left to right, standing: J. Moore (A. Warne & Co), Peter Blow (Wm. Shipstone
& Co), R. A. Sallis (Machin & Kingsley), G. T. Mandl, Vic Pacey (Spicer-Cowan),
E. S. Cormacey (H. Cormacey & Co), D. E. Blow (Bradbury & Smith), H. Gould
(London Boxboard Co), Seated: R. G. Cherry (Machin & Kingsley), Dr T. R. A.
Beukema (Cartonfabriek Beukema & Co), J. W. C. Bagshaw (Harry B. Wood).

Annual Dinner of Technical Division Spring Conference London 1978.
Hance Fullerton, G. T. Mandl, G. H. Nuttall

G. T. Mandl & Co. Ltd, 21st Anniversary Party at Stationers Hall' 1968
Back Row—Left to right: Roy Hurford, Sandy White, George Mandl,
Ron Green, Harold Gould, Tony Denny. *Seated—Left to right:* Terry
Brown, Mrs Schranilova, Mary Nicholson, Unknown, Gillian Dann.

Presentation of Paper Industry Gold Medal to G. T. Mandl by Timothy Benn, Chairman Benn Brothers, 1981

Inaugural meeting of the Paper Trade Gold Medal Club at Stationers' Hall, 1981
l. to r.: standing: ERIC HAYLOCK, PETER WHITING, HUGH BALSTON, GEORGE MANDL, BILL BAILEY, LEONARD PAGLIERO, DR TOBY RANCE
l. to r.: seated: JOHN CURTIS, DR GEORGE RIDELL, MICHAEL LAMBERT, GLANVILL BENN, DR JULIUS GRANT, PERCY ELLIS

Hand-made Paper being made at Netstal in 1979 to commemorate the
Tercentenary of the Paper Mill.

end of 1949, when he established a mill agency, first in partnership and later on his own account, starting with the sale of Dutch boards from NV Cartonfabriek Beukema & Co, Hoogezand. In subsequent years he obtained a number of Scandinavian agencies and built up a substantial tonnage.

The business continued to expand, and his first mill acquisition took place in 1962 when he bought The Fourstones Paper Mill Co Ltd, at Hexham. A £1 million development programme has recently been completed at this old established mill. (See *Paper*, 21 April 1980.)

In March 1964 Mr Mandl was appointed to the boards of Thomas & Green Ltd and H. Allnutt & Son Ltd, in which he subsequently acquired a substantial interest, later becoming the principal shareholder. Fourstones and Thomas & Green were merged into Thomas & Green Holdings in 1972 with Mr Mandl as the sole shareholder.

In 1967 he established a company in Denmark for the conversion of coffee filters, and in 1974 acquired an interest in Papierfabrik Netstal AG, Switzerland. He now has majority control.

All three mills, dating back to 1680, 1705 and 1763, were acquired on the point of closure, and re-structured into new, viable speciality units with a high degree of vertical integration.

In 1978 Fourstones acquired the Kattan Disposables Company in Manchester, extending its hospital disposables converting operations, and following the recent collapse of the Brittains Group, Thomas & Green acquired the Arborfield Mill near Peterborough, for the conversion of book coverings and sterilisation papers.

INDUSTRY ACTIVITY

Apart from the drive and enthusiasm Mr Mandl continues to show in his various businesses, he has for many years played an active role in the affairs of the paper and board industry through its trade associations.

He became a member of the Paper Agents' Association in 1949, and a Liveryman of the Worshipful Company of Stationers & Newspaper Makers in 1956. He joined the then British Paper and Board Maker's Association in 1962, serving on its council from 1963 to 1973, and on the Commercial Board of the British Paper & Board Industry Federation from 1974 to date. Mr Mandl has been particularly active in the Woodpulp Committee, of which he was chairman from 1967 until 1980, and is a UK delegate to the EEC Pulp users group in Brussels.

Other Committees with which Mr Mandl has been associated include the Export Committee since 1969, serving as deputy chairman during 1974–75, and the Waste Paper Committee since 1973. He was a member of the Coated Paper and Board Makers' Association from 1964 to 1968, holding the office of hon treasurer and deputy chairman in 1967.

He is an active member of the Technical Division, which has published a number of his papers and he was elected chairman of the National Paper Museum Committee in 1980.

Mr Mandl became a member of the Council of PIRA in 1975 and has been an active supporter of that organisation ever since. He is also a member of the International Paper Historians and has written two books on the history of his mills.

Mr Mandl's Gold Medal paper, entitled The Case for Common Sense will be published in *Paper* on 6 April.

PAPER INDUSTRY GOLD MEDAL
PRESENTED TO GEORGE MANDL

(Reprinted from *Paper*, 18 May 1981.)

A feature of the annual dinner was the presentation of the Paper Industry Gold Medal, presented by *Paper*, to George Mandl, who is also a member of the NAPM.

Mr T. J. Benn, chairman of Benn Brothers Ltd, publishers of *Paper*, who made the presentation, recalled that this was the 15th occasion on which the medal had been presented.

One of the many and important roles of journals such as *Paper*, he said, was to identify, recognise and publicise significant individual business achievement. Indeed, at the present time, when business achievement was at an absolute premium, it was arguable that this was amongst the most important contributions which *Paper* could make.

It was against this background that the Paper Industry Gold medal for 1981 had been awarded to George Mandl, whose contribution, in a positive way, to the paper and board industry of the UK, over a 25 year span, had been outstanding.

"In making this presentation", Mr Benn continued, "I am conscious that the business of which I am chairman was founded in one room in the East End of London, just over 100 years ago. We have survived and prospered, by matching our own resources and initiatives, alongside those of hundreds of other manufacturers and traders up and down this land. May we long have the opportunity to prosper alongside the initiative and drive of such as George Mandl."

Mr Mandl said that he did not just wish to thank *Paper* for the generous institution of the Gold Medal, or the industry for its extreme tolerance in giving this high award to one of the very few foreigners "in this ultra-conservative trade", but also his colleagues for having enabled him to achieve what the Award Committee had put into their citation.

"I do not wish to abuse the hospitality of the NAPM, of which I am the smallest member, a distinction incidentally which they share with the British Paper and Board Industry Federation, by exceeding the three minutes budgeted for this occasion, and I shall therefore be unable to tell you where this industry of ours is going, except to say to those who may think it had already gone, to be a little less despondent.

"Looking back over the list of 14 mostly illustrious names of those who have preceded me, I am particularly happy to have two of my old friends, who are previous recipients of the medal, as my guests here tonight. They are Michael Lambert, 1971 and Bill Bailey, 1976."

PERCEPTIVE INSIGHT

(Leading article in *Paper*, 4 May 1981.)

Readers who have not already done so are recommended to read the Paper Industry Gold Medal Award paper by George Mandl, 'The case for common sense' (full text in *Paper*, 6 April).

To make a point and to explain the reason for this recommendation we would suggest that perhaps some attendants at the recent annual dinner of the National Association of Paper Merchants, where the award was presented, might have wondered about this addition to the proceedings. Some might not have known about the Mandl paper and some, unlikely as it is, might not have known the author.

Background to the medal starts from 1967 when the first award for services to the paper and board industry, and a written paper associated with that award, went to Leslie Farrow of Wiggins Teape. You couldn't have a better start than that and in successive years there have been some equally remarkable efforts from such notables as Cecil King, James B. Scott, Percy Ellis, Michael Lambert, George Riddell, John Curtis, Cyril Warmington, Toby Rance, Stanley 'Bill' Bailey, Peter Gardner, Peter Whiting, Leonard Pagliero, Julius Grant. Through those years *Paper* has presented each paper without the temerity, or even brief, to edit but with the advantage of being able to judge reactions.

George Mandl has done it again in causing a stir in the breast of some who usually avoid reading items beyond a 100 words or so. One senior citizen paper merchant said (to *Paper*): "I don't usually read long articles but I happened to read George's paper in the train going home. It was fast reading and afterwards it occurred to me to read it again—more slowly. There's an awful lot of truth in what he says."

The reactions we speak of have been all word of mouth but one reader, Richard Reeve Angel, a director of Whatman Reeve Angel Ltd, wrote to Mr Mandl direct. With permission of both, these are the words:

'I have just read your Paper Industry Gold Medal lecture in *Paper*. I write to congratulate you on your clarity and on your perceptive insight into the problems which have been, as you explain, so largely self imposed.

"It has always seemed to me a very clubbish industry. The high capital cost of entry has kept out newcomers and the trade association meetings and dinners have fostered the lifetime membership atmosphere. People feel they belong to the Paper Industry. Under these circumstances few wish to admit they can no longer pay their subscription. In other words, management hang on far longer than they should and the shareholders end up picking up the bill.

'Thus objectivity flies out of the window when faced with the human instinct to seek comfort from close association with people you think you can trust to have the same views as your own when the going gets rough. 'Continued employment for our workpeople' is usually invoked by those who really mean continued employment for themselves. It's all very understandable and especially so when you publicly espouse capitalism but privately mean a patrimonial system of management.

"It means however that our message will simply not be heard. It hurts too much."

FUTURE PATTERNS OF PAPERMAKING

LIKELY DEVELOPMENT OF THE UK INDUSTRY

(Reprinted from *Paper*, 20 June 1983.)

The paper industry in the developed countries of the world is going through a structural change which can only be compared with the impact of the paper making machine on the hand-made paper mills of the 1840s, George Mandl told a recent PITA conference in London. His analysis had broad implications in the UK

In the United States change has been more gradual than elsewhere, as it has taken place by the same companies within one country. In Europe it has taken the form of vertical integration of pulp mills in the Nordic countries. Paper making units with capacities of 10–20 000 tpy, which had been in existence on a similar scale for over 100 years, are suddenly facing competition from fully integrated single machine units with a capacity of 10–200 000 tpy.

In the absence of a raw material base, it will be impossible for the UK to compete successfully against these units. The future structure of the British paper industry will depend on its ability to maintain a certain number of low volume high priced speciality mills and the utilisation of its unused waste paper resources, in the region of two million tonnes, for the recapture of the waste based board market. It may also be possible to develop a new technology to utilise the balance of mixed waste into a new raw material for bulk grades of paper and board, able to compete with imports.

In order to assess the possible future of the British paper industry it is necessary to take stock of the present situation, and analyse the reasons for the large number of mill closures which have taken place in recent years. Paper and board are not consumer end products, and with the exception of household tissues and a small amount of stationery, the entire output of the paper industry is sold to other industrial users, where it is consumed in administration, packaging, and to a lesser degree, as a raw material for further industrial processing.

With the wholesale closure of British industry which we have been witnessing in the last decade, imports have been steadily rising, to such an extent that Britain has become a net importer of manufactured goods for the first time since the industrial revolution.

It is obvious that an imported motor car, refrigerator, television

331

set or shirt is bringing its paper content with it and British paper makers have lost this market simultaneously with the closure of each industrial unit. It is evident that this development is showing a greatly distorted picture of UK paper and board consumption, as the paper content of industrial goods being imported is not recorded anywhere, whilst the consumer is still using the same quantity of paper as he has been previously.

As the per capita consumption of paper is normally taken as a barometer of the standard of living, the recent fall in the UK consumption figure should not necessarily be interpreted as a fall in the standard of living, as no such decline has taken place so far.

ECONOMIC PROBLEMS

The astronomical cost of paying for the amount of imported industrial goods, as well as the maintenance of unemployment benefits to an ever-growing number of unemployed, is being paid from the revenue of the North Sea oil, which not only manages to balance the external account but very frequently puts it into surplus. I am not going to enter here into the likely picture of what will happen when the North Sea oil runs out, but I leave it to your imagination to think of the consequences. The recent marginal drop of crude oil prices has depressed the rate of exchange of sterling, highlighting its economic dependence on North Sea oil.

It is also not my task to go into the reasons why so much of British industry has now closed its doors for ever, but to analyse the consequences of this closure and its impact on the future of the British Paper Industry. The above circumstances in themselves would have been enough to cause the paper mill closures we have been witnessing, as it is evident that a greatly reduced industrial activity cannot support the full capacity of the domestic paper industry.

While the UK was battling with the structural and economic problems I have outlined above, another much more serious development was beginning to take shape, influencing the paper and board industry in all the developed countries of the world, who produce virtually the entire 170 million tonnes of paper and board and consume 80% of it, while 80% of the remaining population of the world consume the remaining 20%.

For more than 100 years, the structure of the paper industry in the developed countries of the world has not changed a great deal. Paper machines very similar to those still in use throughout the Common Market have been in existence since before the First World War, and everyone has been used to average structures of 20–30 000 tonnes per mill containing between one and four machines.

In the early 1950s, a new structure began to emerge in the form of paper machines with capacities in excess of 1000 tpd. While these were initially used in North America for the production of kraft linerboard, they soon began to spread to newsprint, and later to writing and printing grades which had hitherto been the sole domain of the small and medium sized mill close to the consumer market. The change in the United States has been more gradually carried out by the same companies within the same country and the same market but the impact in Western Europe has been totally different. The UK was one of the first countries to convert a newsprint machine, at Bowaters' Kemsley Mill, almost 7 m wide, into a modern and successful woodfree unit with a capacity of 80 000 tpy, but this isolated step in the right direction was not able to halt a development which was beginning to emerge in Sweden and Finland.

The cost of producing chemical wood pulp in the Nordic countries has been rising sharply compared to the North American continent, and it became evident that vertical integration would become a necessity if the market share of the world's major wood pulp market in Europe were not to be lost completely to North America and the rising capacity of low priced hardwood market pulp coming out of Brazil. The first integrated woodfree mill of only 40 000 tpy in Southern Sweden in the mid 1960s was soon followed by much larger units in both Sweden and Finland, showing an unmistakable pattern of a policy decision to take the Western European market, regardless of the fact that substantial over-capacities existed at a time when new mills in the region of 150 000 tonnes per machine were being built.

The economic advantages of these units are obvious. The drying process of pulp is eliminated at a considerable saving of energy, as is the breaking up of the pulp in the non-integrated mill. Machines of between 6–8 m width and speeds well in excess of 1000 m/min, pushed labour unit costs down to less than one-third of those in conventional paper mills such as we know today. State subsidies ensure that these new capacities will sell their entire output regardless of the losses incurred in order to conquer the markets necessary for the maintenance of their future business. In spite of the fact that this action clearly infringes the Association Treaties of Sweden and Finland with the European Community, this process cannot be halted and a restructuring of the European paper industry over the coming decades therefore appears to be inevitable.

While the West German economy has not had to battle with such severe economic problems as the UK, it is nevertheless facing very severe problems for its own paper industry. These have so far been partially resolved by the construction of very large woodfree mills controlled by Finnish and, to a lesser extent, Swedish, interests, located in development areas and therefore subject to Government subsidies, and will no doubt continue for a considerable time, in spite of the fact that pulp will have to be supplied from their parent companies. A similar development has also taken place to a lesser degree in France.

In the traditional waste paper based mills a totally different situation has developed in Germany, where 10–20 000 tpy fluting and test liner mills have been replaced by half a dozen machines operating around 100 000 tpy. This development has not only caused the closure of a large number of old established medium sized mills in Germany itself, but has created severe competition for North America and Scandinavia. On a smaller scale a similar development has taken place in the area of unlined and white lined grey board as well as folding box-board, which can give some indication as to the structural problems which have led to the closure of approximately one million tonnes of waste based board production in Great Britain.

It is evident that the reduction of industrial activity in the United Kingdom requires a certain alignment of its capacity for packaging material in both solid and corrugated board. The closures have, however, taken place on such a scale that at present waste based board is being imported into this country, while a vast surplus of mixed waste has to be disposed of by local authorities at very considerable cost and cannot be exported due to its imbalance of value and freight.

It therefore appears very clear that one of the areas in which the future of the UK paper industry must lie is in the recapture of this market, in spite of the fact that the initial return on capital invested is bound to be unsatisfactory because of the overcapacity in Europe, and the determined fight of those who hold the market at present to retain their market shares. It is equally obvious that any such units would need to consist of the most modern and efficient equipment with manning levels so far unheard of and unacceptable within the UK but currently practised in Germany and elsewhere.

The final and most important aspect of any future development of the British paper industry would have to consist of an entirely new technology, based on the recovery of suitable fibres from the substantial surplus available of mixed waste, and their conversion into bulk grades of paper which would have to compete successfully with the integrated mills using expensive forest resources and energy in Scandinavia, as well as large efficient waste mills in Germany and elsewhere. This is no mean task but it should be undertaken while the financial resources of North Sea oil are still available to the British economy in order to prepare it for the day when, hopefully, it returns to the community of industrialised nations.

I have no quick formula as to how this very difficult task is to be achieved or financed. All I can say is, that unless the United Kingdom succeeds in using its surplus of some two million tonnes of mixed waste into suitable fibre, and converting it on machines of a capacity in excess of 100 000 tpy, its future on the present already greatly reduced scale is not going to be very bright.

I should like to say a few words of warning against the increased use of waste pulp substitute grades. These grades are available in a limited supply which has recently been further reduced due to the closure of some paper converting industrial units. The demand for pulp substitute grades is bound to continue to outstrip supply regardless of the shrinkage of the UK paper industry. Increased usage of pulp substitute grades would only result in pushing up the price for the UK mills and thus reduce their competitive advantage in using pulp substitute waste instead of wood pulp.

The future in the area of low volume, high added value products and vertical and forward integration into end products will be subject to very considerable pressures as companies at present operating in certain traditional markets will be pushed out by the new Scandinavian capacities and will probably begin to encroach on smaller specialised mills.

In the end, the companies with the best technology, the highest productivity and modern equipment will win the battle in this particular area. It is clear, though, that the future British paper industry cannot and should not rely on these products alone, as it is likely to continue having competitive disadvantages in the form of energy and transportation costs for the traditional export share of such products to other markets as well as defending its own market from European imports of similar products.

HAND-MADE MILLS

The hand-made mills of the early 19th century had to face the competition of the paper making machine, which was very slow to take off in its initial stages in the early 1800s but soon gathered momentum and virtually pushed the vat mills out of existence over a 50-year period, replacing an average 50 tpy a year unit by a 500 tpy unit. In just the same way, the giant new machines are likely to push out the 10–20 000 tpy mill in the same ratio 150 years later.

The process has already begun but it has been so slow that most of us have not been aware of it. It is, however, beginning to gather momentum and it is unlikely to take 50 years this time. My guess is that the next 10 is nearer to the mark. We shall then begin to see a structure emerging not dissimilar to that of 150 years ago. A small number of hand-made mills survived the onslaught of the paper making machine for well over a century and finally converted themselves into bank note, filter and other highly specialised units.

In trying to assess the likely structure of the UK paper industry in the 1990s, we can expect to see either a handful of speciality mills with possibly one or two large units making waste based board and

335

corrugating material with a total output of some one and a half million tonnes, or a totally re-structured paper industry producing four million tpy and covering half of domestic demand, consisting of not less than two million tonnes of bulk grade machines in the region of 100 000 tonnes capacity, using the waste paper resources other than pulp substitute grades, and successfully competing in the end product with integrated production in the Nordic countries.

UNIQUE POSITION

The UK is in the unique position in the world of having a seven million tonne paper market and a declining three million tonne paper industry which is unable to utilise the potential 2·8 million tonnes of collectable waste which cannot be exported.

The ability to achieve this formidable task will be in the hands of the technologists of the paper industry. If they accept this challenge, the industry will have a bright future. If it fails, the present decline is bound to continue.

EUROPE: A COMPARISON OF INTERNATIONAL COMPETITIVITY

As can be seen from the statistics of average output per mill, it will be extremely difficult, if not impossible, for mills averaging in size between 16 000 tonnes in Italy and 48 000 tonnes in the Netherlands to compete successfully against mills averaging 105 000 tonnes

PAPER AND BOARD PRODUCTION

Country	Production 1970	1981	% Change
	(million tpy)		
Belgium	0·8	0·9	+13
Denmark	0·2	0·3	+50
France	4·1	5·1	+24
Germany	5·5	7·8	+42
Holland	1·6	1·7	+6
Italy	3·5	4·9	+40
United Kingdom	4·8	3·4	−29
Finland	4·3	6·1	+42
Norway	1·4	1·4	—
Sweden	4·4	6·1	+39
Austria	1·0	1·7	+70
Switzerland	0·7	0·9	+29
Total	32·3	40·3	+24

AVERAGE OUTPUT PER MILL

Country	Production 1970 (000–tpy)	1981	% Change
Belgium	22·73	49·28	+116
Denmark	21·27	44·62	+110
France	17·00	29·93	+ 76
Germany	19·30	39·00	+102
Holland	29·98	48·08	+ 60
Italy	9·13	16·13	+ 77
United Kingdom	28·27	27·26	− 4
Finland	91·17	133·37	+ 46
Norway	34·68	49·04	+ 41
Sweden	64·10	105·70	+ 65
Austria	17·84	45·16	+153
Switzerland	21·50	32·86	+ 53
Average	22·72	38·20	+ 68

MILL CLOSURES

Countries	No. of mills 1970	Mills closed by 1981	% Closures
Belgium	34	16	47
Denmark	11	5	45
France	243	71	29
Germany	285	85	30
Holland	52	17	33
Italy	379	78	21
United Kingdom	171	47	27
Finland	47	1	2
Norway	41	13	32
Sweden	68	10	15
Austria	57	20	35
Switzerland	34	6	18
Total	1422	369	26

in Sweden and 133 000 tonnes in Finland. The 1981 figures do not yet include the latest woodfree projects in Sweden and Finland, which are likely to push up the average figures for these two countries, with the added advantage of vertical integration on site with a

337

wood pulp mill. The entire paper industry in the EEC, with the exception of bulk waste using mills, will therefore be at very considerable risk in the immediate future.

If the decline in the UK output is to be halted, this can only be done in the area of waste based board and corrugated case making materials. Given the right investment in machinery, the UK should be able to recapture this market rather than continue to burn the surplus waste paper through local authorities, and import its requirements from the EEC.

The development of new technology for other grades of paper based on waste recovery is likely to cause considerable technical and financial problems in the UK and cannot therefore be relied upon to be the salvation of the declining volume which has occurred but research in this direction should, nevertheless, be encouraged by the industry and government.

The retreat into specialisation cannot be expected to provide the answer as the volume cannot be placed on the domestic UK market and there is not sufficient competitive advantage to rely on substantial exports.

The general upsurge in UK paper and board output can only take place when there is a general recovery in industrial activity and goods at present being imported, including their packaging, are once again domestically produced.

G. T. Mandl

PAPER—GROWTH WITHOUT PROFIT

(A lecture given at the International Paper Historians Meeting in
Manchester, September 1978, published in the *IPH Year Book*.
Statistics updated to 1984.)

The economic cycles of the paper industry and its problems in industrial relations are well known phenomena of the present and
recent past.

What is less known, is that the history of these problems goes far
back into the early beginnings of hand-made paper making in the
middle ages.

I am not attempting to present here any paper-historical discov-
eries, indeed most of the facts and figures contained in my paper are
already well known to paper historians.

I am merely trying to highlight the strange repetition of cyclical
over-production in an era of uninterrupted and sometimes explosive
growth from the middle ages to the present day.

When we consider the earliest known per-capita consumption of
some 0.1 kg in the sixteenth century for some 4 million inhabitants
in England and compare it with the present 135 kg for some
50 million over 400 years, one visualises an almost incredible and
continuous prosperity of anyone only remotely connected with the
manufacture of paper in spite of the continued decline in price
expressed in real terms.

The value of 1 lb of paper represented a man's daily wage for
16 hours 400 years ago. The present equivalent earnings represent
5 minutes' work. The value being based on 25p per lb of paper and
an hourly wage of £3.60, both of which can be challenged with
justification as being too low (1984 figures.)

Indeed, as we trace the economic progress of the paper industry
in England over the last four centuries, we see only very isolated
periods of prosperity, followed by long years of depression, causing
many mill closures and bankruptcies. The development is very
similar all over Europe.

Let us therefore look back into history and briefly follow the
pattern of development in order to understand the reasons for the
hardship in place of wealth which the enormous growth of our
industry appears to have indicated.

Paper making came relatively late to England. By the time Tate's first mill was established in Hertfordshire in 1490, several Continental countries already possessed a large number of prospering mills. This first mill failed and it was not until the end of the 16th century before the manufacture of paper began to take a firm foothold in the British Isles.

Paper first appeared as a new, imported product in the 14th century competing with domestic parchment and vellum. As competition grew, the price of paper fell by 40% during the 15th century, whilst at the same time the price of parchment rose by 20%, denoting already at that time the conservative nature of the British Scrivener and his reluctance to accept a newfangled product.

The same tendency can be observed in the 16th century, when domestic production of paper started to compete against established imports from Italy and France, later followed by Holland.

The inflationary tendencies of that time pushed parchment prices up a full 70%, whilst paper prices barely followed at between 30% and 60% according to the grade and origin.

It was not until the advent of the printed book that demand for paper began to grow at a rate that made it impossible for parchment or vellum to follow suit.

In spite of this demand it was not until 1588 that the German jeweller and financier, Spillman, was able to establish the first successful paper mill in Dartford, with a great deal of royal and official support.

Earlier attempts were frustrated by lack of skills and the strong guilds of continental paper makers who made sure that none of their members migrated to England thus preserving this lucrative market for themselves.

Moreover, a regular trade in English rags existed to all the main paper making centres on the continent of Europe, which the English merchants concerned were eager to preserve and petitions to forbid the export of rags were regularly turned down by the authorities.

No wonder therefore, that the early English paper maker, John Tate, is on record as having to close his mill and complaining: "At the last, said he, the man perceaved that made it, that he could not fourd his paper as good cheape as that came from beyond the seaze, and so he was forced to lay downe making of paper. And no blame to the man: for men would give never the more for his paper because it was made heare."

Bearing in mind the insignificant domestic production, consumption at that time can be estimated from the following import figures through the Port of London: 1560: 26,000 reams; 1588: 41,000 reams; 1621: 81,000 reams; 1634: 106,000 reams. In 1677 the highest point of 157,000 reams was reached, before the beginning of the 18th century brought the figure up to 213,000 reams in 1701. It then started to fall away under the impact of growing domestic production to 90,000 reams by 1720.

In terms of per capita consumption one can estimate that 4 oz (113 g) of white paper was consumed per head of population in England around 1600 (estimating 60,000 reams of 20 lb = 500 tons divided into the then population of 4 million). The cost of a quire (24 sheets) of between four and five pence was equivalent to a worker's daily wage.

The following 120 years saw a rapid increase to a consumption of 3,860 tons consisting of 2,760 tons of domestic production, imports of 1,100 tons and exports of 40 tons, resulting in a six-fold increase in consumption by 1718 of 24 oz (680 g) per head of the 5.5 million population, about the level of some of the underdeveloped countries in the third world today.

Even Spillman's mill in Dartford, made famous by Churchyard's poem, failed, following the death of his son, John, in 1641, after a brief existence of only 50 years, and the family lapsed into poverty.

Quality, due to lack of skilled labour, was still the major obstacle in the share in growth in British paper consumption of the domestic mills, who were beginning to establish themselves in growing numbers in Kent and Buckinghamshire, in order to be close to the raw material source of rags and the Paper Market of London.

A record of 1637 shows a dispute between paper makers on the river Wye between High Wycombe and the Thames and local inhabitants, who claimed that "the paper made is so unuseful that it will bear no ink on one side, and is sold at dearer rates than formerly".

Brown paper and pasteboard continued to be the predominant output of the growing number of British paper mills. Their number is estimated to have grown from 100 before 1700 to 200 by 1712.

Whilst the best white paper was still being imported, demand for wrapping and packing paper as well as pasteboard for bookbinding grew rapidly, thus providing work for an increasing number of mills, and they began to spread also to Wales, Scotland and Ireland.

A further stimulus to domestic production was the increase of import duties from 5% in 1690 to 15% by 1700.

The continued political tension with France created antagonism against French imports and brought periods of complete prohibition of French goods entering Britain, such as between 1678 to 1685, 1689 to 1697 and 1703 to 1713.

The immigration of Huguenots after 1685 brought about a further considerable stimulus to domestic production with the skill and spirit of enterprise these Protestant paper makers brought with them, Portals being a well-known example.

Small mills fared better in the 17th century, as they do today, although they sometimes sacrificed hygiene to profits, as can be seen

341

from a report of 1697 from a mill near Canterbury, where brown paper and flour were being processed simultaneously: "The mill is set agoing by the water and at the same time it pounded the rags for the paper and it beat oatmeal and hemp and ground wheat together, that is at the same time".

Another example of 1713 indicates that Darley Mills, Derby, consisted of a corn mill, paper mill, fulling mill, hemp mill and leather mill on the same site.

The freehold value of a small paper mill around 1700 was estimated to range from £500 to £1,800, not very different from the price of £1,250 paid for the Fourstones Paper Mill during the depression in 1930.

Most mills were, however, not bought, but rented and the landlord frequently contributed substantially towards the cost of conversion or repair, in order to secure an income from his property.

Labour of about 10 persons per vat (including women and boys) was to a large extent provided by the paper maker and his family and credit of 3 months or more financed by discounting bills was common for both raw material and paper, demonstrating the thin cover of working capital.

From these beginnings arose the enterprises of the early Industrial Revolution, which again failed to bring prosperity to the paper maker, in spite of growth of undreamed of proportions, in the wake of the invention of the paper making machine around 1798.

The population of England increased from 5.5 million in 1700 to 9 million by 1801, and the newly formed United Kingdom of Great Britain and Ireland had a population of 15 million.

Increased activity stimulated by the invention of the steam engine called for increasing quantities of wrapping paper, quite apart from the rising demand of printings, due to the rapidly increasing circulation of daily and weekly newspapers.

The increased population in turn provided a part of the additional rags required for the manufacture of paper and large quantities had to be imported from as far afield as Russia and the American Colonies to satisfy demand.

The introduction of the Hollander beating engine around 1750 helped to increase productivity, with which the old stampers would not have been able to cope.

By 1800 the number of mills rose to 417 in England and Wales and 32 in Scotland, with some 750 vats.

Most of them were still one or two vat mills, but there were far larger enterprises with four or more vats at work.

The largest business was operated by Whatman Junior in Maidstone with eight vats at three mills, who in his most prosperous period, 1780–90, made a gross profit of £4,000 on sales of £14,000 p.a. and spent about £1,500 on wages, a figure of 15% on sales (excluding profits) which is similar to the average the industry is paying today.

His successor, William Balston, took over so many debts and overinvested in to what then became the largest mill in the British Isles, that he had to make a number of settlements with his creditors in order to escape bankruptcy. The mill finally reached financial stability when Balston was well over 80 years of age.

Apart from the technical integration of a flour mill and paper mill on the same waterwheel, vertical integration in marketing also took place between the stationer and paper maker, but selling was always more lucrative than making.

With the growing demand and shortage of rags, a short-lived sellers market began to develop in the late 18th century and some larger firms embraced the trade of rag merchant, paper maker and stationer at the same time.

The Napoleonic wars had a very strong inflationary influence in England and paper prices rose by 50% between 1790 and 1800 and reached 100% by 1814.

Following the publication by Dr J. C. Schäffer's experiments to make paper from other vegetable fibres in Regensburg in 1765-71, The Royal Society of Arts offered a reward for rag substitutes in paper manufacture. Although some awards were made for the use of bark, jute, straw and other materials, they never reached commercial production. In the meantime the price of fine rags soared from 35s per cwt in 1780 to 58s by 1804.

The financial failure of the most important invention of the paper industry by Nicholas–Louis Robert's patent of 1799 acquired by the brothers Henry and Sealy Fourdrinier is well known. The Fourdriniers, owners of one of the most prosperous firms of paper merchants in London, went bankrupt in 1810 having lost more than £60,000 transferred from their stationery business into the research, improvement and promotion of the paper making machine.

The paper makers, having discovered the financial insolvency of the patent owners to institute legal proceedings, shamelessly exploited the patents without payment of royalties.

Over 40 paper machines were built and sold by Bryan Donkin between 1807 and 1822 on which no royalties on the patent had been paid.

A petition to Parliament to pay a contribution out of public funds as compensation for the Fourdriniers' efforts was debated for a long time and finally brought a meager recompense in the form of a £7,000 award in 1837, by which time no less than 279 Fourdrinier machines were in operation in the U.K., according to Henry Fourdrinier's estimate of one machine equalling 5 vats.

The advent of the paper machine caused a 15-fold increase in paper output between 1800 and 1860, and prices fell under the impact of

343

over-production by about 60% in the same period from 1s 6d per lb (£170 per ton) in 1800 to 10d (£95 per ton) in 1836 and to 6½d (£60 per ton) by 1859. By 1860 hand-made production represented only 4,000 tons out of 100,000 tons paper production, serving a population of some 29 million in the U.K.

Between 1851 and 1867 the number of newspapers increased from 563 (incl. 17 dailies) to 1,294 (incl. 84 dailies). *The Times* increased its circulation from 2,000 copies in 1790 to 10,000 in 1830 and 65,000 in 1861, when it also reduced its price from 4d to 3d per copy.

The successful introduction of mechanical groundwood as an alternative to rags on the continent in the 1860s did not take place in England because of the lack of suitable timber and water power. The invention of the method to produce esparto pulp by Thomas Routledge of Eynsham Mill between 1856 and 1860 resulted in a plentiful supply of the necessary esparto grass from North Africa, a trade which persisted to the tune of some ¼ million tons well after the second world war.

Paper mills were being established all over the country and numbered 384 by 1860. Only five produced between 1,500 and 2,500 tons a year and 160 between 50 and 250 tons a year, whilst 90 were still producing 40 tons a year or less.

The 100,000 tons of output at £60 per ton represented a turnover of £6 million. The total capital invested in the industry was estimated at between £7 and £10 million, highlighting the capital intensity still experienced today. (Capital invested equals 1–1½ years' sales.) This figure represents £18,000 to £26,000 per mill, borne out by sales such as Chartham for £20,000 in 1862.

The economic picture would not be complete without a brief reference to labour relations. The secret and strict guilds of the continental paper makers of the middle ages are well known, most of whom were in fact employees, rather than employers.

The combinations of journeying paper makers in England and France forced improved pay, beer money and hours by strike action as early as the 18th century. In England "The Original Society of Paper Makers" emerged in 1735.

In 1796 the employers submitted a petition to Parliament, to prohibit the so-called Combinations of Workers in the Paper Industry, in order to put a stop to continued demands for increases in pay and the refusal to work in mills where Scottish or Irish labour was being employed at lower rates.

Although the Act of Parliament was duly passed, it proved quite ineffective, as did the lock-out of a large number of English mills organised in the same year. Workers in mills up and down the country were in constant communication with each other, thus ensuring a very united front against the employers.

The industrial strife brought no benefit to either side and soon agreements began to emerge shown in the following verses dating back to that time:

> "May masters with their men unite,
> Each other ne'er oppress
> And their assistance freely give
> When men are in distress.
> We covet not our masters' wealth,
> Nor crave for nothing more,
> But to support our families,
> As our fathers have before.
> Then may the God that rules above
> Look on our mean endeavour,
> And masters with their men unite
> In hand and hand for ever."

The two clasped hands remained the emblem of the Paper Division of SOGAT, the present-day successors to the early Paper Trade Union Movement.

A regular Association of Employers did not exist until 1872, because of competition and mutual distrust, except in periods of extreme need, such as the petition on Excise Matters in 1765.

Paper-makers met regularly on a regional basis in certain inns, such as The Committee of Master Paper Makers that met at The George and Vulture tavern in Cornhill in the 1790s. An attempt was also made to control rag prices by a resolution "that none of the 48 signatories should pay any more than 48s per cwt for rags, and that the stoppage of all the mills for a month would be the most effective way of forcing down rag prices".

At the meeting the following month, however, it was clear that the agreement had not been adhered to.

In the meantime paper consumption in the U.K. rose 70-fold from 100,000 tons in 1860 to 7.6 million in 1984, of which, once again, more than 60% is imported. The per capita consumption in the British Isles increased from 3 kg for a population of 30 million to 135 kg for 55 million.

Prices, on the other hand, continued to fall without interruption for over 70 years from £60 per ton in 1860 to £20 by 1905, as the following example, taken from my own mill, Thomas & Green, shows, as published in the *British Printer* in July 1905:

"A couple of sample sheets of Thomas & Green paper placed before us suggest some interesting comparisons. The one was made in 1860 at 6d per lb, the other made in 1905 at 2¼d. The latter, a little over one-third the price, is immeasurably the superior of the older paper in quality, colour, hardness and finish. All this points on the one hand to a constantly increasing standard of production, and on the other to a noteworthy decrease in price. It is a practical illustration of the hard and continual fight paper makers have had during the past half-century to make ends meet on a steadily falling market."

Except for the brief, post first world war boom they declined further during the depression of the thirties to reach £15 by the outbreak of the second world war.

The number of mills fell steadily from almost 400 in 1860 to 98 in 1984, and the decade between 1962 and 1972 alone was responsible for some 50 mill closures. The U.K. domestic production fell by almost two million tons to just over three million tons.

The present severe economic problems and heavy losses in the Nordic countries clearly demonstrate that proximity to raw material resources, low power costs, modern units and high productivity alone do not spell out prosperity even for those mills, who by their competitive pressure have been the principal cause for the closures in the U.K.

This, and most of what has preceded it, shows that "le plus ça change, le plus c'est la même chose".

ENGLAND AND WALES

Year	Population (millions)	Per capita consumption (kg)	Price per ton (writing paper) (£)	Annual wage (paper worker) (£)	Total consumption paper and board (tons)
1600	4	0·1	37	5	500
1720	5·5	0·6	84	10	3,500
1800	9	0·7	140	30	6,500
1860	25	3·8	60	80	90,000
1938	40	74	15	160	3·1 million
1955	45	80	80	500	3.7 million
1963	48	104	100	600	5.1 million
1978	50	130	450	3,000	6·5 million
1984	50.5	135	550	6,000	6·8 million

G. T. Mandl

AUS DER GESCHICHTE DER HOLZSCHLEIFEREI UND PAPPENFABRIK IN MERKELSGRÜN BEI KARLSBAD

(Reprinted from *SPH Kontakte*, no 41, January 1985, pp 710–712.)

Am 10. Juni 1870 stellte Martin Wittig in Merkelsgrün an die Bezirkshauptmannschaft in Sankt Joachimstal das Ansuchen zur Errichtung eines Zeughammers und einer Zeugschmiederei. Am 4. Juli 1870 wurde von der Behörde der Lokalaugenschein vorgenommen und im Anschluss daran die Bewilligung erteilt. Martin Wittig hatte die Zeugschmiederei nur kurze Zeit im Besitz. Er verkaufte dieselbe an Eduard und Natalie Beyreuther.

Diese erbauten im Jahre 1872 anstelle der Zeugschmiederei und des Zeughammers ein Sägewerk. Es erheilt die Hausnummer 18. Eduard Beyreuther lieferte sehr viele Bretter und Baumaterialien nach Karlsbad und pflegte seine Kunden regelmässig samstags zu besuchen, um Bestellungen entgegenzunehmen und Geld einzukassieren. So auch am 18. Januar 1879. Auf dem Heimwege kehrte er im Gasthaus zu Grossenteich ein, stürzte dort in den Keller und starb an den Folgen des Sturzes. Die Witwe Natalie Beyreuther kam in Zahlungsschwierigkeiten. Bei der am 3. August 1880 beim Bezirksgericht in Sankt Joachimstal stattgefundenen Exekutions-Feilbietung wurde die Brettsäge vom Spar-und Kreditverein in Schwarzenberg— der eine grundbücherliche Forderung von 6400 Gulden hatte—erstanden. Sie ging dann über in den Besitz des August Zabel—welcher diesen Zahlungsschwierigkeiten ebenfalls nicht nachzukommen vermochte. Die Brettsäge kam wieder zur exekutiven Feilbietung.

Tagfahrten fanden statt am 6. November und 14. Dezember 1883—eine dritte am 17. Januar 1884, bei welcher Friedrich Hermann Findeisen und Emil Gustav Tost die Brettsäge in Merkelsgrün Nr. 18 und dann die daneben befindliche alte Hammerschmiede in Salmtal Nr. 25 für 27000 Gulden erstanden. Findeisen und Tost erhielten am 6. Oktober 1888 von der Bezirkshauptmannschaft in Sankt Joachimstal die Bewilligung zur Erbauung einer Holzschleiferei. Von diesen Besitzern wurde also 1888 die Pappenfabrikation eingerichtet. Die beiden Besitzer hatten mit dem neuen Unternehmen wenig Glück und bald mit Zahlungsschwierigkeiten zu kämpfen. Einmal fehlte es an

Geld—dann trat wieder Wassermangel ein, und war genug Waser—
dann mangelte es am notwendigen Holz. Sie verkauften die Fabrik
an E. Kötting u. Komp.

Diese Besitzer erzeugten weissen und braunen Holzstoff und
braune Lederpappen. Am 16. Februar 1895 wurde über die Firma
Kötting und das Vermögen der Gesellschafter Findeisen, Tost und Otto
der kaufmännische Konkurs verhängt, welcher nachher mit Bescheid
vom 30. Juni 1895 des Kreisgerichtes in Eger aufgehoben worden ist.
Es kam zu einem aussergerichtlichen 40 prozentigem Ausgleich. Die
Firma ging gleichzeitig in den Besitz des Ernst Naundorff aus
Zwickau über.

Unter diesem geldkräftigen Besitzer erfuhr die Fabrik eine bedeu-
tende Vergrösserung. Um auch bei Wassermangel den Betrieb
fortführen zu können, wurde der Dampfbetrieb eingeführt, um den
Trocknungsprozess zu beschleunigen—eine automatische Heissluft-
trockenanlage erbaut. Die Erzeugnisse der Firma—braune Lederpappen—fanden einen guten Absatz.

Mit Bewilligung vom 8. April 1905 des Bezirksausschusses Sankt
Joachimstal verkaufte die Gemeinde Merkelsgrün an die Firma Naundorff die Grundparzelle Nr. 81 im Ausmasse von 375 Quadrat-
klaftern = 0,135 ha, welche später als Obstgarten des Wohnhauses
am linken Ufer des Baches diente. Der Kaufpreis betrug 1700
Kronen. Im Jahre 1908 verkaufte die Gemeinde an Ernst Naundorff
die am rechten Ufer des Wistwitzbaches liegende "Gmoiwies"
zum vereinbarten Preis von 13400 Kronen. Dieser ehemalige
Gemeindebesitz zerfiel in drei Teile verschiedener Grösse—in die
untere, mittlere und obere "Bummlwies". Ein Teil wurde je nach
Alter des Stieres dem jeweiligen Stierhälter zur unentgeltlichen
Benützung abgegeben.

Nach den Tode des Anton Loeschner im Jahre 1905, "Hammer-
schmiedtonl", erwarb Ernst Naudorff im Jahre 1912 von den hinter-
bliebenen Geschwistern das Haus Nr. 46 im Salmtal. Anstelle des
alten, baufälligen Hauses erbaute er ein Arbeiterwohnhaus.

Nachdem Ernst Naundorff die Fabrik 25 Jahre im Besitz gehabt
hatte, verkaufte er sie am 24. Januar 1920 an Sigmund Mandl aus
Troppau für einen Preis von 2 Millionen Kronen, für seine beiden
Söhne, Dr. Gottfried Mandl und Wilhelm Mandl. Als Besitzer wurde
Dr. Gottfried Mandl eingetragen.

Nach seiner Heirat mit Hanna Mandl, geborene Ascher, wurden
beide Eheleute 1922 als Gesellschafter im Handelsregister Eger eingetragen, und die Firma wurde eine offene Handelsgesellschaft. Mit
dem eingebrachten Kapital der neuen Gesellschafterin erbaute Dr.
Gottfried Mandl durch Verlängerung des Oberwasserkanals eine neue
Pelton-Turbine mit einer Leistung von 500 PS.

Mit Aufstellung eines Kollerganges und Holländers wurde die Auf-
bereitung von Altpapier zur Erzeugung von Graupappen ermöglicht.

Ausserdem wurde eine neue, vollständig mechanisierte Hänge-Trockenanlage in den Jahren 1922–23 eingebaut. Anschliessend erfolgte die Errichtung einer Kartonagefabrik, um einen Teil der produzierten Pappe selbst zu verarbeiten.

Im Jahre 1926 beschäftigte das Unternehmen acht Beamte und 70–80 Arbeiter. Jährlich wurden 5000 bis 6000 m³ Holz verarbeitet, welches aus der ummittelbaren Region sowie aus anderen Landesteilen bezogen wurde. Die Jahresproduktion 1926 lag zwischen 1700 und 1800 Tonnen Leder-, Grau-und Spezialpappen mit einem Bedarf von rund 4000 Tonnen Braunkohlen aus den Revieren in der Umgebung. Durch den Ankauf des Gasthauses "Zur Waldschenke" im Besitz der Familie Knaut in Ullersgrün Nr. 22 und Ausbau des damit verbundenen Saales entstand eine weitere Anzahl Arbeiterwohnungen. Alle Arbeitnehmer wurden bei der Bezirkskrankenkasse in Sankt Joachimstal versichert.

Die kaufmännische Abteilung wurde nach Prag verlegt und ein Büro in der Senovážná Nr. 8 erichtet. Das Unternehmen firmierte als Ernst Naundorff's Nachfolger. Im gleichen Haus entstand durch die Initiative von Dr. Gottfried Mandl die erste gemeinsame Verkaufsstelle für Karton "Kartonia" unter Leitung von Dr. Koutek.

In der darauffolgenden Wirtschaftskrise 1929—31 konnte das Unternehmen nur mit grossen Schwierigkeiten die Produktion aufrecht erhalten, und es mussten keine Leute entlassen werden. Im Laufe der Dreissiger Jahre wurde die Kartonagefabrik vergrössert. Die technische Leitung hatte seit 1930 dipl. Ingenieur Fritz Glasser, und die Produktion lag in den fähigen Händen des Werkführers August Pertack und die Kartonagefabrik Josef Schmidl.

Infolge steigenden Absatzes erwarb die Firma im Jahre 1936 die maschinelle Einrichtung der stillgelegten Pappenfabrik Weigend bei Brüx.

Es wurden vier weitere Pappenmaschinen sowie andere Einrichtungen aus diesem Unternehmen übergeführt. Gleichzeitig wurde 1937 ein neuer Kessel eingebaut, und ein zusätzlicher 150-PS-Motor brachte die Gesamtleistung der Wasserturbine und Dampfmaschine zu einer Spitzenleistung bis 1000 PS.

Nach dem erfolgten Umbau stieg die Produktion auf 3000 Tonnen Pappe pro Jahr, bei zehn Pappenmaschinen. Die Kartonagefabrik verarbeitete mit Ausnahme von Spezialpappen die gesamte Produktion, und es wurden zum Teil Fremdkartons dazu gekauft. Die Belegschaft stieg auf über 200 Personen an.

Im November 1938 kam das Unternehmen unter kommissarische Leitung von dipl. Ingenieur Fritz Glasser und Helmut Pinhak und durch Verfügung des Regierungspräsidenten in Karlsbad durch eine Zwangsveräusserung in den Besitz der Eheleute Hans und Marie Kreibich aus Grossschönau, welche unter dem Firmennamen H. & M. Kreibich Kommanditgesellschaft bis Mai 1945 firmierte.

Wahrend der Kriegsjahre wurde ein neuer Trockenkanal errichtet sowie die Kartonagefabrik weiter ausgebaut. Im Februar 1948 wurde das Unternehmen verstaatlicht und ging in den Besitz der *Západočeské Papírny* in Pilsen über.

PATENT SPECIFICATION

Application Date: April 20, 1938.   No. 11821/38.

513,775

Complete Specification Accepted: Oct. 23, 1939.

COMPLETE SPECIFICATION

Improvements in or relating to Cartons and the like Containers

I, GOTTFRIED MANDL, Paper Manufacturer, citizen of Czechoslovakia, of 4, Francouzska, Prague XII, Czechoslovakia, do hereby declare the nature of this invention and in what manner the same is to be performed, to be particularly described and ascertained in and by the following statement:—

Cartons and the like containers having overlapping closure flaps and a band encircling the package to seal the same are already known. With such known containers one closure flap covers the complemental flap for the whole of its

The use of these additional bands makes the packing work more difficult and lengthens the time required for packing, also increases the tare weight of the package and the packing costs.

These disadvantages are removed according to the present invention wherein cartons and like containers with an end or ends or side or sides consisting of overlapping closure flaps are constructed with one or both of the closure flaps provided with incisions, recesses or loose flaps, or a combination thereof to permit a portion or part of the underlying flap to rest upon